# LOUD AND CLEAR

BOOKS BY ROBERT J. SERLING

LOUD AND CLEAR

THE PRESIDENT'S PLANE IS MISSING

THE LEFT SEAT

THE ELECTRA STORY

THE PROBABLE CAUSE

# LOUD AND CLEAR

The Full Answer to Aviation's Vital Question:
Are the Jets Really Safe?

BY ROBERT J. SERLING

1969
DOUBLEDAY & COMPANY, INC.
GARDEN CITY, NEW YORK

To the memory of the late Captain Erich (Pinky) Paselk of Northwest Orient Airlines, who in a brief but treasured friendship gave me a glimpse into the souls of those who love both the sky and the majestic silver birds privileged to caress its beauty while challenging its wrath.

# CONTENTS

1   "Two Thirds of an Iceberg . . ."    1

2   The First Ten Years    35

3   "It's What's Up Front That Counts"   54

4   "They Bought the Farm . . ."    88

5   The 727—The Libeled Airplane    148

6   How Do You Walk Away?    180

7   Fire Away    212

8   ". . . Skipper's Shot!"    236

9   Collision Course    256

10   The Critics    287

11   The Yonder in the Wild Blue    311

    Postscript    325

# 1

## "TWO THIRDS OF AN ICEBERG . . ."

One day in May 1967, five men boarded a gleaming new jetliner freshly hatched out of Boeing's massive factory in Renton, Washington.

The plane was a three-engine 727, affectionately dubbed the "three-holer" by crews flying the tri-jet. This one bore the red, white and blue markings of Northwest Orient Airlines, with NWA's traditional scarlet tail, but for the job it was to do on this warm spring day it could have been any one of the nine hundred and eighty-seven Boeing jets delivered to the world's airlines up to this date.

This particular aircraft was N499US, ship number 499 being the last of Northwest's original order of thirty 727s. It was about to engage in what the industry terms an acceptance flight, a series of searching inspections plus ground and flight operational tests conducted by personnel of the purchasing airline. It is a thorough, sometimes brutal examination of an airliner. If an automobile buyer put a new car through inspections and tests equivalent to an acceptance flight, the process would consume at least two full days, not counting time for any necessary corrective work.

You are going along on this acceptance flight. It is an airline operation that the flying public is never privileged to observe; for that matter, only a handful of pilots have engaged in such flights. Most airlines use test crews especially trained for the job, since it calls for many operations quite different from those familiar to line pilots.

Your companions today are a special test crew. All three flight crew members, with many years' experience as regular line pilots, are well acquainted with a line crew's needs and viewpoints, a fact which fits neatly with the peculiar demands of test work. In charge of the acceptance flight is Captain Paul Soderlind, whose

official title lists him as Northwest's Director of Flight Operations—
Technical. He ranks among the world's finest pilots. A tall, soft-
spoken, balding man, he was awarded the coveted Air Line Pilots
Association's Annual Air Safety Award plus a Flight Safety Foundation award and a medal from the FAA "for extraordinary service,"
all for his flight tests, studies, lectures and other work involving
the operation of jet airplanes in severe turbulence.

The copilot is a younger man, Dean Sunde. He is slim, dark
and handsome, and has a wry, rather puckish sense of humor.
The flight engineer, like Sunde a permanent member of Soderlind's
division, is Glen Doan, who also is a qualified pilot. He is older
than Sunde, outwardly more serious and shares with the copilot
an obvious respect and affection for Soderlind.

You are breakfasting with your crew at 7 A.M. in a motel close
to Seattle-Tacoma International Airport. A waitress has put down
the coffee when two men join the group. Soderlind introduces
them. The first is Len Larson, Northwest's Superintendent of Engineering Services, who will be handling the voluminous paperwork
that must transpire between NWA and Boeing before the 727 is
turned over to the airline (it was said by some wag that the weight
of the paperwork must equal the weight of the airplane before the
transfer can be consummated).

"He's very, very important," Soderlind chuckles. "He's got the
check."

The second arrival is George Dalin, Northwest's Superintendent
of Quality Control. Dalin (Soderlind calls him "our advance man")
arrived in Seattle a day early and spent all of that day inspecting
the exterior and interior of the airplane. He checks everything from
the quality of the airplane's construction to the operation of the
coffee makers. A scratch on a window, for example, would send
Dalin straight to a Boeing man with a quiet but firm request for
immediate replacement.

"She's pretty clean," he advises Soderlind. "A few minor items
but they've all been taken care of. They're still installing one of
the galleys but should be finished by the time we get to the airplane."

Soderlind explains that Northwest used to—and most airlines still
do—conduct an acceptance flight with a Boeing test crew in Seattle
before formally accepting a plane. But Boeing's Production Test
flight crews and their line maintenance men do such a good job

of presenting "clean" airplanes to the customer, Northwest is satisfied with a "fly-away" acceptance. Under an agreement with Boeing, NWA formally accepts and pays for the airplane before the
acceptance flight test. Its crew then conducts all of the test items
during the delivery flight to NWA's home base at Minneapolis-St.
Paul. This procedure has advantages for both companies. It releases
a Boeing test crew for other duty, it makes good use of the otherwise unproductive but necessary ferry flight time to Minneapolis-
St. Paul, and it gets the airplane into scheduled service one day
earlier. And with the tremendous productivity of a jetliner, the
importance of that extra day's availability cannot be underestimated. A 727 can gross about twenty-five thousand dollars every
working day.

"Is this the first time the plane has been flown?" you ask.

"No," Soderlind answers. "Sandy MacMurray's boys—Sandy is
Boeing's Chief of Production Flight Test—they'll have flown it
anywhere from one to five times to get it ready for us. How many
flights has 499 had, Len?"

"Three. And all squawks cleaned up, they tell me."

Soderlind nods approvingly.

"Boeing is as anxious as we are for a perfect delivery," he explains.
"And Sandy's flight crews really know how to go over an airplane.
Maybe you didn't know this, but Boeing puts a warranty on a new
jet just as an automobile manufacturer does on a car. The basic
warranty is for two years or the first five thousand hours of flight,
whichever comes first, plus an airframe service life policy for thirty
thousand hours. That can amount to nearly a lifetime as far as the
airplane's usefulness to the airline is concerned. Then there are the
individual warranties of the vendors—the subcontractors who supply the various components. These are usually good for two years."

"Boeing pays for the acceptance-ferry flight," Larson adds, "and
for fixing whatever squawks we find on our test flight, even after
we give them the final dough."

You wonder out loud what the flight will cost Boeing.

"About seven hundred bucks," Larson says. "That's mostly for
fuel. Northwest pays our salaries, of course. Want to see the check
we'll give them?"

He takes an envelope out of his pocket and hands it over. Your eyes focus on the amount. Three million, five hundred and one thousand, two hundred and fifty-six dollars and fifty cents. The attached stub carried this information:

> In payment of balance due on delivery of Boeing model 727-51C aircraft No. N499US serial number 19290, being the last of four Block G aircraft under purchase agreement No. 86. Base price $4,996,795.00. Add change orders 10-15 $3500. Less advance payment of $1,499,038.50

"What are change orders?" you ask.

"Special modifications Northwest requires," Larson replies. "For example, as I remember, that thirty-five hundred bucks was for relocating the flight recorder to the rear of the fuselage, a more 'crash-worthy' location. Incidentally, that five million dollar price tag doesn't include the seats or the galleys, or a lot of the electronics equipment. There's about one hundred fifty thousand dollars worth of radio and navigation gear that comes extra. One galley runs about twenty-five thousand dollars and the ninety-three seats cost another sixty-five thousand."

Soderlind interrupts. "Time to get to work. You got a car, Len?"

"Yes, sir. I'm ready whenever you guys are."

The ride to Boeing's Commercial Delivery Center at Boeing Field takes only fifteen minutes. It is a Saturday and the Delivery Center looks less hectic than on a weekday. Larson drives up to the gate guarding the Delivery Center where Boeing's flight test crews conduct their production test flights and the line crews work off any squawks that are found. The Northwest men show their identification badges and the thought strikes you that for what is in the envelope Larson is carrying, the guard could have been a bit more enthusiastic in his welcome.

You walk into the Delivery Center building and through clean but rather Spartan corridors, glancing at the signs hanging over the entrances to various small offices. Soderlind tells you the rooms are used by Boeing customers, many of whom maintain permanent representatives at the Center. The signs are an airline roll call: *TWA . . . UNITED . . . AIR FRANCE . . . AMERICAN . . .*

Finally you come to the Northwest office. Its most prominent item of furniture is a big desk on which Soderlind places a large red loose-leaf book marked "727 SHIP MANUAL," plus a small mountain of what appear to be other engineering and operations manuals.

"You guys can go on out to the airplane and start the ground checks while I talk to Seattle Dispatch and work out a flight plan," Soderlind says to his crew.

Larson, Sunde, Doan and Dalin leave. Soderlind pulls a pad of forms out of his flight bag and begins working out the flight plan. He is planning to fly Jet 90 to Billings, Jet 32 to Aberdeen and Jet 34 (these are the jet routes he will use) on into Minneapolis-St. Paul. He uses a navigational computer—a circular slide rule—that is as much a part of a pilot as his uniform. First he checks with NWA's Seattle Dispatch office and gets a complete briefing on the weather, airport conditions and all the other factors that must be considered. He figures on a fuel load of twenty-three thousand, seven hundred pounds for the en route portion of the flight, at his desired altitude of thirty-three thousand feet where the temperature will be 58° F below zero. He adds another nine thousand pounds of fuel for the one hour of special test flying that will be required. To this Soderlind tacks on the fuel that will be needed if it becomes necessary to proceed to an alternate airport, and, of course, enough reserve fuel for a minimum of forty-five minutes.

This painstaking computing of the fuel load is a little academic, Soderlind admits, because on the acceptance flight the crew merely wants all tanks full—fifty thousand pounds in round numbers—so they can more closely duplicate the weight and performance of a scheduled flight. He goes on to explain:

"About one hour's worth of the required testing—things like compass checks, stick shaker checks, gear and flap operating time checks, and others—can't be done during the en route portion of the flight, so we'll take time out in the Billings, Montana, area for the 'local' work. We normally do this at Billings for a number of good reasons. The weather there is usually good and the traffic is light. The fact that I was born and raised there has absolutely nothing to do with it."

A Boeing employee sticks his head in the door and announces, "She's all cleaned up and ready to go, Captain Soderlind."

Soderlind smiles and phones Seattle Dispatch with his flight plan —a conglomeration of meaningless hieroglyphics to your layman's eyes, but which in reality is a carefully computed blueprint that predicts times between checkpoints and fuel to be used, based on such factors as altitude, winds, temperatures, gross weight and planned true airspeed.

"We can go out to the airplane now," he says, "but first you have to sign this little piece of paper."

The "little piece of paper" turns out to be a waiver of all claims against Northwest if anything goes wrong. Its wording is very much to the point and slightly disconcerting.

> In consideration of his participation in a flight of a model 727-51C, N499US, aircraft operated by Northwest Airlines, Inc., on May 27, 1967, the undersigned agrees to assume all risk of accident and loss of every character including personal injury, death and loss or damage to property, and agrees that Northwest Airlines, Inc., shall not be liable for any loss, damage, injury or death whether caused by the negligence of Northwest Airlines, Inc., or its agents or otherwise, which arises out of or is in any way connected with such flight.

You sign it, handing the paper to Soderlind with a wistful "Kindly refrain from negligence, Captain."

"Don't worry," he grins. "Many of the things we'll be doing on this flight will be a little different from a regular scheduled flight, but we won't scare you too much. Every gizmo on the airplane will be checked in all its normal and emergency functions before we'll let the machine carry any passengers. Let's go."

You enter the 727 through its rear belly stairs, noting as you walk through the cavernous, empty cabin that all the seats are covered with plastic jackets. Dalin and Larson are still checking various pieces of cabin equipment while simultaneously keeping their eyes on the Boeing workmen finishing up the installation of the galley.

"Everything's fine," Dalin tells Soderlind, "including the coffee maker."

With that slip of paper you recently signed fresh in mind, you cannot help asking if the checked-out items include the inflatable emergency chutes.

"You don't need to worry," Soderlind assures you. "Every item on the airplane, including the operation of the toilet flush buttons, has been gone over."

You enter the cockpit while Soderlind stows his "brainbag"—the flight kit that every pilot carries to hold the manuals, computers and other tools of his trade.

"I love the 727," he remarks, "but its cockpit isn't the biggest in the world when it comes to room for flight kits."

Sunde already is sitting in the right seat, armed with a twenty-page document, the top of which carries the simple title "NWA Acceptance Test—Boeing 727-51." He is down to the eighteenth item on the two hundred and twenty-seven item list that starts out with such prosaic equipment as rudder pedal adjustment, instrument panel fasteners and the cockpit seats themselves.

"How far have you got?" Soderlind inquires, taking out a duplicate document.

"Eighteen—fire warning lights, bell cutouts, and 'shut-off' items."

"Everything okay so far?"

"You bet. Everything good down to where we are so far."

"How about the seat placards?" Soderlind asks with a slight grin. "Thought our visitor might like to check that out."

"Better follow him through," Soderlind says. "Most important item in the cockpit. Look down at the back of my seat and read me that red placard."

You comply, doing a double-take at the message. "SEAT MUST FACE FORWARD DURING TAKEOFF AND LANDING."

"Do they figure you might want to face sideways on takeoff or landing?" you ask incredulously.

Soderlind laughs. "Must be. That placard's on every Boeing pilot seat I've ever seen. I've never taken the trouble to find out why."

Doan announces that he's going outside for a walk-around inspection, and hoists himself out of the flight engineer's seat. Soderlind and Sunde resume work on the forty-seven cockpit items that still must be functionally checked before the engines are started.

*Fire-switch operation of fuel valves, hydraulic pump lights and generator breakers . . . thrust levers . . . flight recorder . . . overspeed warning . . . stick shaker . . . pitot-static heat . . . parking brakes and light . . . flaps and slats, positions 0°, 2°, 5°, 15°, 25°, 30° and 40° and annunciator lights . . .*

Every system that can be functionally checked on the ground is checked there, not only to ensure its proper operation, but because the checks can be run on the ground without worrying about other traffic on actual flying of the airplane. Although nearly everything will be rechecked in flight, the ground work means the flight checks can be accomplished more quickly and with less diversion of attention.

One thing that impresses you as Soderlind's crew conducts the ground checks is the voluminous backup equipment in almost every area—a redundant, duplicate system for use if a primary component goes haywire. Hydraulic and pneumatic brake pressures must be within certain limits. Flaps and slats must extend and retract in a specific number of seconds using the normal hydraulic system, and in a longer but nevertheless just as specific time using the alternate electric flap operation system.

When all of the jet's systems have been functionally inspected, the three engines are started. Now Soderlind and his two colleagues are going over engine instrumentation . . . *engine pressure ratio* (the crew calls it "Eeper") . . . *low compressor RPM . . . high compressor RPM . . . exhaust gas temperature . . . fuel flow . . . oil pressure . . . oil temperature . . . pneumatic pressure . . . engine vibration level . . .*

All this is checked both with the engines idling and at takeoff thrust. Every reading is carefully recorded. Such abstract-sounding things as N1-for-surge-bleed-valve operation, wing anti-ice overheat warning, reverse thrust temperature detent values—it is all Greek to you but each is carefully scrutinized and recorded. Finally the engines are each accelerated from idle RPM to takeoff RPM with a "thrust lever burst."

"They must accelerate from idle to takeoff thrust in not more than eight seconds and there can't be more than one-second difference among the three engines," Soderlind says.

On 499, as the fuel flow and temperature gauges move rapidly in their tiny, instrument-encased orbits, all three engines reach takeoff thrust in just over six seconds and Soderlind nods happily. The final pre-flight check is partially to pressurize the cabin and check the "air data" instruments to see that there are no leaks in the static system lines to the airspeed indicators, the altimeters, and other important flight instruments. There are none. Soderlind's list thus far is a long series of checks by the word SATISFACTORY and there are none by the word UNSATISFACTORY.

"Let's go get a cup of coffee and tell Len he can buy it," Soderlind announces.

The paperwork involving the official transfer of N499US from the

Boeing Company to Northwest Airlines, Inc., takes about thirty minutes—the final act being the handing over of the keys to the cockpit door. You walk back to the plane and sit in the cockpit jump seat behind the two pilots.

Takeoff.

From the world of the flight deck it is a thrilling yet simultaneously routine procedure. Exciting in a visual sense, for the view from the flight deck is something a passenger never sees—the 727 gulping down the long ribbon of concrete and the quiet but firm voice of the copilot as he calls out the significant airspeeds.

". . . $V_1$" (the maximum speed at which the takeoff can be aborted) . . .

". . . ROTATE!" (when the pilot begins to lift the nose so the airplane will lift off the ground) . . .

Soderlind pulls back gently on the column, and the nose comes up about sixteen degrees. The 727 climbs effortlessly, as if there were a giant pushing at her with a huge hand under her belly.

During the climb to thirty-three thousand more functional checks are completed. Climb trim, control centering, the "barber pole" position (the Mach/airspeed warning band), autopilot coupling to the VOR (Visual Omni Range) course, captain and copilot airspeed indicator agreement, engine performance, thrust lever trim and a host of other things.

About thirty minutes after takeoff, Soderlind asks Sunde to request a clearance from Air Traffic Control for an approach and landing at Missoula, Montana. When the clearance comes through Soderlind reduces engine thrust to idle and begins the descent from cruise altitude. And now begins a special phase of the flight, not related to the acceptance testing.

"Northwest serves what we call the mountain stations," Soderlind explains. "Missoula, Helena, Butte and Bozeman, all in the mountains of Montana. These airports all present operating problems considerably different from our other stations, primarily because they're closely and almost completely surrounded by or are very near rugged mountainous terrain. Not only that, the four stations are an average of only about sixty-five miles apart, or about fifteen minutes as the jet flies. This means that a large portion of the flight is used in climb and descent maneuvering and this, in mountainous terrain, calls for somewhat different procedures. Several months ago, we flew a 727 into all of these stations to get a better

feel for the peculiar problems involved. So on this trip, Ben Griggs
[Vice President of Flight Operations and Soderlind's boss] asked
that we take another look at the Missoula and Butte operations.
That's what we're starting now."

At Missoula, Soderlind flies a simulated ILS (Instrument Landing System) approach to Runway 11. There actually is no ILS at
Missoula, but one is simulated for the purposes of this flight by
flying a pre-computed profile of altitude vs DME (Distance Measuring Equipment) miles from the Missoula VOR/DME station on
the airport. The approach is down the valley that extends northwest of the airport, in clear weather, and Soderlind and crew
carefully evaluate clearance from the mountains on both sides of
the flight path.

"Looks good, boss," Sunde says. "I think an ILS on Runway 11
would work out fine."

Soderlind makes a touch-and-go landing and on the pull-out reduces the thrust on the center engine to idle. The 727 doesn't even
breathe a little bit harder.

"It's a good test," Soderlind explains as he climbs to cruise altitude
and heads toward Butte. "The center engine is the most critical
to lose since there's more drag than if either pod engine were
inoperative."

The approach to Butte is even more interesting because the airport has high mountains close in on all sides.

"As one of our boys put it," Soderlind chuckles, "the best way
into Butte is on a stepladder."

There is no control tower at Butte but Sunde calls the FAA's
Flight Service Station for traffic and field condition advisories. Although it's not as bad as it looks, you are sure the right wing tip
is brushing the trees as Soderlind circles for a landing on Runway
33. The captain points out that the maneuvering area is limited,
which is the precise reason for these careful survey flights.

The landing is rough and Soderlind grins ruefully while Sunde
murmurs disrespectfully, "Tell me when we're on."

Although the runway is about sixty-eight hundred feet long,
Butte's high altitude, in effect, shortens that length. The thin air
at this more than a mile above sea level airport makes for higher
than normal landing speeds.

"With this factor, and a slight downhill slope the way we landed,
you don't worry about greasing it on," Soderlind remarks in a half

apology. "Getting it on the ground before using up much runway is a hell of a lot more important than a smooth touchdown. You can't stop these things in the air."

When ready for takeoff, Soderlind takes a minute to explain to the FAA man in the Flight Service Station that he'll be throttling an engine on takeoff for test purposes. There is a discreet silence for a moment before the FSS attendant answers, "I'm glad you're doing it and not me."

You worry aloud about this deliberate throttling of an engine on takeoff.

"Don't worry," the captain says. "We don't go around risking a five million dollar airplane. Or our own skins either. We know the performance of this machine down to a gnat's eyebrow, and we don't operate from runways where, if an engine failed at the worst point, we couldn't either stop or continue the climb-out with adequate obstruction clearance. You might be interested to know that every tree, house, pole and every other kind of obstruction is plotted in the area off the runway edge, and the performance computations take every one into account. Sure, in the thin air of a mountain station like Butte, the airplane isn't going to perform like it does at sea level. But it's a simple matter of adjusting the weight to the runway length, elevation and other factors. In other words, we reduce the load to the point where our engine-out performance is still adequate."

"When we reach $V_1$," Soderlind tells Sunde, "throttle number two to idle."

The 727 starts rolling, its turbines howling like a thousand panthers. Doan, the flight engineer, is eying the engine instruments like a hungry hawk so he can immediately warn Captain Soderlind of any trouble.

"$V_1$," Sunde calls, and in one motion pulls the number two thrust lever to idle.

"ROTATE!" Soderlind pulls the nose up for the lift-off.

You look down those sixty-eight hundred feet of asphalt, a little over a mile long but a rectangularly shaped postage stamp to your layman's eyes—particularly with a foreboding mountain directly ahead, its shrub-spotted bulk squatting peacefully under the warm sun.

Your heart beats a little faster. The 727 shoves her snout into the air and breaks ground, clawing her way over the mountain ahead with impertinent ease.

"Quite a machine," Soderlind murmurs. You have the feeling he would enjoy getting out and patting the 727 affectionately on her metal hide.

The throttled engine is left at idle until cruise altitude is reached, to simulate completely the situation where a scheduled flight might lose an engine on takeoff and have to continue to Billings or somewhere else.

"Does that last takeoff mean you can operate the 727 into Butte?" you ask.

"Not until more work is done on improving airport approach aids and other facilities," Soderlind replies. "There's no question about the 727's performance abilities as far as the mountain stations are concerned, but special procedures will have to be developed, too. You look a little green around the gills. Were you scared?"

"A little," you confess. "That damned runway looked about as long as the sidewalk in front of my house."

"There really wasn't anything to worry about," he assures you (slightly too late). "We know what this machine will do under just about any set of conditions. Well, let's head over toward Billings and start the local test work."

This phase of the acceptance flight is started about seventy-five miles west of Billings, and the first item is the stick shaker checks. These involve the simple process of reducing thrust and holding the nose up until the airflow over the wings reduces to near the point where all lift is lost. The stick shaker is a stall warning device and Soderlind wants to determine the accuracy of the system that warns the pilot when lift margins are getting too low. The checks are done with the flaps at different positions, and the airspeed at which the stick shaker operates is compared carefully with the proper "book" figures. It's an interesting experience, to say the least, and again something no passenger will ever encounter because a qualified airline pilot is not going to let his lift margins get too low. But if it happened, the stick shaker would provide plenty of warning. It lets a pilot feel a stall developing on his controls before a stall actually occurs.

Soderlind makes three stall warning checks. The first is with the flaps set at zero or in the cruise configuration. The warning according to the book is supposed to occur at one hundred and fifty knots at our particular weight. The nose comes up and the airspeed drops off gradually. There is a rattling sound when the stick shaker actuates, so called because it really shakes the control column. The 727 trembles in the buffeting of a near-stall, as if shaking her body in protest. Soderlind recovers by lowering the nose, extending partial flaps and applying near-takeoff thrust.

"The shaker sounded at one-five-three," Soderlind reports. "Three knots above the book, but actually right on the nose. The difference is due to our altitude. Now we check it with fifteen-degree flaps."

This time 499's shaker comes on at one hundred and nineteen knots, just one knot above the book value. With forty-degree flap the shaker is heard at ninety-eight, again within one knot of the book number. Soderlind is eminently satisfied and goes on to other tests, such as turning off all the control boost switches to see how the 727 responds without its "power steering."

Next the flaps and landing gear are each operated with their emergency backup systems. Lowering the landing gear with the emergency system calls for inserting a crank in three separate holes in the floor—one for each gear—and cranking a specific number of turns in a specific pattern. It takes a lot longer than the normal gear extension, which Soderlind has already tested and timed.

Soderlind tucks the snout of the 727 down to a lower altitude and the brown and green terrain of Montana flashes under the swept-back wings. Directly ahead is a small town and the altimeter is unwinding steadily until it reads only fifty-five hundred feet above sea level.

"That's Rapelje coming up," Soderlind tells you. "I was raised there from the time I was one year old until we moved to Columbus when I was eleven, and then to Billings a year later. Went to school in that brick building right in the center of town. Kinda like to come over the old town whenever I get the chance. It's so small, the city limits signs for both ends of town are on the same post. It's not only small, it's dry. I remember one year after a long dry spell, a drop of rain hit one of the farmers on the south side of town and he fainted. Took two buckets of sand to bring him to again."

Rapelje apparently is taking Soderlind's nostalgic visit with admirable calm. You don't see any citizens looking up at the 727 as it screams over the few buildings. You wonder what's going through the mind of this calm, so quietly efficient airline captain. Remembering his boyhood? His dreams of becoming a pilot? His early years in a farm community so tiny and peaceful that the 727 almost seems to have flown back in time, an unwelcome intruder showing off its technological muscles to a world that couldn't care less?

By now 499 is ten miles past Rapelje and Soderlind eases up the nose to climb back to thirty-seven thousand for the remainder of the flight to Minneapolis-St. Paul.

During the climb the crew goes through a fuel-dumping procedure, ejecting between sixty and seventy-five gallons from various tanks and drawing from Doan the wry comment that "we oughta send the bill to local mosquito control."

At thirty-seven thousand feet Soderlind checks engine acceleration and surge characteristics by rapid thrust lever cuts, one engine at a time to check for proper restart capability.

Everything works fine but Soderlind recalls with amusement the time they were running engine shut-down checks on a new Boeing 707.

"We got a call from an American flight just behind us," he laughs. "He tells us, 'Northwest, do you know you've got a slight pucker in your left contrail?'"

As you start the descent from thirty-seven thousand feet in preparation for landing at Minneapolis-St. Paul, you note that Soderlind pulls the thrust levers all the way to idle. You ask how this multiton monster is going to stay in the air.

"Most jet descents from cruise altitude," he explains, "are made with the engines at or near idle thrust. Although the engines produce a small amount of thrust even at idle, for all practical purposes the airplane is gliding. The 727 is so aerodynamically clean—we call it 'slippery'—that from this altitude it will glide nearly a hundred and thirty miles. Far more, incidentally, than the smallest and lightest of private airplanes. Not only that, it does it at an average of about three hundred and eighty knots, or four hundred thirty-five miles per hour."

The final few remaining tests are completed during the approach and landing. You taxi in to Northwest's main base, a complex of windowless hangers, offices, parking lots, shops and storerooms that cover some seventy-six acres. Soderlind, Sunde and Doan hold a conference over the voluminous notes they have made during the flight. The attitude indicator on the captain's side has been intermittently sticky. A generator frequency meter is inoperative. One radio headset is faulty, and Sunde has written up an item on "poor audio quality when using first officer's mike." The weather radar acted up about thirty minutes out and Soderlind has also entered a squawk about the squelch on a communications receiver, plus "loop rotator switch on right ADF [Automatic Direction Finder] sticks."

"Not bad," Soderlind says. "When you consider putting together thousands upon thousands of parts, it's truly amazing that we find so few items. It always takes several regular trips before any new airplane is 'squawk-free.' And, of course, we're literally a faultfinding crew—that's our function—so we expect to find things to complain about even on a plane that's just about perfect. Yep, our mechanics will have a few hours' work before 499 goes into service, but she'll be carrying passengers by tomorrow morning."

You deplane through the rear belly stairs, half hoping in your inevitable Walter Mitty mood that the mechanics may figure you were one of the test crew. The mechanics couldn't care less if you were Charles Lindbergh climbing off their airplane. They're concerned only with the squawks in the logbook that Soderlind hands them. As Paul Soderlind said, 499 has to be carrying passengers the next morning—swiftly, efficiently, comfortably and safely.

You accompany him to his office in Northwest's general offices adjoining the hangars. Your eyes fall on a cylindrical package on his desk. It's wrapped like an airline calendar but it is twice the length and far bulkier. Larson had handed it to Soderlind before leaving Renton.

"I'm just curious," you comment. "What's inside?"

"Instrumentation plans for the Boeing 747," Soderlind grins. "You know, the jumbo jet we'll be flying by 1970. We wanted to take a look at what the boys in the blueprint room dreamed up for this baby's cockpit."

His eyes sparkle as he fondles the long package.

"That 747, now. Seven hundred thousand pounds of gross takeoff weight, at least ten stewardesses, eleven lavatories and six galleys —and Boeing says she'll handle as easily as the 727. What an acceptance flight *that* will be!"

The public's view of a scheduled airline's operations can be compared to what one sees when he looks at an iceberg. Only one third of a berg is visible. The same is true of commercial aviation. A passenger comes in contact with skycaps, ticket agents and stewardesses. His visual view of an airliner is limited to a glimpse of the plane as he boards, then the inside of the cabin, the pretty faces of the cabin attendants and the sometimes overly hectic procedure of retrieving his baggage.

What he does not see is what has been done to assure him of a safe flight. He has every right in the world to take safety for granted. He should feel complete confidence in crew, both cockpit and cabin. He should assume without a second thought that the plane on which he is flying has been carefully, scrupulously tested and maintained. He should relax in the knowledge that a massive, enormously complicated and expensive air traffic control system is keeping his aircraft safely separated from other planes.

It is reasonable to assume, however, that the majority of passengers do not have a total sense of security about flying. The volume of commercial air travel has mushroomed. Ten years ago 40 million Americans flew the nation's scheduled airlines. In 1967, the total surpassed the 130 million mark and by 1975, according to the most conservative estimates, at least 330 million persons will use U.S. scheduled air transportation. But it is still a pretty good bet that acceptance of the airplane has not necessarily been accompanied by a drastic lessening of fear.

It is my firm belief, gleaned from more than twenty years of close contact with the airline industry, that lack of knowledge is the prime reason behind fear of flying—a lack of knowledge about the "other two thirds of the iceberg." The little glimpse of an airline acceptance flight was just one example, actually a comparatively minor example, but typical of airline safety practices.

What you will read in the following pages will be no sugarcoating, no whitewash job, no viewing through rose-colored glasses. There are serious areas of weakness in air safety. But the accomplishments have too often been obscured by the black headlines accompanying a fatal crash, by critics who get more attention when they emphasize the negative while ignoring the positive, by Congressmen who use the rarity of an air disaster for personal publicity and uninformed concern that borders on the phony. Commercial aviation has enough problems without also having to combat falsehoods, scare stories, unfair accusations bordering on libel and—most important of all—an abysmal failure on the part of carping critics to acknowledge aviation's achievements even as they attack its failures.

No one in the airline or manufacturing industries, no government official concerned with aviation safety, resents an attack motivated by honest concern involving known areas of safety weaknesses and vulnerability. Those of us who admire commercial aviation, who treasure its past, who promote its present and who believe in its future, are simultaneously not unaware of its faults. A mistake in aviation is akin to an error committed in a professional football game. A boner in the latter means six points for the other team. A boner in aviation can mean death. There is no room in commercial aviation for the alibi. But there is considerable room for explanations of mistakes made, for searching examination of what caused the mistake and for determined efforts to keep the mistake from ever being committed again.

Someone—I wish I knew his name, for it is more of an axiom than a mere quote—once wrote that "Experience is the name you give to the mistakes you made yesterday."

This aptly sums up aviation's search for greater safety. In telling that story, it is only too easy to dwell so heavily on the mistakes that the story is warped out of perspective. For every step backward, for every failure to take a step forward, aviation literally has sprinted a mile ahead.

No accident, fatal or non-fatal, is ever condoned; unless it was an act of God, it stemmed from somebody doing something wrong—on the drawing board of an aircraft designer, in the cockpit, in a hangar where a mechanic got careless or in an airline front office where an executive decision amounted to a calculated risk involving safety. But dwell on this one statistic: for every fatal crash involving a U.S. scheduled airliner in the past five years, there have been approximately 1.6 million routine flights that took off and landed in routine safety—often under weather conditions that would have grounded an airliner only a decade ago. Add to this the fact that virtually all of those 1.6 million flights were completed faster, more comfortably and with far greater efficiency than any passenger could have experienced ten years before.

Somebody must have been doing something right. And *this*, too, is the story of commercial aviation—a far more important story, if less dramatic, than the story of mistakes. Most books written about air safety, however well-meaning or well-intentioned, have done a disservice by concentrating on the latter. So do most newspaper articles and so do the occasional statements and/or speeches made by Congressmen on the subject of air safety. Obviously 1.6 million safe flights don't warrant headlines or several pages in the Congressional Record. But the overemphasis put on the one accident per 1.6 million flights inevitably results in public distrust, fear and even avoidance of air travel.

Najeeb E. Halaby, one of the most intelligent, personable and devoted men who ever entered government service, made this statement when he headed the Federal Aviation Agency (now Federal Aviation Administration):

> "At base, safety—the absence of hazard or danger—is a subjective, relative quality. What is one man's safety may be another's hazard. Each has his own version. Safety, then, lies in the eyes of the beholder . . . Aviation depends on the public—on customers at the ticket window—no matter what the statistician may say, or the aviation writer, or the administrator of the FAA—for our common purpose, there is one all-important truth. The airplane is as safe as the man in the street thinks it is.

> "We face then the severest judge of all. There is nothing that mitigates the judgment of this man on the street. He gives no attention to the obstacles that are being overcome. He cares not for the many heroic 'saves' of our airline pilots or the controllers. He is unaware of the exacting care of our aviation mechanics. None of these stays with him. His judgment is as mercurial and emotional as the headlines of a daily paper. And his judgment, arising as it does out of fear and excitement and haste, demands of our transport industry nothing less than a lengthy period of operations free of disaster and death."

The growth of faith in air transportation has been incredible, surpassing the fondest hopes of those in the industry. Five years ago, only 10 per cent of the nation's population had flown in a scheduled airliner. By 1967, more than 42 per cent of all Americans had taken air trips. But this remarkable increase still leaves a sizable percentage of those who have never flown—for reasons varying from fares to fear. It is the latter group which concerns this writer.

It was mentioned earlier that more than 130 million Americans used scheduled air transportation in 1967 and the figure for 1968 was heading for 150 million. But these totals, however impressive, are somewhat misleading. The 130 million represent tickets sold, not individual passengers. Most air travelers take more than one flight a year. The most recent estimate (a 1967 Gallup poll conducted for TWA) of actual number of Americans who have, at one time or another, flown commercially was 47 million. This leaves about 65 million adult U.S. citizens who have never flown at all. With forty thousand new airline passengers boarding daily, 60 per cent of the adult population will have taken an airline trip by 1970 and the number of non-air travelers will have dwindled to around 40 million—but still a large number, and a total that must inevitably involve fear as a major deterrent.

There have been numerous market studies of the flying and non-flying public, but with air travel expanding so fast most of them are out of date before their ink dries. One statistic has remained fairly valid, however: only about 15 per cent of the total passengers take approximately 50 per cent of the flights. This fact is due largely to the use of the airlines by businessmen, who comprise about 80 per cent of the so-called "heavy fliers" market—Americans who make at least five air trips annually. Again, these percentages may be not only outmoded but meaningless in another few years because of the surge in first-time passengers. The airlines' youth, military and family fares have introduced millions of young Americans to air travel, and these, presumably, will use scheduled air transportation when their careers are settled and their earnings assured. But use of the airlines still does not negate fear; fear or at least real nervousness is known to be present even among those who fly regularly, and it also is a factor in reducing the number of trips a person may make each year as well as keeping Americans off airplanes in the first place.

A survey made by Louis Harris a few years ago (for American Airlines) asked more than twenty-five thousand persons in fifty-five hundred households—a good-sized sampling of both regular air travelers and infrequent passengers—why they fly.

Speed was cited as the primary attraction—by a whopping 67 per cent. Comfort was another major reason, with 66 per cent mentioning such air travel advantages as more relaxing, cleaner and less tiring. More time at destination and less time away from home was cited by 47 per cent. Such items as attentive stewardesses, service, safety and economy were relatively far down on the list. And the top three primary reasons actually involved speed as the dominant factor. Safety was mentioned by only 17 per cent, indicating the presence of some fear even among those who utilize air transportation.

Strangely enough, there have been virtually no extensive surveys made on the subject of fear of flying. In all the traveling by air I do, however (about forty flights a year), I have yet to meet a passenger who would not admit to some nervousness, and I have talked to many who confess they are afraid even though they fly as often as I do. It is safe to say that all the comforting statistics in the world are not capable of reducing the element of fear to any appreciable extent. In other words, most people fly even though they *are* afraid.

Why a fear of flying?

It is, as I said before, illogical if one weighs the chances of involvement in an airliner crash against the chances of injury or death in such prosaic pastimes as driving a car, taking a bath, riding a bicycle, cleaning guns or sailing in a pleasure boat. All of the above have more annual fatalities than the death toll in scheduled air transportation. More people were killed in pleasure-boating accidents in 1967, for example, than in *all* aircraft crashes combined— thirteen hundred and eighteen in boats and thirteen hundred in private, business and common-carrier airplanes.

Fear of flying *is* understandable, for the air is an unfamiliar dimension and anything unfamiliar can breed fear. But it also is illogical, because many of us fear it merely because it is unfamiliar and yet blithely accept far greater exposure to danger simply because the source is familiar. The automobile is a perfect example. Millions of Americans every day step into a car that is potential disaster on wheels, deliberately ignoring such hazards as worn tires, faulty windshield wipers, tired shock absorbers, burned-out or dirty headlights, and—most important of all—they drive that car with only a fraction of the skill that the greenest, newest airline pilot displays at the controls of a transport plane.

Critics of the yardstick the airlines use for judging their safety record—fatalities per 100 million passenger miles flown—love to sug-

gest that a better yardstick would involve time exposure to accidents. If hours of exposure rather than miles traveled were used,
they argue, the airliner would come out a poor safety second to
the family automobile. In other words, because a jet can travel six
hundred miles in the same time an automobile covers not more
than sixty, it is fairer to compare the chances for death while
flying one hundred hours with the same one hundred hours in your
car.

Actually, it is almost impossible to arrive at an accurate comparison because airline mileage figures are exact, whereas private
automobile mileage can only be an estimate. But if mileage is not
a good yardstick, let's use another—namely, the number of times
you step into your automobile compared to the number of airline
flights that occur. The latter figure already has been cited—1.6
million flights for every fatal crash. Does anyone imagine, regardless of how good a driver he is (or thinks he is), that he could
make 1.6 million automobile trips without having a serious accident? There are comparatively few drivers in the United States
with perfect safety records. There are even fewer who can expect
to go through their lives without getting involved in at least one
serious accident. Yet if we use the U.S. airline safety record for
1967, an average year in the jet age, safety-wise, it would take a
person flying steadily for twenty-four hours a day a total of more
than eighty years before he could expect to be fatally injured in
a crash.

The "nobody walks away from a crash" conviction is a major
source of flying fear, but this too is somewhat illogical; very few
motorists walk away from an automobile accident in which impact
occurs at fifty or sixty miles an hour, a statistic which bothers
pitifully few drivers.

Admittedly, the usual yardstick of fatalities per 100 million miles
has statistical weaknesses—for one thing, it refers to revenue passenger deaths only and usually does not include crew. Nor does
it include deaths in crashes caused by sabotage, although deliberate
murder is not a fair input if we are judging an *accident* rate. So,
ponder another yardstick—simple mileage traveled.

Take the airlines' fatal accident rate for any of the past five
years and apply it to mileage. You would have to fly at least 250
million miles before you could expect to be involved in a fatal
crash. You would have to travel only about 40 million miles in an

automobile. That would make the commercial plane more than six times safer than the automobile.

Hours? The U.S. jet fatality rate in 1966 was one fatal accident for every eight hundred and fifty thousand hours flown. Again, there is no comparative rate for automobiles because it is impossible to arrive at the precise number of total hours driven. But judging from the daily automobile death toll, let alone holiday deaths, it does not seem unreasonable to assume that there is more than one fatal automobile accident for every eight hundred and fifty thousand hours spent on the nation's roads—when annual automobile fatalities themselves invariably exceed forty thousand (they reached fifty-three thousand in 1967).

(This observer is convinced that the automobile-vs-airliner argument has reached the point where husbands and wives might well consider driving to the airport in separate cars and then taking the same plane instead of the other way around. In the course of researching this book, I completed a nine thousand mile routine trip by air and then had three near-accidents driving home from the airport.)

Let us grant the contention of critics that it *is* possible at least to estimate the time exposure ratio of airplane-vs-automobile. Making the obvious assumption that the hours in which automobiles are driven far outstrip the hours in which airliners are flown, the critics claim that your own car is 30 per cent safer than a transport plane! In other words, for every accidentless hour you spend in a plane you could spend three hours in an automobile.

Unfortunately, no set of statistics is entirely reliable—figures can be twisted or interpreted to fit almost any point of view, to buttress any side of an argument. So let us ask just one question: If flying is 30 per cent more dangerous than driving the family car, why do insurance companies—the most cold-blooded, impersonal and objective statisticians in the world—charge airline pilots exactly the same rates for life insurance as persons in such tame occupations as clerking, law or even driving a taxicab?

Remember that if one buys this time exposure logic, one also must accept the fact that an airline pilot flies up to seventy-five hours a month, which happens to be double the exposure of a passenger who makes one round-trip transcontinental flight a week. If seventy-five hours a month are spent in a mode of transportation truly 30 per cent more dangerous than the automobile, an airline pilot would be paying far higher premiums for life insurance. There are several professions deemed hazardous enough to warrant higher insurance rates, among them being those of the dock worker, lumberjack, jockey and—believe it or not—bartender! Before 1937, insurance companies refused even to sell life insurance at any premium to pilots. Significantly, after 1937 their premium rates kept dropping steadily in direct proportion to the decreasing airline fatality rate until today a doctor pays higher premiums than a transport pilot.

As former FAA Administrator Halaby pointed out, all the statistics and/or logic available are not sufficient to quell fear on the part of the public. It is bad enough that the average person is naturally nervous to begin with. Add to this the psychological shock of the occasional crash, plus what he reads or hears about the alleged or factual loopholes in air safety, and it is a wonder that air travel has grown as fast as it has. This is the real damage uninformed or false criticism accomplishes.

Can anything be done to reduce or even eliminate fear of flying?

A few years ago, eight leading psychiatrists, psychologists and sociologists held a panel discussion on this subject of such vital interest to the airline industry. Representatives of the Air Transport Association and individual carriers attended, although they were not allowed to participate except to answer specific questions or discuss certain points raised by the panelists themselves—and only at the invitation of the moderator.

The eight panelists all had national and international reputations in their respective fields. It would have been difficult to select a group of higher professional standing. Before the seminar, the members received briefing material in the form of a background memorandum. The participants were briefed on previous fear surveys and what they have shown as to causes of fear; what the industry has done in the past to solve the fear problem, and statistical data on the composition of the air travel market.

The seminar was in general agreement with the most commonly accepted sources of fear—such factors as claustrophobia, fear of falling, fear of height, belief that no one survives a crash, fear of losing contact with the ground, etc.

But in acknowledging these various factors as primary causes of non-flying, the panelists were virtually unanimous in their belief that too little is known about the whole subject. They considered current and available data inadequate, incomplete and possibly outdated. It was significant that perhaps 80 per cent of the two-day discussion covered fears on the part of those who *do* fly. In discussing how the airlines can influence those who *do not,* the participants kept emphasizing their collective conviction that nobody really knows very much about this sizable segment of the public and its anti-flying motivations, and that much research lies ahead before a definite and major campaign can be waged in this area.

While the panelists expressed agreement with the usual and most obvious sources of fear cited above, they also raised some other interesting possibilities. For example:

—The nature of a crash and its attendant drama may have a tremendous effect. Such accidents as those which killed a number of prominent citizens of Atlanta, and the U.S. skating team tragedy, probably have a more shocking and lasting effect than the average accident.

—A very underrated problem may be the effects of an accident on those who knew the victims involved. One panelist suggested that if a hundred persons are killed in a crash, a fear factor is spread directly to at least five thousand "proximities"—the relatives, friends and even acquaintances of those who died.

—The natural tendency of a person to exaggerate a flying incident is probably a minor but very real source of transmitting unjustified fears. The average passenger, particularly male, is very likely to "blow up" an experience from what it actually was—routine—into a close brush with death. Inasmuch as civil aviation inevitably encounters routine "non-normal" incidents daily, there is no way to judge the extent of this bragging habit in spreading anti-flying prejudice and fear.

—There may be a class structure to fear of flying, and this would involve not apprehension about death but of social circumstances. Do many persons refuse to fly because they do not know what to wear or are worried about not "looking right" in the midst of other passengers? Do they feel "planes aren't for the likes of me"? Is there even a "fear of destination"? Several panelists questioned whether airline advertising that concentrates on glamorous destinations actually may contribute to a class fear category. This was one of the major areas in which the participants agreed there should be more research, in the belief that the industry may have to work out separate campaigns to aim at different class levels.

The panelists raised a number of important questions for which there were no ready answers.

Is it possible that fear of flying is most prevalent among those who fly a little? Who may say "I fly four or five times a year and that's enough because if I fly any more my number's likely to be up"? Who regard commercial aviation as a giant Russian roulette game with "forty-five thousand chambers," as one participant put it?

What do people think makes a flight dangerous? Are they more afraid of landings and takeoffs than of flying at thirty-five thousand feet? Would they rather experience engine failure or get stacked up over New York? Why do passengers choose certain seats? Do any deliberately sit by emergency exits? How many wives won't fly on the same planes with their husbands? What is the extent of the "bragging" factor? What are the specific effects of an accident or serious incident on fear in terms of cancellations?

These were just some of the questions and potentially rich research areas raised by the seminar. The participants felt that available data and perhaps much of the industry's current thinking is based on research that is vague, rhetorical and superficial—almost a grab bag of ideas and beliefs stemming from totally inadequate information.

One of the most significant and surprising views expressed by the panel was its own lack of knowledge about air safety. These were highly intelligent men, most of them frequent or at least occasional air travelers, and presumably with a much sharper realization of the safety situation than the average person.

Yet the panelists expressed unanimous amazement at the safety statistics furnished them as part of the pre-seminar background material. They said they had no idea air travel was so safe.

A great deal of time was spent discussing recent experiments which demonstrated that it is possible to manipulate emotions, such as fear, by establishing cognizance of a given situation. In somewhat simpler terms, the panelists suggested it is theoretically possible to substitute excitement for fear—for example, convincing a passenger that a takeoff is thrilling, not frightening.

Some of this discussion wandered a bit into the wild blue yonder. One panelist proposed that the airlines stop playing soft music before takeoffs because it actually contributed to fear. Music that is spirited, peppy or even martial, he suggested, would achieve the substitution of excitement for fear.

Probably this distinguished panelist was not being serious on this score, but the panelists were most serious about changing the atmosphere aboard planes as a means of reducing the fear factor.

It was agreed, for example, that keeping passengers busy tends to allay or at least hide fear. It was noted that a mother being kept busy with a traveling baby never seems to get airsick—and airsickness often can be traced to fear. In-flight movies were brought up, and the panelists expressed great interest in this device as an anti-fear weapon. When a TWA representative was invited to comment on this possibility, he pointed out that the carrier's movies were designed mainly to alleviate boredom, not fear—which prompted the panel's response that alleviating boredom might alleviate fear.

In this respect, the panelists felt there is a wide field for experimentation on creating a more favorable atmosphere not only in planes themselves but even in airports. They did not agree on methods to achieve this atmosphere, merely on the need for it. For example, they considered the interior of an average transport a possible source of apprehension in its very layout—the long tube or cave idea. It was suggested that the airlines take a single jet and try out a new interior design—one that has the necessary economic capacity but also provides more of a social, club car atmosphere.

One specific suggestion for this cabin layout experiment: a compartmentalized aircraft with separate sections for those who like to drink, those who like to walk around, those who want to read and/or be alone, those who want to smoke, etc. The panelists conceded that cabin revisions are subject to the need for good load factors, but claimed that the airlines have more flexibility in aircraft interiors than they imagine. At any rate, an experimental interior was one of the seminar's proposals for acquiring more data on fear of flying and how to combat it. (The new Boeing 747 "jumbo jet" with its separate lounges plus galleys and toilets in the middle of the cabin aisle instead of next to the walls is more of an actuality than an experiment in elimination of the tube effect.)

The possibility of extending this "atmospheric attack" to airports also was admittedly theoretical, but one that the panelists believed would warrant experimentation. Putting movie theaters into major airports was one idea. Attractive, educational and interesting airline displays was another—such as a typical cockpit layout, a cabin mockup, a display on how air traffic control works or even a motion picture depicting the experience of flight.

As in the case of the suggested experimental interior, there was no definite agreement on what should or could be done at airports. But there *was* agreement on the need for doing something to alleviate pre-flight fears on the part of new or infrequent passengers, or perhaps the fears of non-flying persons who might come to an airport.

Actually, the panel acknowledged that in many ways the jets have achieved much along these lines—through their lack of interior noise, their cleanliness, speed, vibrationless operation, etc. But the seminar emphasized that the jets have offered no cure-all and in themselves may have raised new fear problems through unfamiliar noises and operating techniques. The panelists broached the thought that many situations which are routine to airline people are capable of causing concern, fear and apprehension on the part of passengers. Throughout all this discussion ran the recurring theme that it is, indeed, possible to transform these concerns into more favorable attitudes.

The seminar was in complete and rather significant agreement on the role that pilots can play in achieving this "transformation." Judicious, carefully handled cabin PA announcements, the panelists said, could be a major tool to the extent of warranting an airline effort to enlist pilot aid in a campaign. But they had these words of caution:

First, the panelists suggested, there should be an inventory of what can occur during a flight that causes fear. Pilot PA announcements should be handled with such an inventory in mind.

Second, the panelists warned, there is the danger of too much pilot information backfiring: one participant suggested the possibility of a "methinks the gentleman doth protest too much" kind of reaction among passengers—namely, "If he's doing all this reassuring, maybe I've really got something to worry about."

Third, it was suggested that nothing can be more frightening than a cabin PA which is unclear or garbled. Several panelists quite seriously commented that improved PA systems, put into the hands of pilots made aware of the effectiveness of good PA announcements, are most essential.

Despite these reservations, the panelists regarded adequate flight information from the flight deck as very promising. They even brought up personal experiences of their own to cite their own reactions. One told of a pilot who explained to his passengers the reasons behind a decision to move away from the ramp and get into a long line of planes waiting for takeoff clearance rather than just waiting at the ramp for the traffic jam to clear. Another recounted several instances where a pilot advised of a fifteen- to twenty-minute delay but was able to take off in five or ten minutes —suggesting a neat little psychological trick of getting passengers to anticipate the maximum inconvenience, then pleasantly surprise them with the minimum.

Only a pilot, the panel emphasized, can explain immediately situations that cause fear and perhaps even instill long-standing prejudice against flying. There may even be room for a good cockpit sense of humor in certain circumstances; one panelist cited the case of sudden loss of altitude which brought from the flight deck a good-natured "Whoops!" This was not exactly a scientific explanation for the drop, but it was the type of deliberate wisecracking which the panel felt to be most apropos on some occasions.

Some panelists went so far as to suggest that passengers might be allowed to listen to takeoff and landing clearances, or the reading of a checklist—if not over PA systems, perhaps through individual earphones.

While some of this may seem petty to an airline—or a pilot— it should be emphasized that the panel regarded it as essential that pilots give passengers an image of complete responsibility, and that such an image can be provided through calm, carefully worded and judiciously timed PA information.

For that matter, the panelists pointed out that cutting down irritation is almost as important as cutting down fear, because here is some evidence that irritation is not unrelated to fear. And the seminar was agreed that lack of information is a source of irritation.

In general, the seminar reached agreement in these areas:

1. Flying is safe and most fears are unjustified.

2. No one, including the participants on this panel, is exactly sure what people are afraid of and the extent to which it prevents them from flying.

3. There are many promising avenues for the airlines to explore

in reducing fear on the part of those who do fly and who would fly more if the experience of flight could be made more pleasurable and more exciting rather than frightening; the size of this group is something that should be ascertained because it may be vastly larger than anyone supposes.

4. There probably is no anti-fear campaign that will hit all targets; rather, the campaign to conquer fear and develop confidence in scheduled air transportation must take into consideration that the target categories may vary considerably, from those who have never flown to those who fly occasionally and can afford to fly more.

Point 4 underlined the seminar's belief that the fear problem actually is two-fold: fear while flying and fear before flying. It also underlined the seminar's conviction that the airlines could not wage any campaign in either of these two areas without assembling more data on what fears are involved among the different audiences the industry is trying to reach.

The panelists agreed there is a potentially "happy marriage" between the airline industry and psychology or psychiatry—in the sense that if the airlines really want to conquer fear, there is no shortage of professionally skilled interrogators, public opinion specialists and scientists capable of conducting controlled experiments, all aimed at accumulating the data necessary for determining what campaign or campaigns would be most effective.

The panelists thought the airlines should be willing to spend the necessary funds on collecting such data and also should be willing to try some experiments which may seem startling or even scatterbrained until it is realized how little we know about fear. For example, several panelists favored a test to measure the output of adrenalin during such flight phases as takeoffs, landings and turbulence.

The seminar was less sanguine about the chances of conquering fear among those who do not fly. The panelists considered this non-flying group largely inaccessible at present, with only the crudest idea of what constitutes this obviously enormous group and what constitutes its fears.

But the panelists did express the belief that the airlines have, in effect, ducked the issue of promoting safety as such—even though it was their unanimous conviction that the airlines have the right to be tremendously proud of their safety achievements.

To this group of experts, the airlines' ducking of the safety promotion issue, while at the same time they were justifiably proud of their safety accomplishments, seemed completely incongruous. The seminar was agreed unanimously, in effect, that the airlines have a most salable product on which they are doing too little selling.

There were specific "selling" proposals made, such as:

—Reviving the use of pamphlets in seat backs, along the lines of American's little "This Is What Flying's All About" booklet (which several panelists praised).

—An industry-wide institutional campaign to emphasize the safety of flight (several panelists recalled American's blunt "Are You Afraid to Fly?" advertisements of several years ago and expressed wonder that the entire industry has not sponsored similar ads).

—Establishment of a central airline information office in one or two major cities on a trial basis; this would be similar to the joint train information system in which the public can dial a single, central source for information on all train schedules. (This had the most emphatic support of any proposal, with all participants agreeing that a vast segment of the public simply hasn't any idea of where to go for general airline information, and that unfamiliarity with airline operations is undoubtedly an indirect fear factor.)

—Setting up an industry speaker's bureau composed of pilots and other qualified personnel who would go out and lecture various groups on air safety, particularly women's organizations; the panelists felt that the airlines have done too little to convince women of air safety.

—While the panelists were cautioned in advance not to get into the area of airline fares unless it was related to fear, the gentlemen could not refrain from expressing the view that getting more people to try flying is one answer. Thus there were a number of suggestions that the airlines revive sight-seeing flights, lower fares to attract large family or group travel and other proposals stemming from their belief that such promotion could tap the non-flying market; in fact, the idea of experimenting with a new type of "social structure" interior, to appeal to groups or families, was related to this area. The suggestion for sight-seeing flights, incidentally, brought some mention of the success American and TWA have had with this type of promotion in recent years.

Obviously, not even this distinguished panel could come up with a definite answer to the fear problem in a day-and-a-half session. What the seminar did achieve was a realization of the enormous extent of the problem. In this respect, the panelists urged that some experimentation along the lines they suggested should proceed immediately, without waiting for the much larger task of accumulating all the necessary data on fear prior to launching any all-out attack.

Such an eventual attack, the panelists emphasized, must largely revolve around efforts to educate the public on air safety because the problem, boiled down to the simplest terminology, is simply that people don't realize how safe flying is. As one panelist phrased it:

"Fear of accidental death is not confined to flying, but in the case of flying it is a unique fear because it is based on gross misunderstanding or misinformation."

That seminar was held in 1964, and as of this writing, there were several airline-sponsored surveys under way in the areas suggested. The results will be interesting and, hopefully, valuable because there still are indications that the airlines remain extremely sensitive about safety and reluctant to mention the subject of fear.

In 1967, Pacific Air Lines—a local service carrier—hired humorist Stan Freberg to compose a series of advertisements aimed at the "afraid to fly" contingent. The first one was a humdinger that shocked the entire industry. It was captioned: "HEY THERE—YOU WITH THE SWEAT IN YOUR PALMS." The text carried the surprising message that pilots, too, occasionally have sweat in their palms, but don't worry, flying is still pretty safe.

Freberg might as well have come out foursquare in favor of communism, sin and LSD consumption. The series was so controversial that it resulted in widespread industry condemnation and caused the eventual resignations of several top Pacific officials, as well as the subsequent retirement of Mr. Freberg from the airline advertising field—by request. Pacific explained, rather lamely, than it merely wanted people to notice the airline; there was no intent to scare anyone.

At the risk of alienating many airline friends, it is the opinion of this observer that while Freberg went a little too far, his intentions were entirely honorable, praiseworthy and rather refreshing. The airlines have come a long way since they used to send

employees to the scene of a crash armed with pails of whitewash—
to obliterate the name of the airline if it was still visible on the
wreckage. But most of them persist in what can be classed only as
an "ostrich attitude." No carrier can defend a fatal crash, which is
the worst publicity possible. But few if any airlines react to the
wild guessing, uninformed accusations and harmful speculation
that inevitably follow a crash—particularly from Congressmen. It
is not enough that the industry relies on the press to scotch rumors
and answer false charges—the press is sometimes as guilty as
Congress.

Curiously enough, the airlines sometimes react violently to
incidents far less harmful than those perpetrated by certain lawmakers and a minority of news media. A case in point was the
1964 crash test staged by the FAA and the Flight Safety Foundation in Phoenix. On April 24, the FAA and FSF deliberately
wrecked an old DC-7 crammed with impact-measuring instruments, dummies and crash survival equipment.

The DC-7, which used to fly for United, was sent down a
special runway that was nothing but a deadly obstacle course—
with telephone poles and mounds of earth strategically placed to
simulate a typical takeoff accident. Spectacular was the only word
for the test, which was well covered by all news media. In fact,
it turned out to be more spectacular than anyone expected. A
last-second tailwind, just as the plane was released via remote
control for its plunge down the booby-trapped runway, increased
the impact speed to twenty miles an hour above the planned
speed. Damage to the aircraft and its interior was considerably
more than the engineers expected—and the pictures were correspondingly more startling.

There was no disagreement on the value of the experiment. But
there was a blistering quarrel over the publicity it received. Briefly,
the airlines believed the FAA did air travel no favor when it gave
the news media free access to the motion-picture and still shots
of the crash. The movies, shown widely on television, were pretty
rough. There were slow-motion color films of the plane bursting
into flames, the cockpit disintegrating as it crunched into a small
hill, dummies in the cabin being tossed about wildly and crushed
by collapsing seats—the airlines feared that such vivid pictorial
material was hardly calculated to win friends for flying or influence potential passengers.

Airline officials complained privately and unofficially after the FAA released the films and photographs. But their resentment came out in the open when the President of the Air Transport Association, Stuart G. Tipton, disclosed he had written a protesting letter to then FAA chief Halaby.

Halaby's answer, in effect, was a blunt "go fly your kite." He said the public had a perfect right to know what the FAA was doing about improving the chances for survival in a landing or takeoff accident. Tipton then replied that the airlines were not objecting to press coverage of the Phoenix tests, but rather to the propriety of a Federal agency handing out gruesome pictures that could only "scare the daylights" out of people already afraid to fly.

Many airline officials felt that some of the more shocking pictures of the Arizona test actually cost them not only potential customers but solidified the fears of those millions who fly only when they have to.

"As for the non-flying segment of the population," said one airline executive, "the average 'I won't fly' citizen, frightened when he reads headlines about crashes, must be even more perturbed when he sees actual films of a crash, interior as well as exterior. Hell, I was a little scared myself."

The FAA's side of the controversy was that the airlines were being oversensitive. First, the agency argued, the public was well conditioned in advance to the fact that the Phoenix crash was a scientific experiment involving an old plane and presumably accepted even the most sensational pictures in that spirit. Second, the over-all effect of all the publicity, including the films and photographs, was one of reassurance—it made the public aware of how much effort is going into the task of making air travel safer. In fact, the FAA insisted, the spectacular aspects of the test may have contributed to that reassurance.

There probably is something to be said for both airline and FAA viewpoints. The airlines had some justification in pointing out that the FAA by law is entrusted with contributing to the advancement of commercial aviation—and that scaring people doesn't classify as an advancement. The tests *could* have been run without publicity and achieved the same scientific results. There was no doubt that the films were brutally effective; I know several friends who claim they remember the movie shots every time they board an airliner.

But the FAA also was justified in feeling that the airlines frequently have given the impression that even discussing air safety problems is bad for business—sort of an "if we don't talk about it, the problem may go away" attitude. It was interesting to note that the industry was not unanimous in scolding the FAA. W. A. Patterson, then Chairman of the Board of United Air Lines, held that the Phoenix tests (there were two staged crashes, the second involving a Constellation the following September) were beneficial in two ways: they contributed to flight safety, and the attendant publicity in turn contributed to public reassurance.

Patterson, who has since retired from an active role in aviation, was one of the few airline presidents who constantly chided his colleagues for ducking discussion of safety issues and problems. C. R. Smith of American was another—he publicly promoted and defended the Lockheed Electra when other Electra operators were taking the name of the maligned propjet out of their advertisements. To men like Patterson and Smith, the publicity given an air safety experiment was at least preferable to the attention given a real crash—particularly one in which emergency evacuation weaknesses cost lives that might have been saved.

In truth, the industry does not have to hide its head, avoid mention of safety whether negative or positive, or apologize for its record. ATA president Tipton once defined safety as "the art of reducing risk to the least possible chance of occurrence." That is precisely what the aviation community—airlines, government and manufacturers—have accomplished with fantastic strides. Granted there have been stumbles and falls. It also can be conceded air travel could be safer. But in making that concession, it is too easy to forget the achievements of the past, the efforts being exerted in the present, and the magnificent, almost unbelievable goals of the future.

And thus it is time to examine, dispassionately, the miracle wrought in the past decade—the first ten years of the jet age.

# 2

## THE FIRST TEN YEARS

On October 26, 1958, a Pan American World Airways Boeing 707 took off from Idlewild International Airport (now Kennedy) bound for Paris and literally got the jet revolution under way.

The proud British might regard this as sophistry, inasmuch as their Comets were flying passengers as far back as May of 1952. But the Comets, stricken with a fatal structural weakness, were grounded two years later and did not carry a passenger again until October 4, 1958, after they had undergone drastic structural changes. The resumption of Comet service over the North Atlantic preceded the Pan Am inaugural jet flight by twenty-two days and to the British went the chronological honors. But while the Comet was the technological pioneer, the larger and faster Boeing 707 and the subsequent Douglas DC-8 were the planes truly responsible for the jet revolution.

And revolution is the only applicable word to what has transpired in the past decade. It was poetic justice that the first scheduled flight of an American-made jetliner was from New York to Paris. Forty-four years before the inauguration of New York –Paris jet service, a famous American penned these words:

> It is a bare possibility that a one-man machine without a float and favored by a wind say of fifteen miles an hour might succeed in getting across the Atlantic. But such an attempt would be the height of folly. When one comes to increase the size of the craft, the possibility rapidly fades away. This is because of the difficulties of carrying sufficient fuel . . . it will readily be seen, therefore, why the Atlantic flight is out of the question.

The author of that pessimistic peek into the future was Orville Wright, a gallant aviation pioneer but a poor prophet. Exactly thirteen years later, Charles Lindbergh did what Orville Wright (and quite a few others) said was impossible. And forty years after Lindbergh's historic flight, there was a scheduled jetliner crossing the Atlantic once every ten minutes during peak traffic hours, carrying more than a hundred passengers at six hundred miles an hour at altitudes of up to forty thousand feet.

Transatlantic traffic alone totals about three million passengers a year and the jets are flying eleven persons for every one who travels by ship. It was the jet that made ocean flights routine, so routine that it is easy to become jaded toward the enormous technical achievements involved. Orville Wright worried about fuel capacity. A Boeing 707 or DC-8 taking off on an overseas flight burns more fuel in the first three minutes than Lindbergh did in thirty-three hours. One engine on a jet transport weighs more than the entire *Spirit of St. Louis*. And when Wright said the Atlantic could be crossed only by a plane carrying a single man, he never could foresee that a fully loaded jetliner's wings would be capable of supporting the weight of one hundred and two pounds for every square foot of wing area—which amounts to carrying a load of automobiles stacked as high as the Washington Monument on each wing.

The jets figuratively shrank the world by 40 per cent, cruising at speeds made possible by only four engines; if engineers wanted to fly a piston-engine plane at six hundred miles an hour, they would have to install forty power plants. A jet is so perfectly streamlined that dirt on the fuselage increases fuel consumption by nearly two pounds per nautical mile. On a New York–Rome flight, a dirty airplane would cost an airline one thousand gallons of extra fuel.

The jet has changed travel habits to such an extent that it produced the coining of a new phrase—jet set. It is more than just a phrase. There was a young woman in Washington, D.C., who flew to Rome every other week to see her fiancée, while he flew to Washington on alternate weekends. Ditto a San Francisco lawyer engaged to a girl in Honolulu. He took a jet to Hawaii one weekend and she flew to San Francisco the next.

It is not unusual these days for couples to fly from one city to another just for dinner and a show, returning home the same night. In Miami two winters ago, a couple of lifeguards got bored with all the sunshine, caught a plane to New Hampshire, spent a weekend skiing and were back at work on the beach Monday morning.

"Instant mobility" is one name given to the phenomenon of the jet age. That is what Stuart G. Tipton of ATA called it in a speech. He was referring to the growing acceptance of air travel thanks to the jet—growing so fast that even the airlines are stunned. In 1939, the U.S. airlines flew 1.7 million passengers during the entire year. They now carry 2.5 million every week.

Traffic in the first decade of the jets has soared 135.7 per cent—from 56 million passengers in 1958 to more than 130 million in 1967. The U.S. population is growing by seven thousand persons daily, but that is thirty-three thousand less than the number of new passengers who boarded the airlines every day in 1968. The latter figure could be hopelessly out of date by the time you read this; as recently as 1966, the total of new passengers daily was only ten thousand. The jet revolution's impact on just one American city—Cleveland, Ohio—will underscore its multiplying germination: Cleveland generated more traffic in 1967 than *all* the U.S. airlines carried during 1940. One forecast predicts that the nation's scheduled carriers will be flying 500 million passengers annually by 1980.

From every side come indications that Americans are treating air travel almost as casually as they do the automobile. One example: only a few years ago, the overwhelming majority of reservations made for business flights were booked at least one week in advance. Now most business reservations are made only a day or two before the intended flight, and a significant number are made on the same day.

Business travel still accounts for most air trips. But the percentage is dropping steadily, thanks to the avalanche of special promotional fares appealing to families and youths. Only one year after the airlines introduced the family fare, the new rate was producing more than 25 per cent of their coach revenues—an almost miraculous market penetration in such a short time. And no wonder. It is possible to fly a family of five coast to coast for $77 per person; just try budgeting the same trip for the same number of persons by car.

Another aspect of the jet revolution is that travel is now getting priority over other so-called luxury items in family expenditures. Many families already have that second car, fairly new television sets and a myriad of home appliances. As incomes increase, there is room in the budget for long trips that would be difficult or impossible in an automobile.

Hawaii provides a good example of the impact of jet vacation travel. In 1947, there were less than fifty-five thousand airline passengers between California and the Islands. There now are more than 1 million a year. In 1947, Hawaii offered a total of fifteen hundred hotel rooms and now has more than fifteen thousand.

Only a relative handful of Americans flew in the year 1932, when a transcontinental air trip required nearly thirty hours and eleven stops. (Today there are approximately three hundred scheduled jet transcontinental trips daily carrying twenty thousand passengers.)

Let's look at that year 1932 . . .

When engines had to be inspected every twenty-five hours and overhauled every two hundred and fifty hours because of their unreliability. (The modern jet engine averages eight thousand hours between overhauls, with a single overhaul costing $90,000 —$40,000 more than the price tag on a single transport plane of the thirties.)

When cancellations because of weather and mechanical troubles were so frequent that pilots carried special forms authorizing passengers to switch to railroads. (In 1967, with jets flying 75 per cent of the traffic, the airlines completed 97.7 per cent of their scheduled mileage—which added up, by the way, to an astronomical 1 billion, 802 million miles.)

When the airline fatality rate was 14.96 deaths for every 100 million passenger miles flown, thanks to sixteen fatal crashes—not a bad rate considering the fact that the airlines had one hundred and eight accidents that year. (In the past ten years, the U.S. airlines' fatality rate has ranged from a high of 0.76 in 1960—a rate due mostly to the Lockheed Electra's troubles at the time—to an all-time low of 0.07 in 1966. Not since 1951 has the rate gone as high as one death per 100 million miles.)

When a new copilot could be hired at 10 A.M. and be flying a regular trip in the right seat by 3 P.M. the same day. (A new pilot today goes through at least six weeks of ground school plus three weeks of flight training, and has to be retrained all over again when he shifts to different equipment or upgrades to captain. The airlines now spend $100 million annually just for flight crew training, a sum representing the industry's *entire gross* in 1940. At any given time, roughly 10 per cent of an airline's pilots are in some phase of new or recurrent training.)

When all twenty-four airlines then operating in the United States offered a total of less than seven hundred daily flights. (A single local service airline schedules that many every day.)

When 80 per cent of the four hundred and fifty planes in the nation's commercial air fleet were single-engine aircraft. (The fleet now numbers approximately two thousand, about eleven hundred of the aircraft being pure jets and another four hundred propjets whose turbine engines are hitched to conventional propellers.)

When the country's biggest airline proudly boasted it would fly one hundred thousand passengers during the year. (The same airline is currently carrying that many every two days.)

When the pilot work force in scheduled air transportation numbered less than seven hundred men. (In 1967, there were twenty-two thousand active airline pilots, who, incidentally, had a two-hundred-times-better chance of staying alive on their job than their brethren of 1932.)

When the twelve-passenger Ford Trimotor was the queen of the nation's commercial air fleet. (Just one airline, American, has figured out that to operate its present schedules solely between New York and Chicago would require four hundred Trimotors making two hundred departures each way, manned by twenty-four hundred pilots and twelve hundred stewardesses and needing four hundred fuel stops at both Detroit and Buffalo. And at today's jet fares, American would lose $25 per passenger operating that four hundred Trimotor fleet.)

The contrast between 1932 and the present, of course, is far more dramatic than comparing the heyday of the pistons—the middle 1950s—with the jet years of the sixties. Yet even the latter comparison offers some startling items.

—The major U.S. airlines are investing more than $8 billion in *new* jet equipment during the 1966–70 period; in 1955, the entire propeller-driven fleet represented an investment of less than $1.2 billion. The $8 billion does not include jets delivered before 1966.

—In 1955, slightly more than a half cent of every airline revenue dollar went for interest payments on new piston equipment. The figure for the jet age averages four cents out of every revenue dollar.

—The price tag on the spare parts inventory for a major airline was $19 million at the start of the jet age. It is now around $60 million for the average carrier.

—The New York Port Authority pre-jet investment at Kennedy Airport was $221 million. Today it has more than $400 million invested, with Kennedy's terminal area alone covering one hundred acres more than the entire LaGuardia Airport installation, including runways.

—A DC-3 did a day's work when it flew from New York to Little Rock, Arkansas. A Constellation or DC-6 and DC-7 could get in, at the most, a one-way coast-to-coast flight. The jet's minimum workday covers a round trip between the East and West Coasts, with utilization hitting as high as seventeen hours just for passenger flights. A single Boeing 727QC (QC for "Quick Change"), which can be converted from a passenger aircraft to an all-cargo plane or back again in less than forty-five minutes, often will be flown twenty hours out of every twenty-four—the non-flying period being used for maintenance. It carries passengers by day and freight by night. During 1968, the airlines were scheduled to take delivery on four hundred and forty-four new transports—just about the size of the entire U.S. commercial fleet in 1932. The industry's 1968–74 re-equipment program amounts to $10 billion for more than thirteen hundred new planes. During 1968, the airlines took delivery on two new jets, averaging $6.5 million per aircraft, every working day of the year. The $10 billion re-equipment program is even more staggering when one realizes that the airlines' net worth in 1967 was only $2.9 billion, and it is just further proof of the jet revolution's extent. In terms of that vital economic barometer, capital spending, the air transportation industry is now the nation's seventh largest.

The jet age has been an employment bonanza in the nation's economy. The airline industry in 1956 had on its payrolls slightly more than one hundred and thirty-one thousand persons. By 1967 total employment had boomed to two hundred and seventy-five thousand, with a 13 per cent gain registered between 1966 and 1967 alone. The airlines used to be happy with a 5 per cent annual gain in traffic. The average for the past five years has exceeded 15 per cent. And the end does not seem to be in sight. Economists estimate that traffic will double in the next half decade—with the resulting need for another four thousand pilots and eleven thousand mechanics by 1970, not to mention what will be needed in additional ground personnel. The stewardess force alone has soared from eight thousand in 1956 to twenty-two thousand in 1967.

The air travel surge also has sparked a corresponding boom in the manufacturing end of commercial aviation. The number of new jobs in the commercial transport field jumped 11 per cent between March of 1966 and March 1967. The Air Transport Association estimates that the U.S. supersonic transport program alone will have an economic fall-out of $20 billion to $50 billion in the next five to ten years. The ATA forecast is based on the expected creation of two hundred and fifty thousand new jobs: fifty thousand for the prime contractors, Boeing and General Electric, plus a hundred thousand for subcontractors, with these one hundred and fifty thousand new jobs creating another ten thousand positions in non-manufacturing industries ranging from communications to real estate. ATA believes the SST project will account for one out of every fifty new civilian jobs created by 1975.

Thus the jet revolution is destined to continue, spreading its influence and effects throughout the nation's and the world's economy. For it is not merely an American revolution; the jet has had world-wide repercussions, even in areas one might think immune to advances of commercial aviation. One example will suffice.

Any GI who fought on the island of New Guinea in World War II will remember it as a steaming, primitive pesthole that reverted to the jungle as soon as the war ended. New Guinea might seem like the most unlikely target on the planet for aviation progress. Yet today the island has one hundred and twenty-six airports which serve five hundred thousand passengers a year. Scheduled airline operations in and out of New Guinea exceed one hundred thousand movements annually. The airplane, and the jet in particular, has metamorphosed what was for centuries a primeval land.

The jet revolution occurred because jet transportation introduced new dimensions of speed, comfort, capacity and efficiency. But these factors would have been worthless without the most important accomplishment of all—new dimensions of safety. This is what made public acceptance of the other factors possible.

The prosaic routineness of modern air transportation has caused the unhappier memories of the past to fade. A 1936 *Fortune* magazine survey offers a stark example of how things used to be. The survey disclosed that if Americans were given a choice between a plane or a train for a journey of more than five hundred miles, 75 per cent would pick the train. That was the over-all percentage; among the men polled, 70 per cent chose the train while nearly 81 per cent of the women preferred railroad travel.

Nobody blamed them, either. The Actuarial Society of America, about the same time, said an airliner was fifty-three times more dangerous than a Pullman. And commercial flying was rated eight times more hazardous than the private automobile.

Compare the *Fortune* survey with a poll conducted in 1963 by the American Newspaper Publishers Association. This time the question was: "If you were making a long trip (over one thousand miles) and flying was the cheapest way to go, would you fly or use some other means of transportation?" The results:

—Of those who travel for business, 95 per cent said they would fly.

—Among non-business travelers, 92 per cent picked flying.

—Among those who did not fly, 64 per cent said they would fly if it were the least expensive way to travel: 23 per cent preferred the automobile and only 11 per cent chose trains.

If the story of commercial aviation is one of gradual public acceptance, it also is a story of gradual improvement in safety. On a year-by-year basis, the airline fatality rate tends to fluctuate slightly. It seems fairer to measure the record at longer range—on the basis of five-year averages. Using the airlines' yardstick—fatalities per 100 million passenger miles flown—the picture is one of steady progress:

|         |      |
|---------|------|
| 1942–46 | 2.10 |
| 1947–51 | 1.51 |
| 1952–56 | .50  |
| 1957–61 | .48  |
| 1962–66 | .22  |

As Daniel Priest, vice president of public relations for ATA, put it in a speech:

"From the passenger point of view, the fatality rate is the key element in measuring the progress of airline safety. Not only has it improved, it *had* to improve. If the airlines had the same fatality rate, 5.20, that they had in 1938, the airlines last year (1967) would have had five thousand, one hundred and sixty-four fatalities instead of the two hundred and twenty-six they did have."

Note, in the five-year averages, how the safety rate improved during the 1957–66 decade. There were many who predicted a rise in the rate after jets began operating in 1958. After all, they were a completely different type of aircraft flying at speeds and altitudes never before reached by commercial transports. They were not only faster but much heavier, with unfamiliar handling characteristics that invited trouble. They were far more unforgiving than a piston-engine plane and if one did crash, the passenger load alone would have a serious effect on the airlines' own safety yardstick. A fully occupied 707 or DC-8 that crashed could involve as many fatalities as six fatal acidents involving fully loaded DC-3s.

But it just didn't happen that way. While the jets did present safety problems (they *are*, without any doubt, unforgiving beasts that must be flown by the book), they also proved safer than the older planes in many respects—they are stronger, more powerful, exceptionally superior in terms of engine reliability, and their altitude capability puts them above bad weather during most portions of a flight. In the seven years between 1960 and 1967, there were one hundred and sixteen fatal crashes involving piston-engine planes flown by the scheduled airlines of the free world. In the same period, there were thirty-five fatal accidents involving jets, and thirty-eight involving propjets. In 1966, with jets accounting for three fourths of air traffic, the fatality rate for the U.S. scheduled airlines was lower than that of trains and buses—and twenty-eight times under that of the private automobile.

The most comprehensive survey of jet crashes was done by Captain William Moss, a flight operations official for Pan American World Airways. It was first prepared in 1963 and later updated to include jet accidents that occurred through 1966. Moss delivered his initial paper before the Flight Safety Foundation's International Air Safety Seminar in Athens, Greece, under a rather dull title: "Special Aspects of Jet Statistics."

But the contents added up to some of the most provocative observations and conclusions ever made about safety in the jet age.

What Moss did was to study the official and unofficial causes of every fatal jetliner accident between 1958 and 1967. At the time he prepared his facts and figures, there were eighty-nine free world airlines operating jets with a total accumulation of about 15 million hours. It was a pretty good chunk of basic source material and Moss even loaded the dice *against* the jets. First, he avoided using the much-criticized statistical base of fatalities per 100 million passenger miles flown. He chose instead the yardstick of hours flown per fatal crash. Furthermore, he included training accidents and sabotage cases—types of crashes which are not fed into the usual safety statistics. Yet even with this more critical ruler, the jets' record was impressive.

The Moss study confirmed a little-realized achievement of the jet age: the fatal accident rate generally has declined in direct proportion to the increasing use of jets. The rate started with one fatal jet crash every one hundred and fifty thousand hours over the first two years—1959 and 1960. It improved dramatically to a rate of one fatal accident per seven hundred and twenty thousand hours by 1965. Then the rate worsened to one crash for every three hundred and fifty thousand hours. Moss traced the increase to what safety experts term the "learning curve"—which is simply the lack of experience in operating new types of aircraft. In 1965 and 1966, there ware several accidents involving the relatively new Boeing 727 and BAC-111—both so-called "second generation"—as well as the brand-new DC-9. The Boeing 727's difficulties will be treated in a later chapter; at this point, it is enough to say that the airlines cannot condone, in good faith, any learning curve. A passenger has the right to expect that all the necessary learning has been done *before* he steps aboard a new type of aircraft. Certainly there will be no room for a learning curve in the days of the jumbo jets and supersonic transports.

But in fairness to the carriers and their training procedures, it is essential to examine the Moss findings a little further. They cast an illuminating light on the primary reasons behind jet accidents.

First, it should be remembered that his survey covered all airlines except those behind the Iron Curtain (Russia's state-owned and -operated carrier, Aeroflot, has an unknown safety record because the Soviet Union does not always disclose fatal crashes unless foreigners were among the passengers). Many foreign carriers such as Japan Air Lines, Britain's BOAC, SAS, Swissair, Alitalia, Lufthansa and numerous others have safety performances as good as that of any U.S. airline. But a few do not and Moss was not trying to whitewash the jets; he included *all* crashes.

Bearing this in mind, the Moss study showed some remarkable causal patterns.

For one thing, 20 per cent of the crashes were on training flights when pilots were exposed to abnormal situations and operating conditions—such as trying to maneuver at low altitudes with power cut on two out of four engines. The most significant finding was that 63 per cent of the crashes occurred during the landing phase, *with 80 per cent of these taking place in areas of the world where only 17 per cent of the landings are made* "and where the quality of navigational aids and traffic control is the lowest," as Moss emphasized. These areas included Asia, South and Central America and Africa.

By contrast, North America—with 62 per cent of the world's scheduled landings—had only 10 per cent of the landing accidents. Europe, which also has superior airport facilities, had 21 per cent of the landings and only 10 per cent of the landing crashes.

One of the nation's top safety experts, Jerome Lederer of NASA (formerly Director of the Flight Safety Foundation), commented wryly on this correlation between accidents and lack of landing aids by pointing out that "a cost benefit study might show that the installation and operation of these aids would have cost less than the accidents their absence induced."

The Pan Am captain found pilot error involved as a possible contributory cause in 83 per cent of the accidents. Weather was cited as a contributing factor in 40 per cent, navigational aids 38 per cent, maintenance 35 per cent, design 35 per cent and sabotage 4 per cent. Moss, a veteran pilot himself, did not duck the hot-potato issue of crew mistakes. He pointed out that in general, pilot goofs were triggered by factors outside the cockpit such as nav aid malfunctions and weather. But he added:

"In spite of these prior contributory factors, it still remains that the flight crew did not *prevent* [his italics] the accident from happening. I maintain that the prime duty of the flight crew is to cope with the failures of designers, of maintenance, of other humans; this is why our airplanes are not fully automated . . ."

Having tagged pilots with a large measure of responsibility,

Captain Moss went on to plead for better tools with which pilots can work. Specifically:

—Improved nav aids in underequipped areas, such as visual glide paths.

—Better cockpit facilities for chart reading at night; Moss believes this outwardly insignificant item is a prime safety matter, with pilots relying on memory for important altitudes because it is too difficult to read and/or so easy to misread charts at night. He declared that improved cockpit lighting would reduce the incidence of hitting mountains on initial descent, hills on initial approaches or undershoots on final approach—all three frequent repeaters in the circumstances of jet crashes.

—Up-to-date operations manuals as well as adequate "by the book" training; "It is not enough to assume that a man will learn the procedures himself, nor is it enough to assume that he will remember them forever," Moss added.

That latter recommendation will later acquire the luster of perspicacity when we delve more deeply into individual jet crashes, several of which involved training loopholes as a major causal factor. In the training category, Moss offered this frank advice to all airlines: get chief pilots who are not afraid to take disciplinary action and who also are not intimidated by top management.

The Moss survey hit hard at a generally unsuspected and vastly underrated area of concern in the jet age-complacency. The dates of occurrence for the forty fatal accidents he studied show clear evidence that many carriers tend to tighten up procedures and precautions after a bad accident, then after a period of uneventful operations they seem to relax until tragedy strikes again. In effect, Moss was the first responsible airline official who supported that famous "rule of three" superstition—the belief that airline accidents occur in groups of three. Moss indicated it is not a superstition or a coincidence, but a statistical fact stemming from complacency. Explained Moss:

"It is human nature to relax your guard after a certain period. Then lightning strikes. We have a series of accidents in close succession, and we tighten up our procedures operationally and maintenance-wise . . . This accomplishes the objective and we control the accident picture—until we are lulled into a false sense of security again and the stage is set for another rude awakening by a series of accidents."

It should be reiterated again that the Moss study, its conclusions
and criticisms, were directed at airlines in general. He found the
U.S. jet safety record markedly superior to the over-all world rate
and he attributed this in part to the fact that the United States
never tries to sweep an accident under a rug. Moss noted that
the causes of only about half the foreign crashes covered in his
report were officially and publicly reported subsequent to the accidents. By contrast, the United States issues full and detailed
reports on all crashes and makes them readily available not only
in this country but abroad.

It is no coincidence that the U.S. safety record is one of the
best in the world, Moss said, "because prompt public disclosure
of accident facts and circumstances . . . has had a marked effect
on the U.S. record."

An equally interesting approach to safety statistics was made by
Robert F. Dressler, a special FAA consultant, in a paper read before
the International Air Safety Seminar at Madrid in 1966. Dressler
took a different tack than Moss in that he broke down aircraft
accidents in terms of three categories—takeoff, cruise and landing—
and weighed the relative safety of all types of planes in each
operational phase.

Dressler's survey covered three hundred and eighteen accidents,
fatal and non-fatal, involving U.S. carriers between 1961 and 1964.
On the basis of this study, he found that:

—Jets were twice as dangerous during takeoff and landing as
pistons or propjets.

—The jets' cruise risk decreased 40 per cent in the four-year
period, to the point where cruise risk was almost negligible compared to the takeoff and landing phases.

—Cruise risk was almost identical for jets, pistons and propjets
alike.

—Pistons were safest in landings and propjets were safest in
takeoffs.

—There was a distinct correlation between landing speeds and
landing risks, the jets' higher landing speeds being a definite
contributory factor in accidents occurring in this phase.

The Dressler statistics seem to cast a jaundiced eye on the jets,
but they should not be interpreted as a flat "jets are more dangerous" conclusion. Obviously they are more vulnerable to landing
and takeoff accidents because in too many instances they operate

at airports designed for piston-engine transports (see Chapter 4).
And Dressler's inclusion of *non-fatal* accidents gave him an entirely different statistical base than Moss's.

Examining any set of safety statistics reminds one of the fable
about the three blind men who touched an elephant and then
described the animal in terms of whatever part of the animal's
anatomy each happened to grab. On one hand, we have the august
Senate Aeronautical and Space Sciences Committee, which in
February of 1967 issued a sharply critical report on air safety.

"Aviation safety shows no signs of improvement," the Committee
declared. "Scheduled air safety statistics show that aviation safety
has not improved much over the past seventeen years."

The report complained about "year-to-year fluctuations," noting
that 1966 was the safest year in U.S. commercial aviation history
("a remarkable improvement," the Committee said) but that 1967
saw a reversion to the fifteen-year average.

On the other hand, it could be argued with admirable logic
that keeping the fatality and accident rate consistently low is no
minor achievement—considering the technical aspects of the jet
revolution. The 1967 statistics would have just about equaled
1966's, as a matter of fact, were it not for two midair collisions
between airliners and private planes—both accidents in which
the airlines involved certainly could shoulder little or no part of
the blame. Just one or two crashes, occurring under circumstances
divorced from airline safety practices, can cause havoc to safety
statistics. It would be fairer to examine the reasons behind transport crashes before indicting the industry for what appears to be
a status quo record. It also must be admitted that even a fluctuating
record, if the average rate is low, has to indicate an enormous
amount of safety progress. The jet age, with built-in seeds of
trouble in the form of more complex planes, swollen passenger
lists and routine operations in weather that once would have
caused flight cancellations, could have been disastrous if it were
not for dramatic improvements and unappreciated accomplishments. It might be mentioned that the most frequent reasons for
jet crashes listed in the Moss study were the same as those which
have resulted in fatal accidents to older planes. Comparatively
few were analogous to jet operations, which makes the over-all
performance of the turbine-powered fleet even more remarkable.

Yet it is not a proud past that concerns many in aviation, but a future that by its own expanding nature *cannot* rely on any fluctuating—however slight—or generally static accident rate. Put the record of U.S. aviation's best year—1966—into the year 1970 and you might have a catastrophic situation. In 1966, the nation's scheduled airlines had three fatal accidents with a fatality total of only fifty-nine lives. But suppose there were three fatal accidents involving jumbo jets or supersonic transports.

The crash of a single Boeing 747 jumbo jet, which will carry between three hundred and fifty and four hundred and fifty passengers, could be the statistical equivalent of three DC-8 or 707 accidents. The same will be true of the American SST. The worst annual death toll for U.S. carriers was three hundred and seven in 1960. Bobbie Allen, former Director of the Department of Transportation's Safety Board and the nation's top accident investigator, is one who believes a rate decline is mandatory.

"When I look at the projected increase in activity," Allen told an Aviation/Space Writers Association meeting in Washington, "I become apprehensive because accident statistics that are acceptable today may become intolerable tomorrow."

The airlines themselves are apprehensive, too, because they readily agree that air travel must be made even safer. Again, safety and economic progress in the industry have been blood brothers. The industry is well aware of what a single jumbo jet or SST crash can mean, not only in terms of human tragedy and statistics, but also in terms of financial loss. James Fortuna, Vice President of United States Aviation Underwriters, has estimated that a three-hundred-fifty-passenger jet has a loss potential of $55 million just in passenger insurance claims, not to mention the $20 million value of the aircraft itself, plus whatever claims might be filed for damage or injury to persons and property on the ground.

A court awarded the family of a man killed in a 1963 jet crash no less than $2 million. A total of one hundred and fifteen damage suits were filed after the collision of a United DC-8 and TWA Constellation over New York's Staten Island in 1960. The claims amounted to nearly $80 million. Many carriers are considering formation of an airline-owned insurance company before the jumbos and supersonics come along.

There have been some startling projections made on the assumption that the airline accident rate will continue to remain relatively static. One authority predicted one hundred and forty fatal crashes on the world's scheduled airlines over the next five years, with fourteen hundred passenger deaths. The gloomiest and most quoted forecast comes from Bo Lundberg, for years head of Sweden's Aeronautical Foundation (and a vitriolic opponent of the SST). Lundberg took the anticipated growth in passenger miles flown, applied the average world accident rate for the past ten years, and arrived at the conclusion that by the year 2000 we can expect ten thousand deaths a year in airliner crashes unless the present rate is reduced drastically—and eleven hundred annual fatalities as early as 1975.

Such doleful crystal ball reflections may be statistically possible but are not very likely, if past performance and future plans are considered. There was a veritable voices-of-doom chorus ten years ago when the jets began operating, and now the same voices are being aimed in the direction of the jet revolution's second stage— the jumbos and the supersonics. What follows in this book should provide reassurance that the airlines intend to make that second stage even safer than the first—not only with the newer planes but in operations involving the older jets.

If anyone thinks the public is not conscious of and interested in air safety problems, he might inspect about thirty folders on the seventh floor of the big Federal Aviation Administration building in Washington.

Each folder carries the label: "IDEAS ON AIR SAFETY FROM THE PUBLIC." They include correspondence from learned aeronautical engineers, complete with blueprints. There also are laboriously scrawled, crude drawings from children. One letter is from an inventor outlining his proposal for a new type of airliner seat. There is another from an eleven-year-old boy addressed to the late President John F. Kennedy. It starts out: "I'm sorry to bother you, but I have an idea on how to make airplanes safer."

This was accompanied by a pencil drawing of a crippled airliner, with a huge parachute attached to the fuselage. Actually, the youngster's idea is the most frequent suggestion made to FAA. The agency answers each one with the patient explanation that even if it were possible to design a parachute capable of supporting the weight of a huge jetliner, such a chute would be so heavy by itself that passenger and baggage capacity would have to be limited.

The FAA answers every letter, no matter how farfetched or crackpot it may seem. In some cases, it merely acknowledges the correspondence with a polite note thanking the writer for his interest in air safety. Suggestions which may have some merit are turned over to FAA's Safety and Engineering Division.

The majority of letters seek financial help for further experimentation. A great proportion present ideas or theories which already are the subject of current testing or which have been discarded on the basis of previous experiments. And curiously enough, most of them have come in since 1960.

Quite a few bring smiles to FAA's engineers—like the one which began belligerently: "I think this idea is good. It's better than the ones you have, which are nothing."

Or the writer who simply informed FAA: "I have a device which will prevent all crashes. Please reply soon."

Many safety proposals are ingenious, if impractical. Samples:

—Build a conveyor belt at airports, the belt moving at the same speed as a landing aircraft so a plane making a wheels-up landing would merely have to set down on the belt. (Wheels-up landings are not a serious problem, seldom result in anything but minor damage, and the belt idea would be too expensive.)

—Put a big cradle on a flatcar which would move down the runway and catch a crippled airliner as it settled down. (Same objections.)

—Equip each airliner with a telescopic tube, through which passengers could be transferred from a crippled plane to another aircraft while still in flight. (Such a tube would have to be at least seventy-five feet long to keep the planes safely separated, and strong enough to allow the passage of persons at about one hundred and fifty miles an hour—all of which adds up to a device so heavy that no transport plane could carry one.)

—Install a loud siren on every plane so the pilot could warn people on the ground if his aircraft was about to crash. (No comment necessary.)

—Put a long steel rod in the nose of every plane, with a steel spring attached to absorb the shock if the aircraft struck a mountain. (No comment necessary.)

—Line airliner cabins with asbestos so that temperatures from post-impact fire could be kept low while passengers were evacuating. (To keep temperatures below 150° F for a five-minute evacuation would require asbestos about two inches thick—thus adding around nine thousand pounds of weight to the airframe. Actually, new cabin-lining materials are being perfected for present and future airliners which provide thermal protection with no weight penalty; they are described in a subsequent chapter.)

—Have every airliner equipped with a capsule that could be ejected automatically on impact. It would contain any last messages from the crew, comments from the passengers and even such valuables as jewelry and wallets. (Pilots are too busy in an emergency to start writing notes for capsules. Anyway, new cockpit voice recorders are required for all jets and would fill much the same purpose. Also being considered is a crash locator beacon, ejected automatically and capable of sending radio signals that would guide rescue parties to the scene of a remote crash.)

—Planes should be able to fire rockets ahead of them into areas of suspected turbulence. If the rocket is caught in rough air, it could send a warning signal back to the plane. (Major research is being conducted on means to detect clear-air turbulence, largely through "sensors" which operate on a heat principle because turbulence is associated with temperature changes. This work will be described more fully in another chapter.)

Next to parachutes for planes, the most frequent suggestion submitted to FAA involves a means of jettisoning the wings if a crash were inevitable. FAA concedes the theory is admirable because this would eliminate a fire danger. But the fuel system of a modern plane is intricate, with complex plumbing and pumping lines throughout the fuselage and wings. Any wing-jettison device would have to disconnect automatically the entire fuel system. Engineers are wary of any gimmick subject to inadvertent activation, thus creating an even worse danger than the one it is supposed to eliminate.

The truth is that the FAA has yet to get an idea from the public which would warrant further investigation—with one exception. A youngster sent in a plan for an airliner seat with crash-resistant qualities. It was good enough to intrigue FAA technicians. But when they looked into it further, they discovered that a similar seat already had been designed and found to be too complicated and heavy.

At least the public is well-meaning and interested in what is being done and what will be done to make flying safer. Yet whatever gadgets, devices and hardware are developed, air safety still depends to a great extent on the skill, training and dedication of the men in the cockpit.

# 3

## "IT'S WHAT'S UP FRONT THAT COUNTS"

Kimes . . . White . . . Carroll . . . Duescher. . . .

Ask any airline passenger if those names mean anything, and the odds are about 100 million to one against any of them being recognized. That isn't surprising but in a way it is too bad. Those four names were responsible for preserving the lives of three hundred and eighteen fellow human beings.

Kimes . . . White . . . Carroll . . . Duescher . . . Each wore the four stripes of an airline captain, four tiny bands of gold or silver on the sleeves of their uniform coats—those four bands that mean the culmination of years of training and an unspoken but sacred sense of responsibility.

Each was "fully qualified to serve as airline captain, having completed the required qualifications for the high responsibilities and public trust of the position," as the captain's "diploma" for one major airline puts it. Individually, they worked for four different airlines—Pan American, Eastern, Trans World and United. But their braided caps could have carried the insignia of any airline. They were typical of their profession, products of the world's finest flight training, and possessing the three qualities that comprise the character of the airline pilot—skill, courage and coolness under pressure.

These are their stories. They are not told to glorify the four men but rather to present them as airline captains whose professional performances could have been duplicated by thousands of their fellow pilots. This is not to disparage what they did, but merely to point out that they saved three hundred and eighteen lives primarily because they came out of an industry training system specifically designed to deal with emergencies. Undoubtedly they *did* perform "above and beyond" normal airmanship. But basically that is what an airline pilot is trained for and what he is paid for—the ability to analyze an abnormal situation instantly and react correctly. Anyone who questions the validity of paying airline pilots up to $40,000 a year should realize that a captain flying a $6 million airplane crammed with trusting passengers can earn the $40,000 in a few seconds. Like Charles H. Kimes.

There were one hundred and forty-three passengers plus a crew of ten aboard Pan American World Airways Flight 843 when it took off from San Francisco for Honolulu on June 28, 1965.

First Officer Fred R. Miller was at the controls as the Boeing 707 screamed down the runway, a two hundred and seventy thousand pound defiance of gravity.

"Eighty knots," Captain Kimes called out. "Ninety. One hundred."

The nosewheel pounded and thumped. The four engines were spewing at least 95 per cent of full-rated power.

"$V_1$," Kimes announced—the takeoff point of no return.

"Rotate!" Kimes's order was followed instantly by Miller's applying gentle back pressure on the yoke. The 707's nose lifted. The main-landing-gear wheels left the ground with a thud that was almost a protest.

"$V_2$," Kimes said. This was minimum safe airspeed. Flight 843 climbed smoothly, its great bulk and immense power providing the peculiar sensory illusion that is part of the jet age—the feeling that the aircraft is hooked to a giant railroad track curving into the sky. The four men in the cockpit began to relax almost imperceptibly, the inevitable tenseness of every takeoff disappearing magically with the sound of "$V_2$" and the moment of miracle that is flight itself.

In the cabin, Mr. and Mrs. Louis Swanson and their two sons—Louis, eleven, and Joseph, seven, settled back in their seats. The Swansons were from McAdoo, Pennsylvania, and had been attending a Lions Club International convention in Los Angeles. They had never been to Hawaii and after the convention they had flown to San Francisco for connections with Pan Am 843.

Young Louis had a window seat just over the right wing. His brother wanted to know if the plane was "up in the air yet."

"Just about," Louis said with the half-bored, patronizing air of an eleven-year-old talking to a seven-year-old. He still was looking out the window at the wing when he froze.

"Mommy, Mommy!" he shouted. "The wing's on fire! Look!"

Mrs. Swanson peered out too. Flames were gushing from the outboard engine. "It's all over for us," she thought dully.

Jorge Rivera, a chemistry student from Hawaii, had felt the thud of the retracting landing gear as it was tucked away into the belly wheel well. But not more than ninety seconds later, he felt another jolt of a different intensity and source. He looked up and saw a faint, glowlike reflection in the cabin. Almost automatically, he glanced outside. The engine farthest away from him was gone and the wing was on fire.

Mrs. Kaleo Schroder, a California schoolteacher traveling with her three children saw the engine leave the wing. The flames seemed to crawl directly toward them. The children began crying. Mrs. Schroder tried to calm them. Her own reaction was curiously unperturbed. The night before, she had dreamed that something was going to happen to the plane and her first reaction was, "Well, it's happening."

Unperturbed was not the word for passenger Minoru Fujioka of Hawaii. He and his wife had just bid goodbye to their eighteen-year-old son, who was enrolling in the Air Force Academy at Colorado Springs. Fujioka was not a religious man. But when he saw the fire sweep the outer portion of the wing, he prayed. Mrs. Fujioka thought only of her son.

"He will never see me again," she said to herself.

In the cockpit, Kimes and his three colleagues felt the 707 shudder violently. A red light just above the instrument panel flashed angrily and a loud bell sounded. It was a fire warning from the number four engine. Kimes could not know it, but a turbine wheel had disintegrated, flying apart with a force that amounted to an internal explosion. Those compressor wheels whirl ten thousand times a minute, impelled by combustion that has been measured at 1600° F—a gigantic blowtorch capable of melting lead or aluminum. The disintegration of the compressor wheel sent steel slivers throughout the engine, smashing the combustion chamber. The "blowtorch" was set free, its unchained heat roaring out of the shattered engine and licking a searing path to the wing.

Kimes, sitting in the traditional left seat of an aircraft commander, could not see what was happening to the fire-threatened right wing. For that matter, neither could copilot Miller, because of the 707's sharp wing sweepback. He saw the fire but did not see the engine fall off and reported to Kimes that the outer starboard wing tank must have exploded. Kimes, acting instinctively, took over the controls. This was no slur on Miller's ability: when an airliner gets into serious trouble, most captains will assume command authority.

When the engine fell off the burning wing, the jet lurched sharply to the right. Kimes glanced quickly at his altimeter. They were at seven hundred feet, nose high about fifteen degrees. He decided to keep climbing; the higher the altitude, the easier it would be to maneuver. Flying a jet at low altitude can be the equivalent of flying an iron bathtub. Even as he tried to digest the emergency, he thought of his passengers. He clicked on the cabin PA mike.

"Folks, we have a little minor problem," he started off calmly. Miller looked at him quizzically.

"Well, maybe it's not so minor," Kimes added in a voice so nonchalant that he might have been delivering a "glad to have you with us today" welcome.

The shuddering had stopped but the 707 was handling like a car with its front wheels completely out of alignment. Thanks to the fire and the shock of the number four engine pod being torn off, approximately twenty-five feet of the right wing was gone and Kimes literally was flying a 707 with not much more than a wing and a half.

He increased power on the remaining three engines, delicately manipulating the two port throttles and coordinating his rudder controls to counter the plane's skidding tendency. He also had enough of a sense of responsibility toward his passengers to realize that they must be terrified and probably on the verge of panic. As busy as he was, he managed to speak over the PA again.

"We've had some trouble," he told them—still in a tone bordering on the placid. "Please put on your life jackets. There is no danger whatsoever. Just keep calm and everything will be okay."

The troubles of Flight 843 by this time had attracted the attention of thousands on the ground, including Lieutenant Melvin Hartman of the United States Coast Guard. Hartman immediately took off in a Coast Guard amphibian plane and flew close to the stricken 707. To the young pilot, the Boeing "looked like a big Roman candle." Kimes was later to express fervent gratitude for

Hartman's alertness and decision to "ride shotgun" on the staggering jet. The Pan Am captain sent two Mayday messages to the San Francisco control tower, but these traditional distress signals went unheard—Flight 843's radios were acting up and the transmissions were too weak for the traffic controllers to hear the calls.

Hartman heard them, however, and acted as a communications relay between the crippled jetliner and the San Francisco tower. Actually, controllers already were aware that 843 was in trouble. One minute after the plane took off, the tower saw the flames erupt from number four engine and advised all flights:

"Stand by. Emergency in progress."

Kimes decided to level off at about thirteen hundred feet. He would have preferred going higher but by this time he was uncertain whether the battered right wing would hold. He continued to nurse throttles and controls, while almost simultaneously making sure that his passengers were briefed on what was now an inevitable emergency landing. Kimes does not recall specifically what he said on the PA, but Mrs. Ruby Leonard—a registered nurse with the Idaho Department of Health—took the trouble to write Pan Am later about what went on in the cabin where she and her one hundred and forty-one fellow passengers wondered how close they were to death.

". . . the captain's voice came over the intercom and in a very reassuring manner he told us that if we would obey orders there was no need to panic; that everyone should put on his life jacket; take off his shoes; place his pillow on his lap; and lean forward . . . He also told us to remove any sharp obstacles [she meant objects] and wrap our hands around our ankles. He appealed to us as adults and told us that he expected us to handle our emotional reactions in a mature way. When he had given us these instructions and everyone was madly scrambling to follow his instructions, the panic was reduced immeasurably . . ."

Although painfully unsure of the integrity of the damaged wing, Kimes decided not to attempt a landing at San Francisco International Airport. He headed instead for Travis Air Force Base fifty miles away, cognizant of its longer runways and superb emergency and rescue facilities. It took guts to make that decision, for he was battling a very natural instinct to get down on the ground as quickly as possible. The cabin was quiet; the six flight

attendants—the purser and five stewardesses—had everything
under control and ready for landing.

Flight 843's takeoff had been logged at 2:10 P.M. PDT. It was
shortly before 2:30 that Kimes began circling Travis, with fighter
planes hovering around protectingly and Hartman's amphibian
lumbering along behind. Now a new crisis arose. When Kimes told
Miller to lower the landing gear, nothing happened. There had
been an apparent hydraulic failure, and there was no time to fool
with the primary system. Miller, Second Officer Max Webb and
Flight Engineer Fitch Robertson opened a floor hatch and cranked
the gear down manually.

Flight 843 landed smoothly and safely at 2:30 P.M. Only nineteen
minutes had elapsed between the engine explosion and touchdown at Travis. Many of the passengers wept as they disembarked,
tears of gratitude as well as nervous reaction. Unfortunately, they
were due for a new shock.

Pan Am ferried another plane to Travis to fly them back to San
Francisco. As it landed at the Air Force base, the nosewheel
collapsed. There were no injuries to the embarrassed crew, but
some of the passengers could have been forgiven if they had
abandoned air travel permanently.

Finally, they boarded a third jet, which returned them to San
Francisco International Airport. En route, Captain Kimes apolo-
gized over the PA for what had happened to the original ferry
plane as well as Flight 843. The passengers laughed and applauded
him. Five hours after their original departure, they left for Hawaii
in a fourth jet—slightly numb from the drinks Pan Am had served
them at the airport, plus a sumptuous dinner. Many were later to
write either Kimes or the airline, expressing gratitude for his skill
and the actions of the entire crew.

There were other aftermaths for Kimes too. He received some
five hundred letters of congratulations, including one from Vice
President Humphrey. An Ohio minister whose young daughter was
on Flight 843 wrote a particularly touching note which said, "I
believe that you had one passenger aboard who occupied no seat
but was present with each passenger and crew member."

With that, Captain Charles H. Kimes was in full agreement.

The forty-four-year-old native of Enid, Oklahoma, answered
every letter personally, with some secretarial aid from Pan Am.
The response to his handling of the emergency—FAA Adminis-

trator Najeeb E. Halaby called it "a masterful feat of airmanship"
when he gave Kimes a special citation—was embarrassing, for
the Captain is a modest man. One firm sent him a $500 check.
Kimes acknowledged it with a letter in which he reminded the
donor:

". . . under any normal emergency I could quite easily pocket
your largess and have a ball . . . But in the situation you write
about I'd have been treading water in a lead life jacket without
the entire cooperation of all my crew and passengers. I do not
say this in false modesty . . . but panic could easily have resulted
had not my flight service crew busied themselves and kept passengers busy with the donning of life jackets, emergency instructions,
etc."

Kimes split the $500 into ten checks of $50 each and gave one
to each of his crew. When a television manufacturer sent him two
TV sets, the captain insisted on the entire crew drawing straws—
and was secretly happy when he lost. At a news conference shortly
after the incident, Kimes remarked to the reporters that "There
has been misunderstanding of my role. I was just one of ten crew
members," he added. "I did nothing outstanding. I don't feel I
should wear a hero's hat. If any acknowledgment at all is in order,
it should go to the training department of Pan American."

The training department deserved credit, but so did Captain
Kimes and the rest of the crew. Kimes and his three flight deck
colleagues collectively were given the 1965 Daedalian Award,
presented annually to an airline pilot who has demonstrated outstanding skill in handling an emergency. At least a dozen major
newspapers printed laudatory editorials, all stressing the theme
that what Kimes performed was a service to aviation and the professional reputation of the airline pilot. But perhaps the warmest
praise of all came from Boeing.

The manufacturer's engineers admitted they never dreamed it
was aerodynamically possible to keep a 707 in the air with one
third of a wing gone.

"We run just about every kind of test imaginable," said one
Boeing technician, "but you never imagine a plane in this kind of
a situation remaining flyable. That cockpit was full of real pros."

In a very real sense, the story of Flight 843 was a tribute to
Boeing, too, for it demonstrated the importance of all U.S. transport manufacturers' "fail-safe" philosophy—a design concept insist-

ing that the structural failure of any single component must not be allowed to progress to other parts. On a plane not designed under this rule, the loss of a huge wing section would be fatal because the remaining structure would be incapable of absorbing the additional load.

Less than six months later, the value of "fail-safe" was to be demonstrated again, once more in a Boeing 707 but also in the hearts and minds of two airline captains whose fates and planes alike were on a collision course in the skies over the small town of Carmel, New York.

The date was December 4, 1965, and the time was 4:19 P.M. EST.

At that precise moment, a TWA 707 and an Eastern Constellation collided at eleven thousand feet. The impact tore off thirty feet of the jet's left wing and severed the entire control system of the piston-engine "Connie"—rudder and elevator boost package, control cables for elevators and ailerons and even the trim tab cables.

By every logical assumption and law of aerodynamics, both planes and the one hundred and nine human beings aboard them were doomed. One wing of the jet was less than one third intact —worse damage than on the Pan Am 707—and there also was fire. The Constellation was in even worse shape, the equivalent of an automobile whose steering column has been snapped in two.

The TWA 707 was Flight 42, San Francisco to Kennedy International Airport. Commanding was Captain Thomas H. Carroll, forty-five. The flight was about forty miles from a navigation checkpoint at Carmel when Air Traffic Control instructed it to descend to eleven thousand feet. TWA 42 reported at that altitude one minute before the collision.

Carroll had flicked on the FASTEN SEAT BELTS sign, anticipating some turbulence as they approached New York. When the collision impact occurred, there was a sharp jolt, but many passengers thought they merely had encountered rough air—until those on the left side saw part of the wing gone and fire break out. One of these horrified passengers was an electronics expert who was in the process of reading a technical report on air safety. It included methods of preventing mid-air collisions.

Five passengers seated on the left side saw the Constellation just before the aircraft paths bisected. One was John Hollings-

worth of Westport, Connecticut, who felt the jolt and then heard
the incongruous sound of breaking glass (which came, he learned
later, from the galley). Only one terrible conclusion went through
his mind: "This is it."

That was close to what Captain Carroll was thinking, too, but
as more of a fleeting subconscious thought. An airline pilot has
no time for such luxuries as meditation when an emergency strikes.
Carroll had the 707 on autopilot, but his left hand was on the
control yoke when he saw a blue and white aircraft at 10 o'clock
high. Carroll's reaction was lightning-quick. He disengaged the
autopilot with his left thumb, put the control yoke wheel hard over
to the right and almost in the same motion pulled back on the
yoke. Copilot Leo Smith grabbed the controls simultaneously.

The 707 rolled like a frightened whale trying to escape a killer
shark. But Carroll quickly realized that the maneuver would not
take them out of collision course. Both pilots reversed the control
forces, with a hard-over wheel turn to the left and a push forward
on the yoke. The 707 had barely begun to respond when the two
planes hit. The first maneuver, a sharp, climbing turn, was intended to take them over the Constellation. The second was an
attempt to dive under it when Carroll became aware that the
smaller plane was climbing faster than the jet in its own avoidance
maneuver.

Carroll fought to get the 707 back to even keel. Smith spoke
twelve terse words into his radio microphone, tuned to the frequency
of New York Air Route Traffic Control Center.

"Just had mid-air collision with blue Constellation. Request
expeditious approach to Kennedy."

The stunned Center gave the jet immediate priority, clearing
all traffic below eleven thousand feet and giving Flight 42 a
straight-in path to Kennedy. But Carroll had more problems than
just a fast clearance. The 707 was reeling. Carroll, Smith and Flight
Engineer Ernest Hall assessed the damage and Smith notified
Kennedy to have crash and fire equipment standing by. The wing
fire had dwindled to mere smoke but the crew was taking no
chances.

As Captain Kimes had acted six months before, so did Carroll—
carrying the double burden of maintaining control and stifling the
almost inevitable panic that must be poisoning the cabin. Actually,
his passengers were too frightened to show panic. The shock of the

collision—the crew felt two jolts but some passengers were aware of only one—sent handbags, coats, briefcases and other carry-on items flying through the cabin. For as long as fifteen seconds, the 707 bounced up and down.

"It was like a hurricane," one passenger recalled later. "I heard the pilot make an announcement but I don't remember what he said. I was too scared."

What Carroll was delivering was the usual "planned emergency" instruction list—loosen ties, take sharp objects out of pockets, women remove high-heel shoes and everybody stay calm while following the orders of the hostesses. He did not mention that a collision had occurred—just that an emergency landing was necessary. Flight 42 swept toward Kennedy, a semblance of stability restored. Carroll flew a three hundred and sixty degree turn to the left over the airport while men in the control tower checked to see if the landing gear was down—Carroll didn't trust the green "down and locked" lights in front of him, and he had indications that at least some hydraulic pressure had been lost.

TWA 42 landed at 4:40 P.M., nineteen minutes after the collision, with Carroll having to resort to reverse thrust alone after he discovered he had no wheel brakes working. When the jet finally came to a stop, about ten passengers emerged via the main door emergency slide. TWA officials interrupted the evacuation when they saw no sign of fire and the remainder of the passengers left in normal fashion. There was only one injury—a hostess knocked off her feet by the collision impact had suffered a bloody nose.

One of the first questions asked by Carroll and his crew was about the fate of the other plane. The TWA captain was to find out later that his own emergency, brilliantly handled as it was, amounted to relative routine compared with the ordeal of Eastern 853 and a captain named Charles J. White.

White was the son of a New York City detective, born and raised in Brooklyn. At the age of nineteen, Charlie White was one of the youngest bomber captains in the Air Force during World War II. In 1948, he voluntarily left his job at Eastern to fly the Berlin airlift and he earned a college degree by going to night school while flying for the airline—two indications of his determination and his sense of duty.

White was to display both qualities again on this day of December 4, plus raw courage. He was commanding Eastern Flight 853, one of the airline's popular "shuttle" trips from Boston to Newark. He had forty-nine passengers aboard—a light load for the shuttle, but this was a Saturday afternoon and air traffic is fairly light on most Saturdays.

They were at ten thousand feet, the nose of their Constellation poking in and out of whipped cream puffs of clouds that occasionally blossomed above a fairly thick cloud deck. Most pilots love this particular phase of flight—skimming along on top of a cloud bank which provides the rare sensation of speed and motion.

The old Connie, one of the most beautiful airplanes ever built with its sharklike fuselage and triple tail, was just emerging from a cloud when copilot Roger Holt saw an object at two o'clock—a heart-freezing sight that caused him almost to shriek a warning to White. Seemingly at their own altitude and on a converging course was a red and white jetliner.

"Look out!" Holt yelled.

Both pilots, as though their arms were hooked to a single brain, pulled back on their yokes. But in virtually the same second the jet began climbing too.

The jet's left wing sliced into the Constellation's tail, severing one third of the structure and leaving control cables dangling like ganglia from a disemboweled animal. Eastern 853 was moving at two hundred and forty miles an hour and the TWA jet was doing nearly four hundred. Yet while the impact shock was violent on the big jet, the crew and passengers on EAL 853 felt only a curiously gentle bump, hardly any stronger than a bit of minor turbulence. The mildness was deceiving; the Constellation was mortally hurt.

The Eastern plane continued climbing momentarily after the collision. White pushed forward on his yoke. There was no response. The Constellation shuddered and stalled. The nose came down and the plane began to dive. White cut the power just as Flight Engineer Emile Greenway gulped nervously at what his panel was showing. Four red lights flashed multiple warnings—hydraulic pressure was dropping to zero.

"Pressure and quantity!" Greenway yelled. "Pressure and quantity!"

He was telling the captain they had lost their hydraulic boost package—the equivalent of power steering on a car. White pulled a lever that normally would have shifted the controls from hy-

draulic to manual, thus allowing him to move his elevators, ailerons
and rudders by applying a lot of muscle. This time White needed
prayer, not muscle. The mechanical linkage had snapped as well
as the hydraulic lines. There was no control. The nose-heavy
Constellation dove headlong toward inevitable disaster, picking up
speed even with the engines throttled down.

"Power!" copilot Holt yelled. "How about the power?"

White nodded. He pushed all four throttles forward. Power was
all he had. He knew it would increase the speed of the dive but it
was the only way to bring the nose up—the higher speed and
faster revolutions of the props would create more lift under the
wings.

The plane plunged through the cloud layer, engines roaring.
The Constellation trembled as the nose came up with agonizing
slowness. Level. Then a nose-up attitude again, a climb that
would result inevitably in a second stall. But White was improvis-
ing now, manipulating his throttles like a piano virtuoso expertly
fingering his keys. With incredible swiftness, he mastered the
throttle combination that gave him enough power to keep the nose
reasonably level.

The Constellation was in a steady left turn. White found he
could straighten out to some extent by carefully nursing the
throttle settings—full power on number one, slightly less on number two, even less on number three and further reduction on number four. The engines on a four-engine plane are numbered from
left to right. What White did was to create a drastic speed differential between the engines on the left wing and those on the
right wing, with the greatest differential between one and four—
the outboards. This tended to raise the left wing and gave White
some measure of lateral control.

He found time now to talk to his passengers.

"This is the captain speaking."

His voice was calm, with not the slightest hint of fear and impending disaster.

"We've had a mid-air collision. Please fasten your seat belts."

He paused, the only moment of indecision he was to display.
How much could he tell them without causing panic? How do
you sugar-coat an announcement of possible, perhaps certain death?

"We're out of control," he said finally—still in a matter-of-fact
tone. "Brace yourselves the best you can for a crash landing.

You won't be hearing from me any more. I'm going to be a little busy up here."

Only one passenger reacted audibly. A woman wailed briefly. Somebody else snapped, "Shut up, lady!" She subsided. The cabin, except for the two stewardesses moving quickly and efficiently with emergency evacuation preparations, was quiet, in a foglike kind of fear.

Flight Engineer Greenway, meanwhile, had raised the New York Center, which had been trying in vain to contact 853. His message came through loud and clear over the usual filtered, metallic static of air–ground communications.

"Mayday!" he called, repeating the word twice more. "This is Eastern eight fifty-three . . . we've had a mid-air collision . . . in trouble . . . we're out of control . . ."

He sent the message while the plane still was diving. A few minutes later, after White's masterful use of the throttles, Greenway came back on the radio to ask for a quick routing to Kennedy —he assumed White would want to land where the runways were longest. The Center, which had ordered all aircraft not to interrupt on the frequency 853 was using, gave Greenway clearance to Kennedy. The captain broke in at this point to advise ATC they couldn't make Kennedy or any other airport. The Constellation was descending steadily and there was nothing the crew could do about it. The power settings that kept the aircraft from diving or climbing were insufficient to maintain altitude. White so advised the Center.

"We'll just do the best we can," he added quietly. "Keep an eye on us, please, and see where we're gonna wind up."

White and Holt studied the terrain below. Directly ahead was a fairly large hill covered with trees. Off to the right was a lake and White asked his copilot what he thought about a ditching. Presumably there would be less danger of fire. Holt shook his head; impact with water can be more severe than hitting the ground unless the ditching is perfectly timed. Furthermore, the passengers would not have more than a couple of minutes survival time in the cold water even if they came through the ditching.

The two pilots looked to the left and saw a grassy pasture on the side of a small hill. It was the only clear area in sight.

"How about that field?" White asked unnecessarily; he had no other choice.

"Let's do it," was Holt's response.

It was getting dark as the Constellation settled toward the field. Behind the airliner was a small private plane occupied by an instructor and student pilot. They had been following the Eastern plane, knowing they were helpless to assist but unwilling to abandon it. The Connie neared the hill and the men in the small plane saw its red anti-collision light suddenly blink off; Greenway had cut off all electrical circuits.

Flight 853's last maneuver could have been classed not only as difficult but almost impossible. White had to bring up the nose just enough to pancake into the slope of the hill. It required split-second timing. If he applied power too soon, the plane would skip over the hill and stall. If he advanced the throttles too late, he would strike the hill in a level nose-first attitude which had to result in a hard, almost certainly fatal impact.

He fingered the cabin PA mike and pressed the transmitting button.

"Brace yourselves," he said. "Here it comes."

White's coordination was perfect but he had some unknown cards stacked against him. In the gathering darkness and from the altitude at which he committed the plane to its last landing, neither he nor Holt could see that the hill was not as clear as they supposed. The Constellation's belly touched the ground with amazing gentleness and the plane skidded up the slope. But just as the crew figured they might have it made, the left wing struck a small tree and tore off. The fuselage and right wing swerved against the far bank of a gully, bounced into the air and struck the ground again. The fuel tanks in the right wing cracked open and a ball of yellow flame billowed a hundred feet into the blackening sky.

By the time the Connie stopped rolling up the hill, its fuselage had split in three places—damage that miraculously saved lives because it provided three additional exits. Passengers, some of them badly hurt, tumbled out of the broken fuselage. Copilot Holt was so seriously injured that he collapsed right after he crawled through or fell out of a cockpit emergency exit. Greenway to this day does not know how he got out and, in fact, does not remember anything that occurred after sending his Mayday message—a frequent traumatic reaction of airmen involved in crashes. Neither the copilot nor flight engineer remembers what happened to White, although they believe the captain may have helped them out of the wreckage.

Only one thing was certain: Charles White never left his plane. His body was found later, not in the cockpit but in the cabin aisle not far from a seat occupied by a dead soldier—the only passenger who failed to get out. Two died later from injuries. It was obvious that the captain went back to the cabin to make sure all his passengers had been evacuated—a final devotion to duty that cost him his life.

Eastern established a college scholarship in his name. He received, posthumously, the 1966 Daedalian Award along with Holt and Greenway. He was buried with full military honors in Arlington National Cemetery and a large plaque honoring his memory hangs in the Eastern terminal building at Kennedy Airport.

On December 20, 1966, more than a year after the collision, the Civil Aeronautics Board issued a report which found an optical illusion responsible for the mishap. The CAB said the cloud bank just under the Constellation in reality sloped downward, giving White and Holt a false horizon. They actually were separated horizontally from the jet by the required one thousand feet—Eastern had been assigned to ten thousand feet and TWA to eleven thousand—but were fooled into thinking that TWA was at their altitude. Likewise, the TWA pilots also took evasion action because of an identical illusion—they assumed EAL 853 was at eleven thousand. The supreme irony was that the alertness of both crews triggered the collision. It would not have occurred if one or both had not spotted the other.

For Flight Engineer Greenway, the CAB report carried a personal and tragic irony. Ten months before the collision, an Eastern stewardess he had been dating seriously was killed in the crash of a DC-7. The Board's "probable cause" verdict was that the pilots took violent evasive action to avoid what they thought was a collision course with a jet—*because of an optical illusion*—and lost control.

United Air Lines Flight 746, San Francisco–Chicago, was a Boeing 720—in reality just a scaled-down version of the 707, six feet shorter and somewhat lighter in weight.

On July 12, 1963, the lives of fifty-three passengers aboard

Flight 746 were in the hands of a captain named Lynden Duescher. He was only forty-two years old but his logbook showed more than seventeen thousand hours in the air. He had been a captain since 1945 and, like many pilots, seemed to reflect the character of his airline—cautious, business-like, quietly efficient.

There are many in aviation who swear different airlines have different personalities, as if they were human instead of corporate, with their crews in some mysterious fashion acquiring the same qualities. TWA, for example, is said to run to the glamorous side and its pilots are frequently of the "Greek god" variety—some airmen claim this is due to the influence of Howard Hughes, who used to own TWA. Eastern's pilots for years had a reputation for resourcefulness and opportunism, which pretty well described Eddie Rickenbacker and his close-to-the-vest policies of running an airline. American has always catered to the business traveler, and not a few of its pilots look as if they had just stepped out of a brokerage office.

Duescher, in effect, *was* United. Quiet, stolid, not much for fancy or flowery PA announcements, and decidedly professional. It was typical that when United absorbed Capital in 1960, UAL pilots like Duescher referred to their new flight deck brethren as "Brand X." Capital was known as a pilots' airline and mirrored the informality of its crews. United, in turn, was rather formal, far more dignified and markedly conservative by comparison. Which described Lyn Duescher—a firm believer in the airline pilot's creed: "In God we trust; everything else we check."

Before leaving San Francisco, Duescher had examined a company weather forecast indicating an atmospheric disturbance building up over Nebraska. Flight 746 was miles away from the suspected area when the captain turned on his weather-warning radar —with traditional, inherent cautiousness, he wanted plenty of advance notice if the flight was going to encounter turbulence.

The Boeing was at thirty-five thousand feet approaching O'Neill, Nebraska, when its radar picked up mild thunderstorm turbulence ahead. Duescher turned on the seat belt sign and told his crew to fasten their shoulder harnesses. The 720 started to buck.

"Let's see if we can climb above it," Duescher said to copilot Eric Anderson. "Ask ATC for forty-one thousand feet."

Permission to climb to the new altitude was granted. Anderson, who was flying the aircraft, eased back on the yoke. One hundred and thirty-six feet behind the cockpit, the massive elevators hinged to the horizontal tail stabilizers moved slowly and Flight 746 began to climb.

The airspeed increased slowly and the turbulence became slightly choppier. Anderson disengaged the autopilot and assumed manual control. The captain told him to reduce airspeed to the standard maximum for penetrating rough air—two hundred and fifty knots. Flight 746 entered an overcast and bucked even harder. Airspeed and altitude started to fluctuate as alternate updrafts and downdrafts punched at the big jet.

One particularly bad updraft tossed the Boeing two thousand feet up, and only ten seconds later an equally severe downdraft shoved it down two thousand feet. Then came another updraft. Flight 746 soared from thirty-seven thousand feet to nearly forty thousand in less than ten seconds. The airspeed hovered around two hundred and twenty-five knots, dangerously close to a stall at this thin-air altitude.

Both Duescher and Anderson applied forward pressure on the control column and increased power to all four engines, trying to maintain both altitude and airspeed. Turbulence increased and the airspeed indicator was dancing wildly. Now came the first buffeting of a stall. Duescher told his copilot to forget altitude and just concentrate on keeping the nose level and airspeed up. But the nose continued to edge higher. Ten degrees. Fifteen degrees.

The control column was full forward.

The nose crept higher. Twenty degrees. Thirty. Forty.

Turbulence shook the plane. Again, the shudder of an impending stall.

Without warning, the bottom dropped out of the sky. A sudden downdraft sucked greedily at one hundred tons of metal—an airliner already trimmed for maximum combat against updraft.

Flight 746 fell off on one wing and plummeted out of control toward the ground forty thousand feet below.

Negative G forces clamped their strangle hold on flight deck and cabin alike. Loose articles in the cockpit began floating in the air, then on the ceiling and finally near the floor. A checklist card drifted aimlessly about, settling eventually on the instrument panel and covering several dials.

In the cabin, objects from the overhead racks launched themselves toward the ceiling. The contents of the rear galley came floating into the cabin. Carry-on luggage leaped from the racks and sailed back toward the rear. A stewardess about to serve a cup of coffee unceremoniously dumped the contents on the floor rug before the hot liquid could jump into a passenger's lap.

There was one passenger who had ignored the FASTEN SEAT BELTS sign, an omission that had remained unspotted by the stewardess. He rose out of his seat all the way to the overhead rack, then descended almost gently to the floor in a prone position. He got back in his seat and this time fastened his belt securely.

Flight 746 was still in the overcast. The nose was pitched down at an attitude of thirty-five degrees. Airspeed increased ominously. Duescher sent the Air Traffic Control Center in Denver, which was working the flight, a chilling two-word message:

"Aircraft uncontrollable."

Airspeed continued to rise. Duescher chopped his throttles and then pulled the speed brake handle.

Indicated airspeed soared to more than four hundred knots. The Mach warning bell clanged. Altimeters spun crazily. Neither the captain nor copilot could read the instruments—still in the overcast, they could have been upside down for all they knew.

Altitude twenty-six thousand. Airspeed four hundred and eighty knots. The Mach warning bell clanged incessantly.

Flight 746 broke out of the overcast, still plunging earthward.

At this moment, it was Duescher's skill and experience plus the structural integrity of a man-made machine pitted against impending disaster. Everything hinged on a tug of war between a pilot's instinctive reaction and the training drummed into the mind and soul of every man who flies a jetliner—"*you fly by the book, not by instinct.*"

Instinct told him to bring the nose up to check the dive. Instinct told him to do something, anything, to diminish that airspeed.

He had to fight the most immediate and natural temptation— to yank back on the yoke, which would have been either useless or fatal; the Boeing was accelerating too fast. Back pressure sufficient to move the control column would have required superhuman strength on the part of both pilots, and even if they had been able to activate the elevators, a pull-up at this terrific speed probably would have caused structural failure.

He momentarily considered lowering the landing gear, which

would have increased drag and maybe induced pitch-up. Panic was battling training. Training won. Lowering the gear might have produced enough drag to tear the plane apart.

He reached for the inboard wing spoiler switch—again, this would have increased drag. But it also might have torn off the wings. Once again, training overrode panic.

Now he tried trimming the stabilizers electrically, but there was no elevator control at sonic speeds.

Altitude twenty thousand.

Nineteen. Eighteen. Seventeen. Sixteen.

Flight 746 was running out of time and space.

Altitude fifteen thousand feet. The air was heavier. It was now or never.

Duescher told Anderson to increase power slightly. The turbines howled above the noise of the Mach warning bell.

The nose came up, almost imperceptibly, but up.

More power, applied with the delicately careful skill of a surgeon's knife. The nose inched upward. Now both pilots gingerly hauled back on the control yoke and this time they felt response. Like a stilled heart massaged back to life, the elevators were reacting.

Altitude fourteen thousand. Thirteen. Twelve.

The nose was level. Airspeed was normal. The lights of O'Neill winked placidly at the jet above, in innocent ignorance of what had almost happened.

Flight 746 crawled back to fifteen thousand feet and continued to Chicago after Duescher advised ATC that the emergency was over.

The fifty-three shaken passengers disembarked at O'Hare Airport. When Duescher left the plane, some of them booed him —unaware that his coolness and resistance to panic had saved them.

United, FAA and CAB officials swarmed over the plane, looking for any sign of structural damage. Not a rivet had popped. The flight recorder was yanked and its tracings examined. *They were virtually identical to those of a Northwest Boeing 720 that had disintegrated in a Florida thunderstorm exactly five months before.*

The Northwest plane had slammed into the same combination of a violent updraft-downdraft vise over the Everglades, shortly after takeoff from Miami. All aboard were killed and what actions the crew had taken will never be known for sure. But Boeing, in a special report on the NWA accident distributed to all 707-720 operators, said structural failure occurred after an apparent attempt to return the elevators to an up position while the jet was diving in an extreme nose-down attitude. The turbulence itself was insufficient to have caused structural failure, Boeing said.

Then-President W. A. Patterson of United wrote a personal letter to every passenger who had been on Flight 746. "I am sure the experience was frightening, to say the least," Patterson conceded. "If we are to be deserving of your confidence, we must be completely frank in providing you with the facts involved in such an incident . . ."

Patterson then went on to relate the circumstances in detail. Speaking of Duescher in particular, and being well aware of the airport boos, the UAL chief added:

"I don't know of any experience where a flight officer kept his head and under such a severe experience had the knowledge of what not to do under such conditions. We can all be grateful to him for the deliberate and cool-headed manner in which he handled and solved such a critical emergency."

A few weeks later, Patterson invited Duescher and his crew to lunch. He handed each man a check amounting to five figures. But Duescher, who remembered those boos, was even more grateful for the letter.

The airline pilot offers the most incongruous contrast in aviation —he is the father image to many and an overpaid bus driver to others. He is variously portrayed as the stern-faced, tight-jawed God of the cockpit and a stewardess-chasing lecher with the morals of a tomcat. He is simultaneously regarded as a dedicated professional and a spoiled prima donna.

It is only too easy to generalize, but in truth the average airline pilot *does* have something of a dual personality. Even his union, the Air Line Pilots Association, wears two hats. It is a tough-talking labor union but it also is a dignified professional organization of considerable technical influence, one whose contributions to air safety have never been fully appreciated. And many, if not most, pilots seem to reflect ALPA's own double image.

The majority, for example, can be as belligerent and anti-management as a steelworker or truck driver during contract negotiations. Yet ALPA is the only union in the United States whose members are overwhelmingly Republican; one of the strongest and most vocal groups supporting Barry Goldwater in 1964 was a "Pilots for Goldwater" committee organized by a number of captains. The relative affluence of the airline pilot is largely responsible for his conservatism. It has been said that ALPA is the only union whose members ride to a picket line in Cadillacs.

The many contradictions of an airline pilot's character make generalizations sometimes unfair. Among airline people themselves, pilots have acquired a reputation for stinginess that would make Jack Benny resemble the last of the big-time spenders. I know of one captain, with an annual salary of well over $20,000, who will walk through a restaurant picking up unclaimed tips from unoccupied tables. Yet the penurious pilot has a logical reason for seeming cheap; flight crews have a built-in sense of financial insecurity, and well they might have. An airline pilot lives under constant fear of having his well-heeled world collapse overnight. A captain gets a stiff check ride every six months, as well as complete proficiency retraining. He also is exposed to a searching medical examination twice a year, and what would be a gentle "take it easier" piece of advice for the average person could mean a career death sentence for a pilot. Any wage earner would lean toward tightfistedness under this kind of pressure.

Conversely, most airline pilots can be sentimental, spontaneously generous and totally loyal. They also tend to possess delightful senses of humor, quick wit and a gift of sharp repartee, which not even the disciplinary demands of the jet age have been able to douse. They love to play practical jokes on stewardesses and enjoy having tricks played on them. Under severe stress, they have been known to produce unexpected wisecracks that dissipated tension like a hot sun devouring morning fog.

A few years ago, an air traffic controller had his hands full on a stormy night with visibility and ceiling nudging minimums. Flights were stacked up all the way to what would have been normal cruising altitudes, and the pilots were hounding ATC for descent clearances, approach clearances and landing clearances.

One harassed controller finally growled into a radio frequency heard by the majority of the impatient crews:

"I'll get you guys down as soon as I can. We're doing the best we know how."

Back came the voice of an unidentified pilot.

"Bullshit!" he said loudly.

The controller was furious; such language is forbidden, and in this case was blackly resented.

"Attention all flights!" the controller barked. "Who said that?"

There was a dramatic pause while the pilots pondered the horrible crime. One by one, they offered their pious denials.

"United 542, negative on the bullshit."

"American 5, negative on the bullshit."

"TWA 22, negative on the bullshit."

"Northwest 301, negative on the bullshit."

"Continental 611, negative on the bullshit."

"Delta 419, negative on the bullshit."

"North Central 510, negative on the bullshit."

The roll call continued for a few more minutes and undoubtedly included a firm not-guilty from the offending flight. By the fourth or fifth response, the controller was laughing so hard he had to turn his mike over to a compatriot.

There was an equally tense situation involving one of the FAA's few female controllers. She was working flights in bad weather and experiencing communication difficulties. She finally asked one pilot, "Is my transmission fuzzy?"

Silence. Then a chuckle.

"I don't know, honey," the pilot replied. "How old are you?"

Professional airmen have a camaraderie, a spirit of comradeship, that transcends the rivalry among their hotly competitive airlines. One can see this at ALPA safety forums, where there is a solid closing of ranks on safety issues and where pilots seem to lose their individual airline identities in favor of a vague kind of fraternalism. Any emergency encountered by one pilot will invoke automatic and immediate cooperation from fellow airmen. Airline crews are often bitter toward private pilots, resenting the fact that a tiny Cessna or Piper on a non-essential, one-man pleasure flight can hold up a transport with a hundred passengers during peak traffic hours. Yet the FAA's files are full of incidents in which airline pilots have gone out of their way to guide lost, inexperienced and panic-stricken private pilots to safety. Typical was this partial dialogue between a United captain and the pilot of a small plane who got into bad weather without instrument training and became not only disoriented but frightened to the point of total panic.

UAL: *"Do you read now?"*

Pilot: *"I read you but I don't know what I'm doing."*

UAL: *"Okay now, just relax. We all get in a spot once in a while. If you'll just relax your hands on the wheel, just for a second, I think we'll calm down. Take your feet off the rudders for a second and then just shake your hands a bit and relax and go back to it and just head east, which is 'E' on the indicator. East heading and hold that for a minute or so. Just nice and straight and I think we can calm down quite a bit and accomplish quite a bit. Okay?"*

Pilot: *"Okay, I got you."*

UAL: *"You have a good airplane under you. It's a real good machine and with just a little help, it will do a real good job for you."*

Pilot: *"We are going due east now at nine thousand feet."*

UAL: *"Very good, very good. Just hold that now and you'll be doing real good."*

Pilot: *"My gas is getting down below a quarter of a tank."*

UAL: *"We all make mistakes. Relax now, and we'll get you out of this . . ."*

Thanks to the United crew, the Traffic Control Center in the area and a more experienced private pilot who took over a little later from United, the lost airman landed safely.

Most airline pilots feel a natural enmity toward the government agency that wields so much authority over their careers—the FAA. Some of this is the kind of ill will a motorist would display toward a traffic cop, a resentment of disciplinary authority. There was a real feud between ALPA and FAA during the regime of the agency's first administrator, Elwood R. "Pete" Quesada. Quesada's successor, Najeeb E. Halaby, made an admirable effort to improve relations and so did Halaby's successor, William F. McKee.

Some pilots still bristle at the idea that an FAA inspector can board their flights any time and monitor their flight procedures. But even this source of friction has been lessened noticeably because FAA was intelligent and honest enough to admit past mistakes—namely, too many inspectors were miles away from the men they were checking in terms of skill and experience. FAA took the advice of pilots and airlines alike, sending their inspectors to airline training schools for qualification on specific types of transports. In the old days, some inspectors had never flown the airplane in whose cockpit they were exerting check authority.

In similar fashion, there has been an admirable improvement in relations between pilots and controllers, a steadily growing mutual appreciation of each other's problems and needs. Tempers occasionally get short, nerves become frayed and there can be angry exchanges—usually when airports and airways get clogged. But airmen have mounting respect for the men who work in those antiseptic pressure cookers that are the towers and control centers. Many pilots visit ATC facilities in an FAA-ALPA-airline program aimed at acquainting pilots with the work of controllers. In turn, more and more controllers are taking advantage of "FAM" (familiarization) flights—the privilege of riding in airliner cockpits to obtain firsthand knowledge of pilot procedures.

It is impossible to cast the airline pilot in a single mold. If anything, the membership of ALPA and the Allied Pilots Association (APA is a pilots' union that represents American Airlines flight crews exclusively) is in essence a collection of rugged individualists. Pilots simply refuse to be typecast and they vary in personalities probably as widely as any other professional cross section in America. Some are inveterate clowns and some are deadly serious, occasionally on the dour side. Some are deeply religious, community-minded and devoted family men. Others are admitted playboys. Many try to forget aviation between trips. But a sizable minority are hard workers in the field of safety—the contributions of the pilot group toward greater air safety are sadly underrated. Many aviation reforms have stemmed directly from pilots' demands, suggestions and even experiment and research conducted on their own time. And in many cases, flight crew thinking on safety has been years ahead of government and industry, particularly in the pre-jet era. Airborne radar, the need for modernized air traffic control, better runway lighting and improved navigation aids are just a few examples.

Perhaps the one thing pilots have in common is love of their profession, an almost mystical appreciation of flight that can be grasped only by those fortunate enough to share that love. (Many stewardesses do, which is why pilot-stewardess marriages usually are successful.)

Their infatuation with flight is a common bond, an emotional explanation for the unanimous bitterness veteran pilots feel toward the controversial "retire at sixty" rule imposed by the FAA in 1959. A layman would find it a fascinating experience to attend the conventions of retired-pilot organizations—several airlines have such groups.

American's "Grey Eagles" was the first and is one of the biggest and most active. If you could be present at one of the annual gatherings of the Eagles, you would notice first of all the above-average physical condition of the recently retired members—those the FAA forced to quit, even though they were (and many still are) capable of passing any flight or medical test.

A few have potbellies, while some look like men only a couple of years beyond a professional football career. All have the telltale crow's-feet around their eyes, that hallmark of men who fly. Typically, the three-day convention agenda schedules only one business meeting, with the rest of the time set aside for fun.

Wander around them and you pick up such snatches of conversation as:

*"Yeh, I remember my first flight. We had three passengers and all of 'em got airsick . . ."*

*". . . Remember old Captain So-and-so? I flew with him six months before the creep let me make a landing . . ."*

*". . . You had troubles your first trip? Hell, mine was back in '30—between New York and Hartford. Thunder and lightning all the way in weather I wouldn't have driven a car in . . . I couldn't find Hartford 'til we were on the ground . . ."*

*". . . You're damned right I remember my first engine failure —I couldn't forget it because it didn't happen until I had twenty-six thousand hours logged . . ."*

They reminisce and swap tales and they can be forgiven if the years have colored a few yarns brighter than the real event. Their nostalgia runs a curious pattern. Most remember their first airline flight with amazingly vivid clarity—some can even give you the name of the stewardess—yet memories are hazy about more recent years.

Almost to a man, they talk warmly—and occasionally with a kind of wry awe—about the various captains they flew with when they were young pilots. The martinets, the practical jokers, the ones who imparted wisdom. Seldom do they mention the present—

only the past, because the past was flying and the present is usually nothing but a memory of happier years. It is not that they are inactive. The majority of the Eagles' four hundred members are in occupations ranging from real estate to operating golf courses. Many have turned their avocations of airline days into vocations in their new lives; again, the propensity of pilots to have a kind of "reserve" business is a manifestation of their financial insecurity, their constant dread of the day when they will be unable to fly.

No pilot has really resented being grounded because of health —usually eyesight, reaction time or heart. But he does get indignant at the prospect of retiring before he wants to—under what he regards as an arbitrary age limit established on a questionable correlation between chronological and physiological age. While it is true that a man in his sixties is theoretically more vulnerable to a heart attack than one much younger, actual experience under the FAA's retirement rule offers absolutely no valid support. Between 1952 and 1967 sixteen U.S. airline pilots died while on duty. The average age was only 43.5, and the chronological breakdown is interesting:

| Age bracket | Number of deaths |
|---|---|
| under 30 | 1 |
| 30–39 | 4 |
| 40–49 | 7 |
| 50–59 | 4 |

Talk to a recently retired Grey Eagle or any other physically fit airline pilot hit by mandatory retirement and you can understand their bitterness; you'll probably begin to share it, because these grizzled veterans can be intensely persuasive.

"Look around this room," one says to you. "You can find men over sixty who can pass any physical examination and any proficiency flight check better than half the men flying today. The airlines are short of pilots, the supply is going to get tighter, and the government still won't let them tap all this experience. It's the most criminal, inexcusable, inefficient waste of manpower in American industry."

"It's a bunch of malarkey that a pilot over sixty is more likely to have a heart attack," adds another retiree, who looks capable of wrestling a bear. "Any doctor will tell you the most dangerous years for a sudden, unexpected major coronary are between forty and fifty, not past sixty. It would have been fairer if FAA had just tightened medical and proficiency tests for older captains and then let the airlines themselves set a retirement age based on individual pension plans."

When FAA put the retirement rule into effect in 1959, only forty captains were affected immediately. But now, each year finds a soaring number of pilots reaching sixty.

ALPA early in 1968 petitioned the FAA to drop the mandatory retirement rule and allow pilots who are sixty or over to keep flying so long as they can pass medical and proficiency tests. The union argued with commendable logic that many of the reasons for forced retirement cited in 1959 no longer are valid. There is no large group of older pilots facing difficult transition from pistons to jets. Many jetliners have three qualified pilots in the cockpit, reducing the hazards of incapacitation. And finally, premature retirement may work against safety. The pilot group is getting older. Nearly 75 per cent of ALPA's 1967 membership roster was in the forty-to-fifty-nine age bracket. By 1972, nearly six thousand airline pilots will be in the fifty-to-fifty-nine age group, compared with twenty-two hundred in 1967 and only three hundred and fifteen in 1959.

This means that if mandatory retirement at sixty stays on the books, the airlines in another five years will be losing a huge pool of their most experienced and skilled cockpit personnel—and this with the critical years of jumbos coming up by 1970. President Floyd Hall of Eastern estimates it will cost an airline $200,000 to qualify a three-man crew for the Boeing 747, thus raising the unpleasant prospect of spending millions on training pilots who start flying the 747 shortly before they have to retire. And it will be the veterans, not the younger pilots, who will be operating 747 trips. This is one issue in which ALPA has drawn general airline support.

An increasingly older pilot population must be considered a part of what has yet to be but might become a major safety problem—fatigue.

The average layman is likely to have a somewhat jaundiced view of any man who gets paid up to $40,000 a year for working about seventy hours a month. There is little doubt, however, that seventy hours of duty in the cockpit of a jetliner are more than the equivalent of the usual forty-hours-a-week job in terms of fatigue as well as responsibility. It was thirty years ago that the airlines agreed to limit monthly flight time to eighty-five hours. That maximum stayed in effect up to the sixth year of the jet age, when the airlines conceded that the jets had created new fatigue problems not anticipated six years before.

One obvious difference is the speed of the jetliner. A pilot flying a piston schedule used to make five round-trip transcontinental flights per month to get in his eighty-five hours. On the faster jets, eighty-five hours would add up to ten flights a month.

Another fatigue factor is purely medical. Jet crews literally live in an atmosphere where cold outside air is pumped into the aircraft, warmed and then expelled rapidly. Such air is almost totally lacking in moisture. This results in a dehydration process which causes loss of potassium from the blood stream and body tissue over a long period. Such a loss can lead to abnormal fatigue.

Fatigue also is involved in what doctors term "diurnal variation" —man's habit of dividing his daily life into roughly three eight-hour periods, eight hours for sleep, eight for work and eight for relaxation. International and transcontinental flight crews, exposed to frequent time zone changes, have this natural, habitual cycle disrupted almost continually. It usually takes three days to get back into the normal cycle, and there will be even more difficult readjustment when the supersonic age dawns.

Finally, there is a certain amount of tension stemming from the jets themselves. They are marvelously efficient, strong and dependable. But they demand more pilot attention and faster decisions—both fatigue-causing factors. I recently asked a captain who has been flying for three decades, including ten years of jets, if fatigue was a problem as far as he was concerned. He wrote me:

"Yes, flying jets takes a lot out of me. I haven't really been able to pin down all the reasons even in my own mind, but I'm bushed mentally and physically even after a relatively short flight. I guess the main reason for jet fatigue is that everything moves at such a fast pace. When a problem comes up and there's need for decision and action, you can't park and think it over. The manager of a multi-million-dollar factory must make important decisions, but he has time to consider them. Just move his multi-million-dollar factory through the air at high speed and the pressure is increased many times over."

The letter continued: "You fly the jet by the book and it's a damned thick book. To stay ahead of any jet, a pilot must stay mentally on the edge of his seat every minute. Take the landing approach, for example. In a typical jetliner, a pilot has only about 110 seconds from the outer marker to the runway. He's flying a machine that weighs about 100 tons and he's moving some 250 feet per second. Even on a normal, routine ILS approach, the pace and workload are high.

"Because of all this, many of the decisions and actions involved in control of the aircraft are irrevocable. Again, the pilot can't stop in mid-air and think them over."

In conclusion, the captain wrote: "I don't know of a single pilot who isn't tired when he gets off a trip, including the routine ones. You can't help being conscious of the fact that you've been operating five or six or seven million dollars' worth of airplane that's absolutely unforgiving of carelessness, bad judgment or poor flying technique. You carry that sense of responsibility around in your guts every second you're on the plane, and when the flight's over it's still sitting inside you like an undigested meal.

"Sure, we fly as few as seventy hours a month. Sounds easy, doesn't it? But three or four hours in a jet is the equivalent of eight or nine hours of hard work, and when I say work I mean mental strain as well as physical exertion. You ask if I get tired? Hell, yes!"

Buttressing the view of this pilot was a survey made a couple of years ago among wives of jet captains flying for two major airlines. The wives were selected instead of their husbands to avoid any reluctance of the men to admit weaknesses, symptoms and physical difficulties. The returned questionnaires disclosed a significant percentage of increasing nervous tension, as portrayed by the wives' complaints. They reported their husbands showing less interest in their children, in recreation and in sex since they began flying jets. Some of this may have been due to the normal aging process, but the responses indicated that fatigue and stress were going beyond the expectable.

"His fatigue, both physical and emotional, seems to be what would be expected over a 10–15 year period, not three years," one wife wrote.

"He's on a treadmill of flying and sleeping, never quite catching up," said another.

"It takes all of his three days off to get rested up for the next trip," a spouse complained.

No comment is necessary on the following observation:

"There is an anti-social, irritable stranger living in this house and you can have him. I want laughing boy back."

It is somewhat difficult for pilots to "sell" the public on such problems as fatigue, partially because of an old suspicion that economics is the ulterior motive behind many pilot safety proposals. Here again is that contradictory double image of ALPA—when airmen fight for some safety measure, are they speaking as skilled, objective technicians, or as union members masquerading a labor demand under the guise of a safety problem?

ALPA for some time has been concerned over its reputation in the nation's press. A few years ago, it asked a public relations consulting firm to conduct an extensive survey among leading aviation and labor writers. The union wanted to know what these newspapermen thought of airline pilots in general and ALPA in particular. The results were not cause for smugness. Less than 30 per cent credited the organization with being a real force in promoting safety, while nearly all the respondents regarded ALPA primarily as a labor union. A disturbing 47 per cent rated ALPA's image as fair, poor or bad.

The survey obviously reflected some lack of knowledge about the nation's air crews and their contributions to safety. For one thing, a crash gets more publicity than a technical achievement—and most accidents eventually are blamed on the men up front.

Inasmuch as pilot error statistically is the leading cause of crashes, it is too bad there are no statistics on the number of times pilot skill has kept a disaster from occurring. Three particularly dramatic incidents have been described earlier. Others, just from the U.S. airlines, would fill a book. Men like Captain R. E. McKenna of United, who landed a DC-6 safely after a freak structural failure knocked off virtually his entire rudder. Or Captain David Rall of Northwest, who ditched a flaming DC-7 off the Philippines and lost only one passenger—an elderly woman with a heart condition.

Some comprehension of what it means not to have an accident

happen—because a pilot has demonstrated courage, technical ability
and calmness under stress—can be gleaned from this Air Force
data on average human reaction times in the air:

| | |
|---|---|
| Time from eye image to brain | 0.1 seconds |
| Recognition time of brain | 1.0 seconds |
| Decision time | 5.0 seconds |
| Decision time to muscle | 0.4 seconds |
| Muscle reaction time | 0.4 seconds |
| Air reaction time | 5.0 seconds |

This adds up to 11.9 seconds elapsing between the time the
human eye spots an emergency situation and when the airplane
itself responds to whatever decision the pilot has made. Remember
that a jet in landing configuration—the slowest phase of flight—
still is moving two hundred and fifty feet per second. There have
been too many accidents blamed on pilot error in which crews
simply ran out of time in which to conquer an unexpected
emergency—or "running out of information and altitude simultaneously," as pilots like to phrase it. Given a reasonable breathing
space, the airline pilot can perform miracles.

One of the most unusual "saves" in aviation history occurred
May 29, 1965, and it involved unprecedented pilot teamwork,
ingenuity and coordination—the safe landing of a crippled jet by
using procedures developed in an emergency test flight a thousand
miles away while the jet circled and awaited the results!

A Northwest Boeing 727, Flight 227 from Newark to Chicago,
took off routinely but quickly ran into trouble. The crew had
retracted the landing gear but the nose gear red warning light
remained on. Captain Harry Muldoon ordered the gear dropped
again to see if repeating the extension-retraction cycle would produce the green lights of normal operation. But with the gear
supposedly down, the red warning light for an unlocked nosewheel kept glaring ominously at the pilots.

At this stage, Muldoon didn't know if the nosewheel was up *or*
down. He flew over the Newark tower for a visual inspection
and got the bad news immediately—the nose gear was fully retracted despite the extension cycle. Muldoon and his crew could
not know the reason, of course, but they did know that some
failure in the nose gear lock system had made extension im-

possible. They tried every conceivable normal and emergency extension system in the book; the nose gear stayed up, which meant that sooner or later Muldoon was going to have to land the 727 with its snout pushing up pieces of runway pavement.

Northwest requires its crews to notify headquarters in Minneapolis-St. Paul of any abnormal situation. The NWA Planning Office received Muldoon's message and alerted Captain Paul Soderlind, Superintendent of Flying. Soderlind, in turn, asked an engineering official named John Reinman to meet him at the Minneapolis Airport on the double. Reinman's title: Weights and Balances Engineer. Soderlind wanted his advice on what would be the key factor in saving Flight 227 from a potentially bad accident—reducing weight forward so the nose could be held off the ground as long as possible when the plane finally landed.

Both Soderlind and Reinman were uncomfortably aware that all concerned, including the airplane, were breaking new ground. No 727 had ever suffered a stuck nose gear before. Boeing had furnished all 727 operators with a nose-up landing procedure, but Soderlind wasn't satisfied that it could provide minimum landing damage. He asked the Planning Office for a 727 to be used in an emergency test flight, and he began conferring with Reinman on what advice to give Muldoon.

"For one thing," the balance specialist suggested, "tell him to start burning fuel from the center tank only. That'll leave as much fuel as possible in the outboard wing tanks. The center tank is forward of the CG [center of gravity] and the outboards are aft of CG. Get it?"

"Got it," said Soderlind. "That'll shift the CG rearward. I'm also gonna tell Muldoon to move any passengers he can toward the rear—fill up all the seats they can in the aft section. Now I'd better raise Muldoon."

Northwest can talk to any domestic flight directly from its main base, and Soderlind established radio contact with 227 quickly. He agreed with Muldoon's decision to stay in the New York area while fuel was consumed, and to land at Kennedy where the runways were longer than at Newark.

"Just stay up there until you hear from me again, Harry," the chief pilot said. "We've got a 727 ready for a special test flight. I have a hunch we can work out something that isn't in that

Boeing manual—some way to keep that nose off the runway at the lowest practicable speed."

Muldoon explained the situation to his passengers and told the four stewardesses to serve complimentary drinks and dinner. He kept Flight 227 in a holding pattern near Kennedy, where trucks were preparing to foam Runway 22R—the prime purpose of the foam being prevention of sparks from the friction of metal on concrete when the nose touched down. If impact caused any fuel leakage or spray, the tiniest spark could mean fire.

At Minneapolis, meanwhile, Soderlind took off in another 727 with two purposes in mind. First, he wanted to determine as accurately as possible where the nose would touch so the foam could be applied to that portion—there wouldn't be enough to foam the entire runway. Second, he wanted to try out a theory which, if correct, would give Muldoon the lowest possible landing speed in a nose-high roll without any danger of a stall.

His idea involved the precise manipulation of the 727's trailing edge flaps and lift spoilers on the wings—literally hinges that reduce airspeed during the approach and landing phases. The Boeing tri-jet, like nearly all jet transports, has flaps and spoilers that can be "split"—in other words, the so-called hinges located outboard on the wing can be operated independently of those on the inboard area. Normally, flaps and spoilers are operated simultaneously, but in this case, Soderlind figured, splitting would be another way of getting that center of gravity moved back toward the rear.

On the swept-back wing of a jet, the outboard portion of the wing is behind the CG and the inboard portion is ahead. Soderlind's brand-new procedure was to extend only the inboard flaps first—increasing forward lift and thus helping to keep the nose up. Then he planned to extend only the outboard spoilers, which would reduce aft lift and thus tend to keep the tail down.

The tricky part was determining the best moment for splitting. Soderlind found out with relative quickness exactly how the special flap and spoiler management could shift CG rearward without affecting the critical low touchdown speed. He discovered that if he used full flaps and spoilers right up through touchdown, he could achieve minimum safe speed and then activate the special split flap settings just after the main wheels touched.

A single test flight confirmed Soderlind's experimental procedures. He briefed Muldoon and advised Kennedy Airport exactly where to foam Runway 22R. By this time, Reinman had computed the exact CG shift accomplished by moving passengers and burning fuel off from the center tank. His figures, plus the data from Soderlind's flight test, told the foam and fire truck crews almost to the exact foot where the 727's nose would first touch the runway. The emergency vehicles moved to the recommended area and Muldoon swung Flight 227 into a long approach.

He had already pre-positioned the flap and spoiler emergency controls so the splitting would take place at precisely the right second.

The main wheels touched down about one thousand feet from the threshold of 22R. About four thousand feet farther, the nose finally settled into the foam in the predicted spot. The 727 rolled another six hundred feet before coming to a gentle stop as the passengers cheered. One man refused to believe that the landing was made with the nose gear retracted until after the occupants evacuated and he could see for himself. Some passengers claimed later it was a smoother landing than they usually experienced.

It *was* smooth, beyond doubt. The only necessary repairs consisted of installing new nose gear doors, adding a tiny patch at the forward end of the nosewheel well and replacing the faulty lock assembly that had caused the trouble.

An official of the Port of New York Authority, which operates Kennedy, informed Northwest that "in all our years of handling various types of emergencies, this was by far the best managed of them all."

There was an important sequel to the incident of Flight 227, however, and one most demonstrative of commercial aviation's cooperative spirit when it comes to safety. Northwest advised Boeing of Soderlind's new technique for landing with a stuck nose gear. Boeing immediately transmitted a full report to all airlines flying 727s.

A few weeks later, a 727 flown by a different carrier had an identical nose gear malfunction. Using the new Northwest procedure, the pilots landed with only superficial damage and no injuries.

# 4

## "THEY BOUGHT THE FARM . . ."

Let it be said at the outset, firmly and fervently, the jet transport
is a brilliantly engineered creation that has demonstrated its inherent safety over the past ten years—against considerable odds
and in defiance of pessimistic predictions.

The drama of the jet age has been its very lack of drama.
The jetliner literally has wrought a quiet revolution, accomplishing
this by getting the public to take for granted not only its speed,
comfort and efficiency but also its ability to provide those three
assets with an all-important fourth: safety.

Significantly, the jet—representing the most drastic technical development in commercial aviation history—achieved safety despite
an explosive expansion that could well have invited disaster. Between 1963 and 1965, jets flew more hours than they did in their
first five years of operations! Considering the fact that the turbine-
powered transport was a radically different kind of aircraft, the
safety record has been a lot better than many experts believed
possible.

In 1967, for example, airlines belonging to the International
Civil Aviation Organization (ICAO) compiled their best safety
record in history, with .39 passenger fatalities per 100 million passenger miles. Scoff again, if you must, at that maligned mileage
yardstick but also consider the fact that this fatality rate was a
prodigious 37 per cent lower than in 1966 and nearly 30 per cent
under the previous safest year of 1965. ICAO itself noted that the
rate showed signs of flattening out between 1955 and 1960, but
then started to drop about 15 per cent each year. Inasmuch as
the jets began taking over the bulk of world-wide traffic in
1960, the only conclusion is that the jets brought increased safety
despite their steadily mounting potential exposure to accident.

We are about to discuss the negative subject of jet crashes, but first it is necessary to examine the positive side of this negative subject. And that is a simple truism: by and large, jets have crashed for basically the same reasons airplanes have always crashed— weather, inadequate ground aids, inferior airport facilities with short runways a prime factor, pilot error, collisions and sabotage. The overwhelming majority of fatal jet accidents are *not* due directly to the operating characteristics of the jet itself. If anything, those operating characteristics have contributed more to safety than they have detracted from it. To give just one example, the jet is indeed an aircraft that refuses to tolerate human mistakes. This may be a quality representing a potential hazard, yet it also is a quality that breeds discipline and respectful caution in the cockpit to a far greater degree than the pistons ever did.

There is another observation one must make in order to keep jet accidents in a properly focused perspective. The jet age has been comparatively free from those aeronautical engineering gremlins known as "bugs"—major design mistakes that turn up only after airliners enter regular service and which remain perversely hidden through the most rigorous test programs. The jets have had bugs, yes, but not of a calamitous nature, which is no mean attainment considering their greater size and complexity and their different operating environment. The jet was such a revolutionary departure from the pistons that it would not have been surprising to see it spawn some serious design mistakes, as earlier transports did— the Electra, DC-6, Martin 202, Constellation and Comet, to mention those airliners once afflicted with fatal "bug bites." All but the Electra were grounded for corrective measures, and the latter was forced to operate under severe speed restrictions pending extensive structural modifications.

This is not to say the jets have been totally free of design weaknesses. As with every transport aircraft, they have undergone constant modifications and improvements as the rugged, day-by-day rigors of airline operations exposed areas of inadequacy. The 707 or DC-8 in which you fly today is a better airplane than either was at the dawn of the jet age. And two virtues of the jetliner have exceeded the rosiest hopes of engineers, both involving safety. One is structural integrity. The other is engine reliability.

The jet's brute strength has been described previously—in those two instances in which jets lost part of their wings and still remained flyable. After the second incident, the TWA-Eastern col-

lision, some unknown wag sent a message over TWA's teletype
system amending the airline's "no go" list—those items which *must*
be in perfect condition before an aircraft is allowed to move one
inch from a ramp. The tongue-in-cheek order, transmitted to all
TWA stations, read:

AMENDMENT TO INOPERATIVE EQUIPMENT
LIST—EFFECTIVE IMMEDIATELY—ALL BOEING
707S MAY BE DISPATCHED WITH RIGHT OR LEFT
WING MISSING.

The reliability record of the turbine engine is best illustrated with
a single comparison. In 1959, the FAA required jet power plants
to be overhauled after only one thousand hours of operation: in
some cases, the overhaul time was eight hundred hours. In 1968,
most turbine engines were going six to eight thousand hours between overhauls, and even this is conservative. Many power plant
experts believe a jet engine, properly maintained and inspected
regularly, could go on almost indefinitely without needing a major
tear-down. The FAA has even begun allowing some airlines to
eliminate major overhauls if they follow a new system of replacing
certain components at regular intervals.

If the designers deserve unstinted praise for what they achieved
in strength and reliability, however, they also warrant a spanking
for their occasional transgressions. The airlines have felt for years
that airframe manufacturers, operating under federal certification
requirements, perform admirably in meeting or even surpassing
those stiff requirements but occasionally are less diligent in areas
where there are no certification standards.

The certification process for the commercial transport itself deserves an explanation. FAA engineers work with factory technicians almost from the start of the first blueprints for a new airliner. The FAA specialists lay down certain specifications and
tests which the final product must meet. Can the plane, for example, suffer engine failure while taking off with a full load on a
hot summer day from an airport considerably above sea level and
still climb safely? Are key structural parts stressed to withstand
sudden jolts or prolonged gust forces? Does cockpit visibility come
up to minimum standards? Are there adequate backup systems for
any control component that might fail?

Certification has played an underrated role in air safety; the rare failures stemming from inadequate certification have obscured the many times the process has nipped bugs before an airplane began carrying passengers. But there are weaknesses and drawbacks, starting with the fact that the FAA lacks the funds for hiring sufficient technical experts (thanks to the Budget Bureau and Congress, the latter a highly vocal demander of greater air safety while it simultaneously and with alarming frequency cuts air safety appropriations). With limited engineering personnel, the FAA delegates some portion of its certification duties to the manufacturers, who, in turn, assign trusted employees to the program.

This delegation of authority has resulted in certification of at least three airliners with fatal bugs—the Constellation, the DC-6 and the Martin 202. All three were certificated despite weaknesses which resulted in serious accidents. The Constellation had an electrical wiring flaw which led to a fatal in-flight fire. The DC-6 had an air scoop which sucked overflow fuel from wing tanks into the heating system ducts. The Martin 202 was built with a key structural part in the wings made of an untested alloy, one which developed metal fatigue in a short time.

Certification work by factory engineers has been vastly improved since the jets, and the liaison between FAA and manufacturers also is far closer than it was in the past. Also significant is the fact that the airframe manufacturers do, indeed, impose on their new planes tougher test programs than FAA requires.

But limited FAA manpower, nevertheless, has resulted in limited certification. Robert E. Stone, United's Director of Flight Safety and an ex-line pilot, told an ALPA safety forum that "one of the greatest faults of certification is that it concentrates on the 'killer items.'" By this, he meant that certification—with its numerically inadequate personnel—must focus on major items most directly concerned with safety.

"This is fine," Stone added, "for we get an airplane that is basically safe, but the little detail items are not covered by adequate certification rules and these drive us crazy."

The UAL official went on to cite such examples as a cabin lighting system that somehow managed to garble navigation and communication signals, or a cockpit voice recorder whose tape kept jamming. Stone said United actually found it could purchase $CO_2$ cartridges in a liquor store which were better than those a safety equipment manufacturer was supplying for the airline's life jackets. United, he said, once bought new altimeters which supposedly would correct themselves for temperature and airspeed variations by means of an electro-servo unit. In actual flight experience, the servos not only didn't work but also made the altimeters more dangerous. UAL has a "top twenty" list showing the twenty air- craft parts that fail most frequently. Stone said that for the first three months of 1966, nineteen of the items on the "top twenty" list for the DC-8 were not covered by certification. The same ratio was true for the Boeing 720.

Every airliner has certain "no go" components—meaning that if a "no go" item is inoperative, the airplane cannot fly until repairs are made. According to Stone, six of the uncertificated items on the DC-8's "top twenty" were of the "no go" variety, and there were eight such uncertificated items on the Boeing 720 list.

As Stone himself pointed out, certification has made massive contributions to air safety and the manufacturers' insistence on going beyond certification standards has made almost as many. Yet with the ever increasing complexity of airliners, disaster needs only a sliver of an opening through which to strike—a jet crash on March 1, 1962, offered stark evidence of this.

It was an American Airlines 707 that left New York for Los Angeles with eight crew members and eighty-seven passengers. Only eight seconds after takeoff, the plane lurched to the left, banked sharply and continued an almost graceful roll until it was on its back. Then it fell, nose down, into the shallow waters of Jamaica Bay. There were no survivors.

The CAB's report, announced ten months later, found that: ". . . the probable cause of this accident was a rudder control system malfunction producing yaw, sideslip and roll leading to a loss of control from which recovery action was not effective."

Boiled down to layman phraseology, the CAB findings deter- mined that a short circuit had occurred in the wiring of a small motor which activates the hydraulic boost system for the rudder. It might be compared to what would happen if the power steering on an automobile suddenly jammed while the wheel was in a sharp turn. In the case of the American 707, according to the CAB, the electrical malfunction resulted in crossed wires, sending the wrong voltage through the circuits and giving the rudder an unwanted hard-over signal that took the pilots by surprise.

The rudder servo unit from the wrecked plane was recovered and examined. Investigators found evidence of pre-impact damage on the wires—scratches, punctures and other unexplainable gouge marks. CAB experts visited the factory where the units were manufactured and watched the assembly process. One investigator noticed a pair of tweezers on a bench and asked the workman what they were used for. The workman explained that he needed the tweezers to grasp a cord which had to be wrapped around the wires. The investigator examined several units that had just come off the assembly line—units on which tweezers had been used—and found damage identical to what had been discovered on the little motor from the American 707.

The CAB's verdict has been disputed by Boeing, American and the FAA. The latter still believes the crash resulted from a wrongly installed bolt (put in upside down by mistake) which fell out of the hydraulic system, rammed excess fluid into one side of the rudder control system and caused a sudden, violent shove that locked the controls while the plane was in a turn. If true, this FAA analysis was just one more manifestation of "Murphy's Law"—namely, "if an aircraft part can be installed incorrectly, someone will install it that way." At least two major crashes in the United States, and several more overseas, have been blamed on application of "Murphy's Law."

The doubts raised against the CAB's verdict in the Jamaica Bay accident were based largely on flight tests which duplicated the rudder control malfunction alleged by the Board. Boeing and the FAA maintained that a short circuit in the servo unit would have resulted in comparatively little force, which, even if totally unexpected, could have been easily overriden by the pilots. Boeing, in fact, deliberately short-circuited the unit without warning on several test flights. The pilots had no difficulty in maintaining control and stopping the roll. As far as Boeing is concerned, the crash is still unexplained—no other jet has had any experience which might throw some new light on what happened over Jamaica Bay. Many pilots bitterly point out that whatever control malfunction occurred, it came when the American flight was just starting a noise abatement turn at low altitude, with insufficient room for recovery. It would be hard to convince pilots that noise abatement didn't play a role in this accident.

We may never know whether a short circuit in wires no longer

than a pencil and only one sixth of an inch thick was responsible
for ninety-five deaths, or whether the cause was a one-inch bolt
costing about twenty-five cents. But in either case, the lesson to
be learned is identical. A jet carries more than three thousand
pounds of safety, standby and emergency installations. Its navigation and communications equipment alone costs more than an entire transport did twenty years ago. Yet safety, or death, may
hinge on such seemingly insignificant items as the thread design on
a tiny bolt or the innocent use of tweezers on a few little wires.
The true tragedy of the American crash was that catastrophe in
the form of a ridiculously tiny Achilles' heel managed to defeat all
the previous efforts made to assure the maximum of safety.

The aviation industry *is* learning the lessons taught by disaster.
And one such lesson is the greater extent to which new planes are
being tested before they fly passengers. This is not to say transports like the DC-8 and 707 were inadequately tested; they underwent what were at the time the most ruthless, extensive test programs in history. But it is an aviation axiom that daily airline flying
sometimes can uncover bugs which defy exposure by the toughest
test flying.

In the early part of the jet age, the new transports were plagued
by a wave of hydraulic failures—first in the 707 and later in the
DC-8. There were an alarming number of incidents in which landing gears refused to come down normally—sufficient to warrant frantic grounding demands by several Congressmen who did not take
time to consider the fact that a stuck landing gear had yet to kill
a single passenger.

The public, which deserves credit for not getting as hysterical
as certain lawmakers, nevertheless must have wondered why jets
came up with hydraulic difficulties after supposedly thorough test
programs. And there must have been some concern generated by
the statements coming from a few Congressmen who, as is so often
the case, leaped before they looked. Not one who pressured the
FAA to ground first the 707 and later the DC-8 took the trouble
to ask for a briefing on what was causing the technical problems.
And the cause was not only simple but symptomatic of the teething
pains suffered by most new airliners that are bigger and more complex than their predecessors.

First, the jet's hydraulic system is ten times more complicated
than corresponding equipment on pistons. In addition to greater

complexity, the system is subjected to drastic temperature changes which can literally "age" some of the components. Some parts have worn out before expected. A jet can take off with the ground thermometers reading one hundred degrees and in a few minutes be cruising at thirty-five thousand feet in outside temperatures of twenty degrees below zero. Older, prop-driven aircraft at one time had fewer gear problems because their hydraulic systems had benefited from years of refinement. Gear failures on the jets are diminishing, too, for the same reason—improvements resulting from experience and better maintenance.

An FAA-industry campaign to cure the gear difficulties in the early jet years was typical.

The FAA and the airlines agreed on nine modifications to the DC-8 hydraulic system and generally similar changes in that of the Boeing. The airlines also instituted stricter inspection and maintenance procedures as well as checking flight crews to make sure they were following prescribed procedures for dealing with hydraulic emergencies. The airlines began filing faster, more frequent and detailed reports on every conceivable type of hydraulic malfunction, no matter how minor.

This enabled the FAA and the industry to prevent insignificant problems from developing into major ones.

In less than seven months, the concerted government-airline effort reduced hydraulic incidents from a peak of sixteen per one thousand hours of flight to five per one thousand hours. The rate today is down to the level or even below that of piston-engine aircraft.

Admittedly, this is no comfort to a passenger at best inconvenienced and at worst frightened when an airliner encounters an abnormal situation, such as a jammed gear. But it is the purpose of this book to emphasize the positive while acknowledging the negative. For every so-called abnormal situation or even real emergency, there are about one and a half million completely routine flights. And this, too, must be realized when anyone looks askance at the weaknesses in scheduled air transportation.

Yes, we are about to examine jet crashes—their causes and their cures. It will not be particularly pleasant reading; it will frighten some readers and it will bring pain to anyone who has lost a loved one or friend in an air crash. But it should not bring indignation, anger or doubts toward a U.S. manufacturing industry that has pro-

duced three out of every four commercial transports flying the
world's airlines, or a U.S. airline industry that lands approximately
85 per cent of its eight million annual flights within fifteen minutes
or less of scheduled arrival times and completes more than 97 per
cent of its scheduled mileage. For every tragedy, there are hundreds
of thousands of triumphs, and that is precisely what a safely completed flight is—a triumph forged by skill, responsibility and devotion to the goal of constant safety improvement.

Pilots have a pet expression for fatal accidents—the typically
casual jargon of the airman who feels emotion deeply but tries so
hard to hide those emotions under a blanket of half cynicism, half
fatalism.

"They bought the farm" is the way they refer to a crash.

Captain Roy W. Almquist, like many veteran airline pilots, flew
for a living but had an avocation to which he devoted most of his
off-duty time. Based in Minneapolis, he also was a banker, president of his local Lions Club and definitely a solid citizen.

On February 12, 1963, Roy Almquist was commanding Northwest
Flight 705, non-stop from Miami to Chicago. He took off on schedule, at 1:30 P.M. Approximately twenty minutes later, Almquist and
the rest of the forty-three persons aboard Flight 705 were dead
and the wreckage of their Boeing 720B was scattered over a wide
area of the Florida Everglades. For the first time since the dawn
of the jet age, a U.S. jetliner had disintegrated in the air.

That one aspect shook the entire aviation industry. There already
had been reassuring evidence that the jets were stronger than their
designers had planned. A Pan Am 707, only a few months after
the start of jet service, had gone into an unexpected dive from
thirty-five thousand feet over the Atlantic. By the time control
was regained (the autopilot had inadvertently disengaged), the
plane had plunged to six thousand feet, exceeding the speed of
sound. It later was determined that during the dive, the 707 had
been subjected to load forces nearly six times the force of gravity,
*exceeding the design limits established by Boeing engineers by a
sizable margin.* The G forces were so great that when the captain
landed, both his eyes were blackened as if by heavy blows.

It was a hair-raising yet comforting incident, for it showed that
the strength of a battleship had been put into the jet's aluminum
skeleton and skin. More than four years of safe jet operations tran-

spired between the Pan Am dive and the destruction of Northwest Flight 705. There had been accidents, but none involving supposedly impossible structural failure.

Yet it was obvious that the NWA 720B *had* suffered structural disintegration, and in the violent turbulence of a thunderstorm. This was a fate not unknown to piston-engine planes, but no one thought it likely that a storm could tear apart a mighty jet. There seemed to be no doubt that turbulence was involved. The record of communications between Flight 705 and Miami Departure Control contained frequent references to severe turbulence and repeated requests from 705 for vectoring out of the storm in the vicinity of Miami International Airport.

At one point, Flight 705's copilot—Robert Feller—advised Departure Control:

"Ah, we're in the clear now. We can see it out ahead . . . looks pretty bad."

"It" was the boiling caldron of a thunderhead, containing storm cells of near-tornadic strength.

Departure Control, rather apologetically, assured Feller it had vectored Flight 705 into what ground radar showed was the least turbulent area. It cleared the flight to climb to its assigned cruising altitude of twenty-five thousand feet.

"Okay," Feller replied. "Ah . . . we'll make a left turn about thirty degrees here and climb."

"Is two-seven-oh your climb-out heading?" Departure Control asked.

"Affirmative," said Feller. "It'll take us out in the open again."

Departure Control gave 705 permission to turn to a heading of two hundred and seventy degrees and climb, even as Feller reported that the turbulence was moderate to heavy. Again, Departure Control assured him that the vectoring course was intended to avoid the worst turbulence and at the same time steer clear of conflicting traffic, the later getting obvious priority.

"Okay," Feller said with a trace of sarcasm. "You'd better run the rest of them off the other way, then."

(When the CAB studied the transmission tape later, it was apparent there had been a persistent conflict between Flight 705 and Departure Control—the crew kept complaining that the vectoring courses were exposing the flight to a bad pounding, and the controller working 705 kept insisting, in effect, that he was doing

the best he could, considering the demands of other traffic. This
"conflict of interest" occurs too often. The CAB report on the accident noted that: "Clearly, both were seeking the safest, most
expeditious route. The misunderstanding resulted from the pilot's
desire to avoid the squall line and the controller's prime responsibility to provide adequate separation from known IFR traffic."
Pilots wish the FAA had sufficient funds for dual radar installations,
one to monitor weather and the other for monitoring traffic, as well
as additional personnel to handle such equipment.)

The last communication from 705 was Feller's laconic, "We're
just about out of seventeen-five [seventeen thousand, five hundred
feet] . . ."

The time was 1:48 P.M.

Less than two minutes later, ground witnesses saw an orange
ball of flame flare up amid the black thunderclouds, then fall to the
ground.

Not until June 4, 1965, did the Civil Aeronautics Board release
its findings on the destruction of Flight 705. Twenty-seven months
is an unusually long period between the occurrence of an accident and the issuance of a "probable cause" report. But the
solution of Flight 705's death involved some of the most vital
safety research in aviation history, for it exposed hitherto unsuspected hazards in the jet's operating characteristics. Incredible as
it may seem, the hazards were not detected in the hundreds of
flight test hours or thousands of airline flight hours accumulated
before the Northwest accident.

Jets had been tossed about by severe turbulence many times—
prior to February 12, 1963, there were thirty-four incidents in
which passengers were injured and/or jet transports damaged—
but not until Flight 705 was wrenched apart did the phrase
"turbulence upset" take on a new and deadly meaning. And the
delayed recognition of this upset problem can only be interpreted
as a combination of lack of experience with serious loss of control
during turbulence, and the unhappy fact that it took a fatal crash
to focus attention on the upset phenomenon.

To understand Flight 705's fate and subsequent upset incidents,
both fatal and non-fatal, it is necessary to reconstruct what must
have occurred in the cockpit when an emergency confronted
Captain Almquist and First Officer Feller with which they were

not prepared to deal—and through no real fault of their own, or of anyone else, for that matter.

They were climbing to their assigned altitude, still being punched around by turbulence, when their 720B slammed into massive updrafts. The nose of the aircraft tilted up sharply and airspeed dropped accordingly—down to the point where Almquist, flying the plane, became alarmed at the possibility of a stall. He reacted as almost any pilot would have at the time. He pressed his left thumb on a small button attached to the control yoke. This is the electrical stabilizer trim switch—known to Boeing pilots as the "pickle switch." This switch is hooked to a small electric motor in the tail section. When the black button is pressed, the motor manipulates the entire horizontal stabilizer.

On ordinary planes, the horizontal stabilizers are fixed, with only the elevators—the hinges attached to the rear of the stabilizers—able to move up or down, providing what is known as longitudinal control: the means of climbing or descending. But on jets, it is possible to move the whole stabilizer area. (David Hoffman, able aviation editor of the Washington *Post*, gave the best analogy of this function when he compared it to a child sticking his hand out of a car window, adjusting or trimming "the angle of his fingertips to porpoise his palm in the windstream outside a moving car.")

Almquist was faced with an abnormally out-of-trim condition—nose up and airspeed evaporating. He pushed the "pickle switch" forward and shoved his yoke forward at the same time. The jet dove, but simultaneously—as the flight recorder showed later—Flight 705 suddenly was caught in the vicious vise of a huge downdraft. With all controls literally locked in a dive position, the jet accelerated sickeningly and rapidly. The CAB's report describes what must have been taking place in the cockpit during these few terrible seconds:

"Besides the distraction of warning lights and ringing bells which were probably actuated under the negative G conditions, loose items such as briefcases, charts, logbooks, etc., would be tossed around. The crew members themselves would be forced upward against their belts and the average airline pilot would probably have difficulty keeping his feet on the rudder pedals and his hands on the control wheel."

It probably took Almquist eight seconds before he managed to get his hands back on the control yoke. In those eight seconds,

Flight 705 went into a vertical dive exceeding five hundred miles an hour and with airspeed increasing steadily. He hauled back on the yoke. The nose stayed down. The dive continued. He continued to apply back pressure in a desperate tug of war against the aerodynamic loads building up on the stabilizers and elevators. It was no contest. The tug of war ended when the loads exceeded the design strength of the stabilizer-elevator section. The elevators snapped off and Flight 705 plunged helplessly toward the swamps below. As the uncontrollable dive rose to almost supersonic speeds the jet began to spin, engine pods and wings broke off and fuel tanks exploded.

Recall the experience of Captain Duescher (Chapter 3). He was challenged by the same emergency as Almquist. He came through because he resisted the temptation to recover control until his own 720 was at a lower altitude where elevator response was possible. This is not to blame Almquist. He was relatively inexperienced in jets—of his nearly eighteen thousand hours of flight time, only one hundred and fifty hours were in the 720. Copilot Feller, with more than a thousand hours in Boeing jets, presented the unusual situation of a first officer being more experienced than his captain in this particular type of aircraft. Almquist was no stranger to thunderstorm turbulence—not with more than seventeen thousand hours logged—but he *was* a stranger to the effects of turbulence on swept-wing aircraft.

Those effects became only too apparent after the Northwest crash, the Duescher incident, several other instances of temporary control loss during severe turbulence, and finally some hard-nose research performed by Boeing, Douglas, NASA and airline flight superintendents. Paul Soderlind of Northwest, who had been a close friend of Almquist, embarked on what amounted to an educational crusade. He wrote probably the most widely distributed safety publication of all time—a discourse on jet behavior during turbulence and ways to combat it. He also toured the country, addressing pilot groups of all airlines.

Literally, Soderlind recommended an entirely different approach. Previous to the Northwest crash, jet pilots had been penetrating storm areas in the same manner in which they had flown straight-wing aircraft into known rough air—slowing down to specified speeds to prevent structural damage. As far as the jets were concerned, there were two dangers in following the old procedure:

(1) the jets were being slowed down too much, creating the possibility of stalls, and (2) pilots were trying too hard to maintain airspeed during severe updrafts and downdrafts, instead of concentrating on keeping their aircraft level.

Soderlind's advice, supported by industry and government flight and wind tunnel tests, was to increase turbulence penetration speeds slightly—he reasoned that the jets were structurally capable of withstanding the greater stresses generated by the higher penetration speeds, and that preventing stalls was more important. Second, he urged pilots snared by severe turbulence not to worry so much about such pressure instruments as airspeed indicators. He reminded his fellow airmen that in turbulence those instruments often are unreadable anyway, and that trying to "chase" them can lead to loss of control. He also warned against actuating the electrical trim switch during turbulence, but to rely instead on manual control of the elevators and, above all, to concentrate on maintaining level attitude—in other words, he was telling them to let the jets almost fly themselves through storms, instead of fighting turbulence. Similar and equally important missionary work was done by Frank Kolk of American Airlines.

Inability to read instruments when an aircraft is being flipped around in a storm has been an aviation problem for a long time. It is a more serious problem with jets because the swept-wing aircraft loses lift more rapidly in violently rough air and correspondingly rapid attitude changes. Because most instruments operate via the pressure of air forced to the instruments by aircraft movement, such attitude changes can result in erratic instrument readings. Airspeed, for example, can fluctuate more than two hundred miles an hour in turbulence as aircraft attitude itself fluctuates. An Eastern DC-8 captain, whose plane was almost rolled on its back in a thunderstorm shortly after taking off from Dulles International Airport, described what can happen during severe turbulence in succinct terms.

"We encountered the most violent jolt I have ever experienced in over twenty thousand hours of flying. I felt as though an extremely severe positive, upward acceleration had triggered off a buffeting, not a pitch, that increased in frequency and magnitude as one might expect to encounter sitting on the end of a huge tuning fork that had been struck violently. Not an instrument on any panel was readable to its full scale but appeared as a white blur against its dark background. From that point on—it could have been ten, twenty, sixty or a hundred seconds—we had no idea of attitude, altitude, airspeed or heading. We were now on instruments with no visual reference and continued with severe to violent buffeting, ripping, tearing, rending, crashing sounds. Brief-cases, manuals, ashtrays, suitcases, pencils, cigarettes, flashlights were flying about like unguided missiles. It sounded and felt as if pods were leaving and the structure disintegrating. The objects that were thrashing about the cockpit seemed momentarily to settle on the ceiling, which made it impossible to trust one's senses, although I had a feeling that we were inverted as my seat belt was tight and had stretched considerably. As my briefcase was on the ceiling, I looked up and through the overhead window and felt that I was looking down on the top of a cloud deck. The first officer said later he had the same impression at the same instant, as we acted in unison, applying as much force as we could gather to roll aileron control to the left. The [artificial] horizon bar at this time started to stabilize and showed us coming back through ninety degrees vertical to a level attitude laterally. At this time, I had my first airspeed reading, decaying through two hundred and fifty knots. The air smoothed out and we gently leveled off at between fourteen hundred and fifteen hundred feet . . ."

That vivid account explains why the airline pilot's traditional recommended maneuver for combating a thunderstorm is a one hundred and eighty degree turn. It also underlines the propensity of some jet instruments to go into a frenetic dance during a turbulence upset. Of particular concern is the artificial horizon indicator; large transports are not flown by the old "seat of the pants" feeling and jets are even more reliant on instrument flying than are pistons. The artificial horizon indicator tells a pilot when he is flying level, climbing or descending, and in many of the most serious turbulence cases studied during the "trouble with turbu-lence" years, crews lost their only attitude references when their horizon indicators went crazy. Inability to "feel" aircraft attitude is particularly hazardous at night or in an overcast.

The new technique of giving attitude a priority over airspeed was a major step in preventing upsets from occurring in the first place; the old reverse priority, airspeed over attitude, resulted in haywire instruments and loss of control before pilots could do anything about maintaining attitude. A second safety bonus was added when the airlines adopted new artificial horizon indicators which are far easier to read and less prone to tumble. And most important, pilot training and retraining have emphasized the new procedures exerting more moderate control forces when counteracting turbulence instead of fighting it.

Significantly, turbulence upset instances have diminished since mid-1964 when the research, better instrumentation and new techniques began to pay off. Jets still run into jarring air—one can no more eliminate turbulence itself than repeal the law of gravity —but not with the resultant loss of control that plagued the industry in the early sixties. It is quite natural, however, for the public to ask why the turbulence problem seemed to catch the airlines by surprise. The crash of Northwest Flight 705 occurred four and a half years after the start of U.S. commercial jet service, and while there had been no fatal accidents attributed to turbulence, there had been more than thirty serious incidents—presumably sufficient advance warning that a pattern and a problem existed.

The answer is that no one recognized the pattern until lives were lost, a situation which seems to be one of the less praiseworthy aspects of air safety progress. This is not to imply that the industry and the government always wait for a fatal crash before action is taken. The opposite is true. The FAA issues "airworthiness directives" almost daily. These are mandatory corrective orders based on the constant flow of reports coming into the agency from the airlines. These reports are watched closely for the slightest sign of a developing pattern that could affect safety. Repeated or persistent malfunctions involving a certain component on a certain type airplane, for example, will bring a telegraphed warning to all carriers operating that kind of aircraft, along with a "fix" order to be accomplished by a certain deadline—sometimes before the plane is allowed to fly again. Frequently, the aircraft and/or engine manufacturers will wire the airlines advising them to inspect, repair or replace components which seem suspect. So widespread and rapid is this sharing of operational experience that the FAA's airworthiness directives often are mere confirmations of what the airlines already have done on the advice of the manufacturers.

In the case of the upset problem, there unquestionably was an element of overconfidence in the jet itself—specifically in its structural brawn. Airplanes had been endangered by turbulence since the beginning of aviation. Airliners had been wrecked by angry storms long before the jets came along. In the pre-jet years, the test flights failed to disclose any particular handling difficulties in rough air that were not true of straight-wing aircraft—that was the reason jet storm-penetration speeds were proportionately the same as those of the older transports.

The Northwest accident that opened an aeronautical Pandora's box officially was blamed primarily on Boeing and to a lesser extent on the airline. Two years after the crash, a Chicago jury ordered Boeing to pay $1.6 million to the widow of one of the victims, and Northwest was found liable for another $400,000 in damages. The widow's attorneys convinced the jury that the 720's horizontal stabilizers were defective and that Boeing waited until after the accident to warn pilots that turbulence techniques should be changed.

Without casting aspersions on any collection of "tried and true" jurists, their verdict was technically unsound. Boeing had no monopoly on the instability of jets in rough air under certain circumstances, any more than its planes had a monopoly on rugged construction. All swept-wing aircraft were subject to turbulence hazards, not because of design weaknesses but because it was not known at the time that they had to be flown differently. True, the certification process failed to go into this.

(It does now. The DC-9 and Boeing 737 were required to fly through severe thunderstorms as part of their certification tests, and those tests included instrument behavior during deliberately induced upsets. The new jets were not only tested for their handling characteristics in severe turbulence but they were even exposed to a fully untrimmed condition—their horizontal stabilizers were positioned full up or full down, and the aircraft then were rolled and dived to make sure pilots could recover safely.)

When the Boeings were having some early upset problems, many DC-8 captains rather complacently decided they were fortunate to be flying what they considered a more stable airplane. In a sense, the DC-8 is somewhat easier to handle than the 707 because its wings are swept back at a slightly lesser angle. Some pilots who have flown both planes claim the DC-8 flies more like a conventional airplane and is more docile than the Boeing. But any complacency on the part of the DC-8 crews was eradicated quickly.

An Eastern Air Lines DC-8 brushed its wing tips against disaster on November 9, 1963, while flying from Houston to Mexico City. Shortly after departing from Houston, it flew into a thunderstorm. The commanding pilot, Mel French, asked Air Traffic Control for a course change because his airborne radar showed turbulence ahead. Copilot Grant Newby was flying the plane and French was still discussing (arguing would be a better word) a different heading with the controller when the DC-8 went into a roller coaster ride—updrafts and then downdrafts of severe and prolonged duration. The horizon indicator might as well have been the "tilt" sign of a pinball machine; it was useless. The jet suddenly dipped into a high-speed dive from just under six thousand feet.

Both pilots tried to pull out, but the control yokes seemed to be riveted in a forward position. Their airspeed, the flight recorder showed later, was more than six hundred miles an hour. They were too close to the ground to bring the nose up by increasing power, as Duescher had done three months before. French had only one recourse and he acted with skill and masterful speed. He reversed thrust on all four engines. He couldn't have done this on a Boeing, whose reverse thrust can be used only on the ground for braking power. But on the DC-8 the engines can be reversed in flight as a kind of auxiliary aerial brake. French's application of reverse thrust slowed the plunging jet just enough for the pilots to regain some elevator control. Their yokes came back, slowly and grudgingly. They managed to get the jet level at around two thousand feet, but this lifesaving maneuver generated enough stress to tear off the number three engine pod and damage a second pod.

French made an emergency landing at Barksdale Air Force Base, outside of Shreveport, Louisiana. Except for the pod damage, the DC-8 was structurally intact—another mute tribute to the jets' inherent strength. But seventeen passengers were injured, four seriously enough to require hospitalization.

Not quite four months later, another Eastern DC-8—Flight 304 —left New Orleans bound for Atlanta, Washington and New York. Its wheels lifted at 2 A.M. Five minutes and forty seconds later, the giant plane crashed into Lake Pontchartrain, Louisiana, nineteen miles northeast of the New Orleans International Airport. All fifty-one passengers and the seven crew members perished.

Among the latter was First Officer Grant Newby, who must have been living on borrowed time. The impact was so great that not a single whole body was recovered.

This was another turbulence accident but one in which turbulence was more a contributing factor than a primary cause. It revolved around a small device called the pitch trim compensator—PTC to pilots. The PTC is a means of offsetting a jet's tendency to "tuck under"—assume a nose-down attitude—at high speeds even while flying level. Mechanically, it consists of a tiny computer which senses the critical airspeed at which tuck-under occurs and automatically sends compensating electrical signals to an actuator. The actuator, in turn, moves the copilot's control column back, trimming the aircraft back to level attitude. The computer triggers the entire process either at Mach 70 (70 per cent of the speed of sound) or at about three hundred and forty miles an hour. As speed increases, the computer steps up the electrical signals, which exert more force on the control yoke as the higher speed requires.

Boeing jets are not equipped with PTC units; pilot manipulation of the "pickle switch" accomplishes all trim chores. The DC-8 also has manual trim but the PTC was added to reduce the amount of trimming its crews would have to perform. Many DC-8 pilots would prefer to handle all necessary trim functions and would just as soon take the PTC off their planes. Others, however, regard it as a valuable aid.

The PTC on the Eastern jet that dove into Lake Pontchartrain was the subject of intensive investigation and, in fact, was the key to the crash. It is perhaps inconceivable to the layman that a malfunction in such a relatively tiny component—one that some pilots don't even regard as essential—could result in the destruction of a $6 million airliner. But to understand how it could happen is to understand better the phenomenon of jet behavior in turbulence, why the PTC was an undetected menace for so long and the means by which this menace was overcome.

Above all, the case history of Eastern Flight 304 and the aircraft involved—N8607—confirms another aviation axiom: few accidents have a single cause. Rather, a crash invariably is the result of a combination of circumstances: a chain reaction of mistakes, omissions and wrong assumptions, none fatal individually but deadly in a collective sense because each can lead to the fatal finality—

whether it be pilot error, a failed part or exposure to abnormal weather conditions. The fate of Flight 304 is a classic example.

The chain reaction that destroyed the EAL DC-8 began in that little PTC. The PTC computer on N8607 had been changed eight times, four in the week preceding the accident. And the computer that was on the jet when it crashed apparently deserved the automotive term "lemon." From April of 1960 to the night of the crash, this particular unit had been removed from various aircraft no less than fifteen times. Six of those removals followed pilot complaints of unwanted extension—in other words, the PTC actuated trim when it was not needed. Yet not a single discrepancy was found and the unit kept being reinstalled, the last installation being on N8607 the day before the crash. Not until after Flight 304 crashed was it learned why the PTC could malfunction in flight and yet pass every shop inspection. The reason was the initial triggering force that led to tragedy. *Not only Eastern but other DC-8 operators were performing PTC functional tests which were incapable of detecting certain computer malfunctions.*

This inspection inadequacy was discovered when CAB investigators took a supposedly serviceable unit from Eastern's PTC stock and put it through the manufacturer's own complete test procedures. The unit failed to pass all these more extensive tests.

On February 24, N8607 was flown from Miami to Philadelphia with no log complaints entered against the PTC. The aircraft was loaded for a flight to Mexico City via Washington, Atlanta and New Orleans. Before leaving, the flight engineer reported that the PTC failed a ground check while he was going through his pretakeoff checklist. Mechanics performed their own ground check and agreed with the flight engineer. That check consisted of activating the test circuit and watching for movement of the PTC indicator or control yoke. The mechanics did not inspect the actuator position or operating capability of the indicator system. The flight was dispatched with a request that the pilots check PTC operation during the trip south.

(It was ascertained later that no examination was made of the actuator because of its inaccessibility. To view the part, it was necessary to remove the copilot's seat. All DC-8s now have an access panel for easy actuator inspection, the panel being located in the nosewheel well.)

The crew performed the in-flight check between Washington

and Atlanta and found the PTC inoperative. N8607 landed routinely
at Mexico City the night of February 24 where its captain noted
in the aircraft logbook that the PTC was inoperative and should be
inspected and repaired when the ship returned to New York the
next day.

Flight 304 departed Mexico City under command of Captain
William Zeng, a veteran with more than nineteen thousand hours
logged and nearly one thousand of these representing DC-8 time.
Because of the inoperative PTC, Zeng's flight plan—in accordance
with Eastern's dispatch procedures—called for reduced airspeed
all the way to New York. It turned out to be a futile precaution.

Passengers who disembarked at New Orleans said the Mexico
City–New Orleans leg was routine except for light to moderate
turbulence experienced in the last thirty minutes. There also was a
cabin attendant change at New Orleans, a steward and three
stewardesses replacing the four cabin attendants who had worked
the Mexico City–New Orleans segment. First Officer Newby transmitted a "304 rolling" message to the tower fourteen seconds before
2 A.M. and the takeoff appeared to be normal.

One minute later, the New Orleans tower advised Flight 304
to contact Departure Control. Zeng, not Newby, acknowledged.
The captain apparently had turned the controls over to the copilot
immediately after takeoff. Personnel in the tower watched the anti-
collision lights of the DC-8 disappear into an overcast about two
and a half miles from the airport.

"Eastern 304, turn right heading zero-three-zero," Departure
Control ordered.

The DC-8 banked obediently, as if giant puppet strings were attached to the wings.

At 2:02 A.M., Departure Control handed the flight over to the
New Orleans Air Route Traffic Control Center and told Zeng:
". . . contact New Orleans Center, radar frequency one-two-three-
point-six now."

"Okay," said Zeng.

This was the last word from Flight 304. About three minutes
elapsed before the Center impatiently inquired of Departure
Control:

"Did you send 304 over? He's not talking to me . . ."

"Yeah, I did," Departure Control assured the Center. "I'll shake
him up again . . . Eastern 304, contact New Orleans Center, radar

frequency one-two-three-point-six, now, please. Repeat. Eastern 304, contact New Orleans Center, radar frequency one-two-three-point-six . . ."

There was no answer. Departure Control, puzzled and now worried, asked the Center: "Hey . . . you got him?"

"No, I'm not talking to him . . . he disappeared off the scope . . . up there, northeast."

"Mine too," the controller manning Departure radar murmured.

"I don't know what happened," the Center said in a voice hollow with concern.

"Eastern 304 . . . one-two-three-four-three-two-one . . . Eastern 304 . . . New Orleans Departure Control calling."

No reply.

A controller in the New Orleans tower picked up a phone connected to Local Control.

"Give me a number for Eastern Air Lines," he snapped. Then, still on another line to the Center, he added: "Hey, Center, call the company, will you? We're trying to get a phone number now . . ."

Departure Control and the Center kept paging Flight 304. The former finally asked if state police should be notified. The Center agreed. Departure Control suggested that the police cars "run the Causeway [over Lake Pontchartrain] because he was in the vicinity of the Causeway on my scope . . . just east of it . . . yes he . . . he was."

Early the next morning, a helicopter spotted an oil slick and floating debris on the lake. The CAB immediately called in various kinds of electronic and sonic underwater detection gear, but the wreckage was not located until late in the afternoon of March 13. Salvage operations began immediately and continued on a twenty-four-hour basis until April 16. By that time, approximately 60 per cent of the aircraft's torn carcass had been recovered from the mud and silt on the lake bottom. Each piece of wreckage was washed and then taken by barge to the New Orleans Lakefront Airport for examination by CAB, Douglas, Eastern and ALPA experts.

There was no sign of structural failure, in-flight fire or explosion. Examination of the engines disclosed that Zeng or Newby had taken the same desperate emergency action, apparently to halt a dive, which Captain French had employed to save another DC-8 from doom four months before. The recovered reverse assemblies showed use of reverse thrust at impact. The only trouble was that Flight 304's crew had run out of sky. They almost made it, at that; the power-plant damage indicated the jet was level at impact.

Both right and left stabilizer jackscrews were found within one turn of a full down position, which made no sense; the pilots obviously were trying to pull out of a dive and would not be applying nose-down trim. Then investigators discovered signs of abnormal wear in several parts that transmitted power to the stabilizer section, particularly failure of a chain sprocket on the stabilizer drive gear. To complete the picture of abnormal stabilizer functioning, the recovered portion of the PTC showed evidence of an "unprogramed" (meaning unwanted or inadvertent) extension. The PTC on N8607 was supposed to be inoperative. Yet it was evident that while the unit was inoperative, it actually had slipped into a nose-down trim condition. Far from being fully retracted, it was extended—sufficiently to give the pilots undesired down trim just as they ran into turbulence and a few other problems. To quote the CAB report issued sixteen months after the accident:

". . . the Board must accept the possibility that N8607, at departure from New Orleans . . . was being operated with a PTC actuator extension, although inoperative, ranging from 0.5 inch to 2.15 inches."

The CAB deduced that as Flight 304 climbed, the unwanted PTC extension literally jammed the stabilizers in down trim. With the aircraft accelerating in the climb, the pull forces on the controls must have increased steadily—to the point where it must have taken extreme exertion by the pilots to override the unprogramed down trim. At this point, it is reasonable to assume, Zeng and Newby reduced airspeed to relieve the unnaturally heavy stick (yoke) forces. This action presumably coincided with the encountering of moderate to severe turbulence. Suddenly the stick forces lessened with the reduction of airspeed, and simultaneously the DC-8 was shaken by turbulence gusts. Unprepared for the relieved stick forces, like a man on the end of a suddenly released rope, the crew overcontrolled the plane while trying to combat the oscillations, and Flight 304 went into a dive from which there was no room to recover.

That hypothetical picture of N8607's death throes is pure theory and, to some extent, second-guessing. But it is based not only on the inconclusive evidence of a malfunctioning PTC (the actuator itself was never located), but also on a number of subsequent test flights which drew an identical portrait.

As soon as the PTC became a prime suspect, Douglas conducted special test flights to determine DC-8 controllability with unprogramed PTC extensions or retractions. The company reported that even with this malfunction, adequate elevator control was available to overpower the unwanted PTC input.

Yet Douglas conceded there was a time lag for overriding what amounted to a stuck stabilizer—and there wasn't much time for Zeng and Newby at their relatively low altitude. Furthermore, later tests on DC-8s by FAA pilots revealed what the CAB termed "an interesting discovery." They showed that with a fully extended PTC, airspeed at approximately two hundred and twenty knots (the estimated speed of Flight 304 when it went into its last dive) and the stabilizers trimmed fully down, any attempt to maneuver by using the elevator system resulted in extreme instability. To quote one FAA test pilot:

"This was true in applying either nose-up or nose-down control. A pilot with this condition existing during turbulent atmosphere would be presented with a very difficult control problem."

Another test pilot found that the combination of an unprogramed PTC extension and a down stabilizer setting seriously affected stick forces as airspeed varied—the forces shifting from very heavy to very light.

Still other test flights added more solidity to the CAB's theories about Flight 304. An independent research agency, under an FAA contract, conducted experiments involving the aerodynamic stability of swept-wing aircraft exposed to longitudinal motions—i.e., up and down turbulence. Said the CAB of these tests:

"Flight testing demonstrated . . . the aircraft could be flown with no difficulty as long as the pilot flew gently, accepting the slow response [of a jet being maneuvered through rough air]. If he attempted to force a more rapid response, as might be done in a gust disturbance, a short-period pilot-induced oscillation resulted. The pilots quickly found this characteristic could be overcome by smaller [lighter, easier or more gentle] corrections. However, it was disturbing to fly because one was never certain when a quick response might be needed."

The investigation of the New Orleans accident also turned up several cases of DC-8 control system misrigging among several airlines, a discovery which led to changes in maintenance procedures. Aside from this benefit, the misrigging cases provided additional evidence to buttress the CAB's reconstruction of what probably happened to N8607. In one instance, the crew on a DC-8 training flight reported control difficulties immediately after takeoff. An inspection disclosed that a new PTC actuator was extended a half inch even when it was fully retracted. The discrepancy resulted from an installation procedure that did not take into account a difference in the size of the bolts in the new unit, compared to those of an older model. On such apparent trivialities is potential disaster based. This misrigged PTC system, according to the pilots on the training flight, forced them to use nose-down trim following takeoff to such an extent that an excessive trim warning light flashed on.

In many respects, Eastern Flight 304 had as many beneficial aftereffects as Northwest 705 because it also shed new light on dark corners of unsuspected hazard. The circumstances differed, but the CAB's investigations delved into many mutual aspects—jet behavior in turbulence being a principal common denominator. While flight experts like Paul Soderlind of Northwest, Frank Kolk of American and others in the industry preached new turbulence-handling techniques, parallel studies by the National Aeronautics and Space Agency fully supported their recommendations. I have dwelt on the turbulence problem at considerable length for a prime reason: it presented an air safety challenge associated almost exclusively with jets, and it was a challenge not fully appreciated at first—a failing which, if it cannot be alibied, can at least be explained and understood. It established one of the few patterns of danger in the first decade of the jets, and a pattern of trouble is easier to solve and correct than an isolated accident which has no apparent connection with other crashes.

Admittedly the pattern was deadly. The crash of a Trans-Canada (now Air Canada) DC-8 shortly after taking off from Montreal on November 29, 1963, was a mirror image of the crash of Flight 304. As late as August 1966, a Braniff BAC-111 disintegrated while trying to fly through a Nebraska thunderstorm. The British-built jet was the victim of an unusually powerful wind shear (a collision between the cold and warm air masses that spawn thunderstorms). The Braniff crash did not seem to fall into the loss of control in turbulence category, however. It was a case where the gust forces generated by the line squall simply exceeded the jet's stress limits, and this was not any example of jet vulnerability. Piston-engine planes have suffered structural failure in thunderstorms too; a wind shear can concentrate the equivalent destructive power of a tornado in a very small area. The weather encountered by the Braniff flight had been predicted and was avoidable; there was undoubedly an element of overconfidence in airborne storm radar on the part of the captain, who thought he could pick his way through the storm. Overreliance on radar also was a factor in a subsequent Electra crash during a thunderstorm, and the National Transportation Board has found it necessary to remind pilots that radar is intended as a storm-*avoidance* tool, not a device for flying through storms.

It is not being falsely optimistic to say that the upset menace has been drastically reduced, if not virtually eliminated. Altered cockpit techniques were only one of the reforms to come out of the deaths of two giant jets. The travel limit of horizontal stabilizers has been reduced in all jets to minimize the effects of mistrimming and prevent overtrimming. PTC inspections have been revised, Weather Bureau dissemination of thunderstorm warnings has been improved. Better instrumentation has been installed on the jet fleet, with new attitude displays giving pilots a true picture even in severely disturbed air.

These are the legacies left by Flights 705 and 304, and every passenger is a beneficiary. Still to be conquered is another kind of turbulence, however, one bearing the initials CAT.

They stand for Clear Air Turbulence. Never has CAT resulted in U.S. passenger fatalities, but it is a constant headache to pilots because it is so hard to predict and its onslaught is almost totally unexpected and frightening. It has caused minor structural damage and injuries. A form of low altitude CAT, frequently occurring just over mountain areas, was blamed for the fatal crash of a BOAC 707 on March 5, 1966, shortly after the jet had taken off from Tokyo International Airport bound for Hong Kong. BOAC pilots have a reputation for cautiousness, and what was to ensue was beyond explanation. The captain, Bernard Dobson, decided to give his one hundred and fourteen passengers a breathtaking aerial view of Mount Fuji, the magnificent sacred cone that lies fifty-five miles from Tokyo.

The mountain is known to be a lair for violent winds. The weather itself was perfect—clear and sunny—but the forecasts predicted exceptionally strong winds in the Mount Fuji area at time of takeoff ranging from eighty-five miles an hour up to occasional gusts of one hundred MPH, which is hurricane force.

Dobson, known as a prudent airman, checked the Tokyo weathermen before taking off, but it was never determined whether the particular forecasts he examined included high wind warnings for the Fuji area. It may be that he relied solely on visibility and ceiling information, which, of course, indicated perfect weather ahead. He also may have been guilty of overconfidence in his airplane—up to March 5, 1966, there probably was not a 707 pilot alive who thought a Boeing couldn't handle high winds.

Whatever the reasons behind his sight-seeing decision, it was a fatal choice. Eyewitnesses saw the jetliner flying toward huge spirals of snow that boiled up like white tornadoes over the mountain. The 707's altitude was almost level with Fuji's height, more than twelve thousand feet. The aircraft seemed to fly between two of the visible twisters and it was as if two giant hands had grabbed the jet. Horrified onlookers on the ground saw one wing separate from the fuselage, followed by the tail section. The 707 fell in flames. All one hundred and twenty-five aboard were killed, including ninety Americans.

A Boeing official who aided the Japanese government in its investigation commented, after viewing the wreckage: "I never believed there could be destructive forces like this."

The BOAC 707 was wrecked by the winds and turbulence associated with high mountains, sometimes known as the mountain wave effect. This is not really CAT; it is more of a first cousin to the clear air turbulence which is prevalent at the higher altitudes. Airliners have been running into CAT for many years, but the jets are more frequently affected because they fly higher.

Research into CAT and means to avoid it dates back to before the advent of jets, but it has been stepped up considerably since 1960. CAT cannot be predicted by ordinary airborne radar, which measures turbulence only when it stems from precipitation. Thus, the radar on airliners is fine for warning pilots of storm turbulence —as far as one hundred and fifty miles ahead. But CAT pounces without warning, out of what appears to be perfectly clear and smooth sky.

Technically, CAT is produced by a collision between two wind forces, one horizontal and the other vertical. The phenomenon is believed to be correlated with temperature changes at high altitudes. What the airlines have been seeking is an instrument capable of sensing these changes far enough in advance to permit avoidance. Back in 1960, an Eastern Air Lines weather expert named Paul Kadlec began riding jetliner jump seats as far north as Canada and as far south as Mexico, charting the conditions under which CAT is likely to occur.

Later, Eastern and also United equipped several jets with instruments registering the temperature of the air in their path. These early detection instruments registered temperature changes in fractions, on specially calibrated dials, but they still proved incapable of giving sufficient advance notice. Usually, the jets on which they were installed hit CAT just about the time the warning was being flashed.

But the temperature-sensing technique was promising enough to warrant refinement and further research. Scientists knew that turbulence, in effect, excites the molecules of the gases that make up the atmosphere. The molecules radiate increased energy which is measurable at several frequencies—such as an X-ray band or infrared waves. Excited gases, of course, rise in temperature, and this was the principle behind CAT detection methods.

In mid-1967, Pan American began flight-testing a CAT detection instrument that picks up the infrared frequency emitted by excited atmosphere. A few bugs have shown up, but the device has been undergoing constant modifications and refinements to the point where the airlines think CAT could be licked. Also encouraging is an Air Force-developed radar which has the theoretical capability of spotting CAT some distance ahead. The radar is so sensitive that it has tracked a single insect (a bee) twelve miles away.

There is widespread hope that CAT can be eliminated as a potential hazard—certainly in time for the supersonic age when no pilot would want to slam into turbulence at eighteen hundred miles an hour.

Despite this hope, however, CAT is far from a complete cure. The current research is typical of many air safety projects which hold so much potential that many in and out of aviation prematurely assume a particular problem has been licked and demand immediate implementation of unproved devices.

The system tested by Pan Am, for example, has some major failings in that infrared readings are not always accurate. A plane equipped with this type of sensor can get distorted readings when it flies into the sun. Reflections from clouds can produce false warnings. And while there is a definite connection between CAT and temperature changes, clear air turbulence also has been associated with such other atmospheric conditions as electrical fields.

False turbulence warnings present a problem of their own. The early CAT sensors tested by the airlines and the Air Force gave false turbulence indications 75 per cent of the time, as well as providing insufficient warning when CAT was present. This seems to be a phenomenon of turbulence itself as well as an indication of the primitivity of the warning devices. Peter E. Kraght, manager of American Airlines' Weather Services, took a close look at the turbulence data collected by the airlines over a long period. He found that even when all the atmospheric conditions known to produce severe turbulence exist, pilots actually encounter rough air only 50 per cent of the time. They run into light turbulence 40 per cent of the time and experience moderate to severe turbulence only 10 per cent of the time.

Nearly half of the world's fatal jetliner crashes in the past decade have occurred during the final approach or landing phase.

This is not any indication of jet vulnerability. The same statistic was true when piston-engine aircraft dominated commercial aviation. The statistic is more of an indication of failure to overcome known past hazards which have been allowed to continue into the jet age. The causes of approach/landing crashes apply to any airplane. That they still exist, in large part, is a partial exception to— almost a contradiction of—aviation's vaunted ability to learn from mistakes.

Inadequate airport facilities, unreliable altimeters, poor weather reporting—these three factors have been resulting in fatal accidents for the past thirty years and it is sad to admit that a major crash could occur tomorrow for one or a combination of those reasons. It is not that aviation has ignored them; the fact that airliners are operating safely and routinely in weather conditions responsible for grounding most flights only a few years ago is proof of progress. But the fact that the approach and/or landing phase of a flight remains the most dangerous is proof that not enough progress has been made.

Captain Robert Buck of Trans World Airlines is a pilot with great respect for government-industry air safety research. At the invitation of FAA Administrator Najeeb Halaby in 1963, Buck spent a month inspecting and studying the government's activities in solving bad weather operations. He was impressed with the dedication and talent of FAA personnel, but he was not impressed with the rate of progress. In his report to Halaby, he made this comment:

"In 1937, the landing limits for airliners at [airports like] Newark, New Jersey, were 200 feet ceiling and a half-mile visibility. These are the same limits today. We have jumped in speed during those 26 years from 170 miles per hour to 600, increased our range from 700 miles to more than 5,000, swelled passenger capacity from 14 to 140, but we have not gained one inch toward all-weather flying . . . we are about to land men on the moon, but we still cannot assure pilots and passengers of safely traversing the last two miles to an airport."

Buck's words were written five years ago, of course, and he would be the first to admit that steps of more than "one inch" has been taken toward all-weather operations since he made his report. But to some extent, his criticism remains valid. The U.S. airlines alone complete nearly one million instrument approaches a year, but the accident potential in bad-weather landings persists. Buck said at the time that his study convinced him there are no "unusual, different or badly neglected" weather problems but rather a general failure to use solutions already on hand. This, too, is still the case five years after his study. From the very start of the jet age, for example, pilots warned that too many runways were marginal in length for heavy jets trying to brake on slick surfaces. Overruns continue to plague the airlines, and while some are due to submarginal landing performances by pilots, many more can be blamed on submarginal runways.

Inadequate runways have played a major role in landing accidents, and there certainly is no mystery about either the problem or the solution. The FAA's original certification process theoretically required a jet to be able to stop in a certain distance on dry pavements, the distance depending on aircraft landing weight. The FAA itself admitted in 1965 that its requirements were on the unrealistic side—a concession that came in the form of an order increasing effective landing runway lengths by 15 per cent under wet and/or icy conditions. For instance, a jet allowed to land on a seven-thousand-foot dry runway would need eight thousand and fifty feet of length if the runway were wet. If the longer runway was not available, the plane would have to reduce its landing weight—which in most cases means taking off passengers or cargo, or both. For the 15 per cent increase in landing length minimums is predicated on runway conditions forecast as of a flight's estimated arrival time. Previously, runway length requirements were identical for dry and wet conditions.

(Overdue was the word for the FAA's action; forty-eight hours after the new rule was announced, to become effective January 15, 1966, a Continental Air Lines Boeing 707 landed on a rain-slick, seven-thousand-foot runway at Kansas City Municipal Airport—and kept rolling. The jet, with fifty-nine passengers aboard, skidded past the end of the runway toward a dike. The captain managed to ground-loop and struck the dike sideways; a head-on collision probably would have been disastrous, but his action prevented any fatalities although the aircraft fuselage cracked open in two places.)

Pilots welcomed the stiffer regulation, even though they firmly believed a 40 per cent increase would have been wiser. They still consider the FAA's additional safety margin inadequate at too many airports where the bigger jetliners literally squeeze their landings. A wet runway exposes any airplane to a hazard known as aquaplaning—and one captain said of this condition, "When aquaplaning starts, the pilots might as well be back in the cabin with the passengers."

Aquaplaning to an airman is simply the loss of tire friction on a wet surface, and it can be as scary as an automobile skidding on glare ice. In fact, automobile drivers encounter aquaplaning of a sort. It occurs most frequently in the early stages of a rain that hits a dry pavement. The combination of water on a surface containing residues of oil, before the rain has a chance to wash away the oil, drastically reduces braking force.

In the case of a heavy aircraft, a film of water on a runway can have the same effect. The plane keeps rolling, resisting all efforts to brake because the tire tread never really touches the pavement. Compounding the aquaplaning problem, surprising to relate, is noise abatement! It seems that some noise abatement procedures result in pilots landing downwind instead of upwind, which increases both the landing speed and the chances of aquaplaning. A Pan Am jet landing downwind at Kennedy International Airport a few years ago aquaplaned off the runway. All one hundred and forty-five persons aboard walked away from the wreckage, and if they could have known the facts they would have been one hundred and forty-five persons who never again complained about noise annoyance.

Runway length is one of those areas in which pilots could be forgiven for muttering "I told you so." The Air Line Pilots Association since 1948 has been urging the federal government to certificate airports for safety just as it certificates aircraft. It makes no sense, according to pilots, to assure the public it is riding on safe airplanes that have to land at unsafe airports. The official ALPA policy on the subject demanded not only adequate runways but also adherence to minimum standards in all aspects of airport operations, from snow removal to elimination of obstructions on approach paths.

From the standpoint of an airline pilot, or that of a passenger, the ALPA policy does not seem unreasonable. There is evidence that the FAA agrees. In June of 1967, the agency began making experimental safety inspections of thirty-two major airports "to identify conditions within the airport environment which may contribute to accidents or incidents, inform airport managers of unsafe or marginal conditions, evaluate the willingness and effectiveness of managers in taking corrective actions recommended as the result of the inspections, and estimate the FAA resources required to perform the safety inspections if the agency decides they are needed."

According to *Aviation Daily*, the first twelve airports checked turned up "improperly or poorly maintained runway marking, improper or non-uniform runway and taxiway light spacing or orientation, poorly maintained or eroded runway shoulders or lips, poor public protection and airport fencing, marginally manned or marginally equipped fire rescue facilities, inadequate safety precautions in fueling areas and improper locations for wind recording devices."

To date, there has been no FAA decision to continue such inspection on a nationwide scale, whether informally or on a certification basis which would put some teeth into the inspection process. Airport managers themselves are divided on the necessity for certification. They are conscientious, hard-working men who are not unaware of safety problems and their own inadequacies, but who point out that the inadequacies usually are the result of lack of money, not indifference. In this respect, Congress is a prime offender; it has persistently slashed appropriations for federal aid to airports, the economy advocates usually including those more vocal members fond of denouncing the airline industry and FAA for not doing more to improve safety.

The airlines, until recently, were not without some guilt in the field of inadequate airports. For a long time, airport officials have complained bitterly that they have never been able to obtain facts or figures or even a majority agreement from the carriers on what airport improvements might be needed in the future.

"If the airlines would tell the airports what their realistic requirements will be five to ten years hence," Foster Jones, director of airports for Louisville, Kentucky, told the 1967 ALPA safety forum, "and sit down with us with the idea of working together for their development to the benefit of the community and the airline, we would have far better airports today. This head-in-sand attitude has been one of the greatest detriments to the development of airports."

Fortunately, the airlines appear to be taking their heads out of the sand, as Jones put it. United Air Lines for two years has had a special staff analyzing every airport it serves with a view to determining what is needed in terms of airspace utilization, runway capabilities, airport access and terminal facilities for passengers and cargo. And the Air Transport Association last year set up an industry-wide committee to work with airport management on correcting present weaknesses and planning for future needs.

Much of this new spirit of airline-airport cooperation, of course, deals with service as well as safety. In the latter respect, airport operators readily concede room for improvement, but they express some natural cynicism toward FAA's growing "shape up or else" mood. Jones, in his ALPA speech, was just one of many airport managers who think the federal government—in almost inevitable bureaucratic inconsistency—figuratively shakes one fist self-righteously while committing sins of its own with the other. Said Jones wryly, as he recited one example:

"The FAA has a requirement for the painting of automobiles used on airports to the effect that they should be high-visibility yellow. This is an excellent idea because they can be seen from the tower and the air, and it also gives the tower operator immediate identification of a stranger who doesn't belong there. Who is the biggest violator? The FAA and the Air Force, promulgators of the regulation! The FAA uses those gray GSA (General Services Administration) vehicles and the Air Force has blue vehicles, two of the hardest colors to see on an airport."

The Louisville airport official also recounted an incident involving a needed runway extension. In order to get federal funding assistance, it had to be built in accordance with guidelines laid down by the FAA's Airport Design Manual. That manual permitted open drainage ditches along or across the ends of runways and within one hundred and seventy-five feet of the edge.

Jones went out one day to check the runway construction and found the contractor installing a retaining wall in a ditch ten feet deep— "He was doing," Jones added, "just what the FAA said . . . needless to say, the ditch isn't there now, but it sure took a lot of argument, phone calls and proof which I had to obtain in the form of statements from ALPA, ATA and others to get a drainage pipe put in."

This may seem like a picayunish gibe at an agency which for the most part does a superb job for aviation. But it is presented along with a gentle reminder that little things cause big accidents —like a one-inch bolt, or a half-inch unwanted extension in a tiny motor, or a ten-foot ditch at the end of a runway on which a jet may not be able to stop in time.

There is, however, a tendency to pick on the airports as scapegoats for the airport safety problem, a problem which can be defined simply as a case where aviation technology has outstripped the airport itself. But a more objective examination uncovers other culprits, such as, to repeat, Congress. Says one prominent airport official:

"Airports have been running to catch up with airplanes since 1945, largely because federal aid has been so erratic that long-range planning has been impossible."

The Airport Operators Council estimates that federal aid to the

tune of about $160 million a year is needed to modernize the
nation's airports between now and 1970. Naturally, part of this
amount would go for services rather than safety, but by no means
the majority. A sizable proportion would have an indirect bearing
on safety—such as money to build new general aviation airports
that would relieve the major terminals of light plane traffic. Yet
current Congressional appropriations call for spending only $71
million annually, less than half of what the airports and airlines
say is needed.

The Department of Transportation is trying to unplug a little-
appreciated bottleneck in airport improvement by emphasizing the
interdependency of all facets of air transportation. There has been
too little planning on a national scale, due largely to the failure
of a provincially minded Congress to understand the complexity
of a modern transportation system. It does little good to have a
huge terminal and inadequate runways or, conversely, a tiny
terminal and huge runways. It is a waste of time to have a modern
airport served by totally inefficient ground transportation. Yet when
Congress enacted the Federal Aid to Airports Act, typically it
saddled the law with countless restrictions which, in effect, ignored
interdependency.

Certainly, there was pitifully little advance planning done for the
jet age as far as airports were concerned—not at the major cities,
but in the smaller ones which clamor for jet service into airports
where the jets would need figurative shoehorns. The Association
of Local Transport Airlines, representing all but one of the nation's
local service airlines, has a membership operating in and out of
more than five hundred airports. As of mid-1967, they were operating under various weight restrictions at two hundred and sixty-
three of these airports. And based on scheduled jet deliveries
through the end of 1968, weight restrictions on jet operations
will be in effect at another one hundred and fifteen airports.

The phrase "weight restrictions" is synonymous with inadequate
runways, and even when runways are improved there is a temptation on the part of many financially hard-pressed airports to bring
them up merely to minimum requirements instead of building in
extra safety margins.

Not even the bigger airports are exempt from sinning against
safety. They are not dangerous per se—not when millions of landings are made safely every year—but their ability to provide safety

under *all* conditions varies to a considerable degree. It might be said that too many of them are only marginally safe under certain conditions. Captain Homer Mouden of Braniff, a leading ALPA expert on landing problems, made this comment in observing that marginal runways can cause difficulties ranging from annoyance to catastrophe: "The margin between the two extremes is often as narrow as the thickness of an aircraft's skin."

Continued Mouden: "Overruns are caused initially by one or a number of unavoidable [and usually compounded] conditions—slippery runways, worn or smooth tires, crosswinds and high or fast approaches due to adverse weather—but the causal factor of all overrun accidents or incidents is that runways are too short for operating under those conditions encountered at that time . . . They have remained the same causative factors for more than twenty years, with no significant change in them during the past ten years of jet airline operation."

There are two primary ways to slow down and stop a jetliner when the wheels are on the ground—reverse thrust and brakes. Both are extremely efficient considering that they have to dissipate the energy generated by one hundred and twenty tons of metal moving at ninety to one hundred and thirty miles an hour. Aircraft brakes are far better, proportionately, than automobile brakes. The capability of this system has more than doubled in efficiency since 1950, improving so much that some pilots believe this probably has resulted in lethargic research into finding other means of stopping airplanes.

But the finest braking and reverse thrust systems in the world can be useless during aquaplaning. And there are circumstances in which pilots cannot use full braking or full reverse thrust—during severe crosswinds, for example. Under these conditions, adequate runway length must substitute for braking efficiency. And under truly abnormal conditions, such as unavoidable aquaplaning, even a long runway can be insufficient. This is why pilots also urge that runways have strong overrun areas, capable of withstanding a jet's weight and providing just an extra margin of safety that could mean the difference between a harmless overrun of the runway itself or a disastrous collision with soft turf and/or obstacles at the end of a runway.

A layman might ask why it is necessary for a skilled pilot to need so much protection—evidently, it might be said, against his own occasionally faulty technique. With rare exceptions, it is not faulty technique that gets a pilot into trouble during a landing. U.S. airline pilots have made about forty million safe jet landings since 1958. In 1960, NASA did a survey of landing patterns and practices which revealed that the overwhelming majority of pilots landed in just about the same way—in almost every case they used up the same amount of runway before touching down, for example. Two years later, the FAA did a similar survey, which showed that most pilots still weren't deviating in the ways they were landing; as the survey emphasized, they were adhering to the "fly 'em by the book" rule hammered into all jetliner crews. There was a bothersome tendency noted in both surveys, however—namely a propensity to "duck under" the glide path slightly during the final visual portion of approach and landing. This could be conducive to undershooting, which is potentially a worse hazard than overshooting. Yet the latter occurs far more frequently and it is obvious that the duck-under habit is not what is causing most runway accidents and incidents.

The frequency of these mishaps can be judged by the experience of just one major airline, which happens to have one of the best safety records in the world and a pilot training program that is copied by other carriers. This airline has averaged, during the jet age, about two undershoots for every one million landings, four overshoots per one million landings and a slightly higher occurrence of runoffs for every one million landings. Each instance represents a potential accident even if one did not occur. The record for the entire industry shows more than $120 million worth of jets destroyed in overrun mishaps since 1958.

It should not be supposed that nobody is doing anything about all this. If more-than-adequate runways are the answer, and it undoubtedly is, what can be accomplished until better runways are built? One solution is not only promising but far beyond the experimental stage. This is the grooved runway, or, as pilots and airport officials have dubbed it, the "runway stretcher."

The nickname is well deserved. Runway grooving involves placing strips of tiny indentations across the width of a runway to reduce or even eliminate aquaplaning and skidding. The first test grooving was installed at the much-criticized Kansas City Municipal Airport after preliminary tests on a NASA runway at Wallops Island, Virginia. The Kansas City grooves, only an eighth of an inch wide, a quarter of an inch deep and less than two inches apart, covered forty-five hundred feet of a seven-thousand-foot runway. The immediate results: skid resistance improved about 20 per cent under both wet and dry conditions. The airport manager reported to the Air Transport Association, which originated the project, that since grooving the one runway there had been almost no diversions to the neighboring Kansas City International Airport (where runways are longer) during heavy rains.

Runways also have been grooved at Washington National and Kennedy International, with Chicago's Midway coming up in the near future. The Kansas City installation cost $87,000, which was shared by eight airlines through increased landing fees. The $178,-500 grooving job at JFK also was shared by the airlines. The FAA paid for the National Airport project. Whatever the cost, the results have been somewhat startling. Pilots using the grooved runway at Kennedy said deceleration performance improved so much that it was the equivalent of adding two thousand feet to the runway length.

At both Washington and Kansas City, grooving proved to be so effective that pilots reported their anti-skid devices weren't even being activated on wet days. Walter Horne, NASA's expert on runway traction, told ATA that all the test data indicated grooving literally turned a wet runway into a dry one. And the majority of airline pilots questioned on their reactions to grooved pavements urged the grooving of all runways equipped with instrument landing systems—in other words, those most frequently used during bad weather.

Grooving is relatively inexpensive safety insurance, compared to the cost of lengthening a runway or installing such devices as arresting gears. A rough ball-park figure is that it would run between $70,000 and $100,000 to groove the full length and width of a runway ten thousand feet long and one hundred and fifty feet wide. Whether the airports, airlines, federal government or a combination of the three should pay the bill is a matter to be settled. What is more important is that grooving seems to work, it is not exorbitantly expensive and it can be done quickly. The British (who often are ahead of everyone when it comes to solving some air safety problems) have been grooving runways at military airports for more than twelve years. Both the British and NASA techniques utilized high-speed diamond cutting wheels which carve out thir-

teen grooves at a time. The job at the JFK runway was started
May 8, 1967, and finished the following July 24—which is a lot
faster than what it would have taken to stretch the same runway
by two thousand feet (at a cost of $1000 per linear foot!).

Pilots have been unable to tell the difference between a grooved
runway and conventional ones. The first U.S. captain to experience
grooving was an American Airlines pilot taking delivery in England
on a new BAC-111. ATA officials asked him to land the jet on a
grooved British runway, half-expecting him to report that it felt
like going over a washboard road in an automobile—as some aviation
authorities in this country feared. His verdict:

"I couldn't spot any difference from what I was used to. There
was no vibration, noise or rumble of any kind."

One possible objection to grooved runways is the possibility that
they could accumulate water and eventually overflow into one
huge puddle. It isn't likely, given anything short of a prolonged
cloudburst capable of drowning the Ark itself. The eighty-four-
hundred-foot grooved runway at JFK has 104 million inches of
grooves which hold eleven thousand gallons of water, or ninety-
three thousand pounds.

The runway at Kennedy, it should be noted, is used only for
landings. ATA and FAA are gathering further data on whether a
grooved runway would have any effect on takeoff performance. It
may be that grooving will be limited to landing runways exclusively,
although right now there is very little evidence indicating adverse
effects on takeoffs.

Significantly, airline pilots continue to call for better runways
and express enthusiasm over grooving as being at least a step in
the right direction, but they have demonstrated very little support
for runway arresting gears, which some lawmakers have pressured
the FAA to make mandatory at all major airports.

Runway arresting gears are a direct descendant of a similar device used since the twenties on aircraft carriers, to bring Navy
planes to a quick stop when landing on carrier decks. The gear
works, too. I was aboard an FAA Boeing 720 on a gear test a few
years ago. The one-hundred-ton jet engaged the gear at a speed
of well over a hundred miles an hour and came to a swift, not uncomfortable stop in about five seconds—only a few feet from the end
of the runway.

The device is relatively simple. Steel cables are wound around huge drums embedded on each side of a runway. A small section of cable stretches across the runway, just high enough to catch a retractable hook attached to an aircraft's belly. The hook is lowered to cable height by the pilot's pushing a button, when he realizes that an overrun is inevitable. The jet's weight and momentum unwinds the cable from its lubricated drums.

In commercial use, the gear would be located about two thousand feet from either end of the runway. Installation for a single runway costs about $250,000–$300,000, but an added expense is the necessity of stressing aircraft frames to accommodate the hook structure and withstand the strain of engagement. This would run about $5000 per plane on jets already built, although less if the hook arrangement were built into a brand-new airframe at the factory. Some Boeing 727s already have been turned out with special modifications for the hooks.

A somewhat similar but less complicated device is a self-erecting net made of lightweight but immensely strong synthetic fibers. One has been demonstrated in France and it has the advantage of eliminating the heavy, cumbersome steel cables that are part of runway arresting gears. The French net barrier was designed specifically to serve as a safety measure during tests of the Concorde, the British-French supersonic transport.

The net is stored in a trench dug across the runway end. It can be activated by a signal either from an airplane or the control tower. The webbing has just enough elasticity to slow a heavy jet, with the dynamic loads being shifted from the net to a friction-braking assembly located on either side of the runway.

Designers claim impact damage to whatever aircraft struck the net would be minimal—certainly less than what would occur during an overrun. In theory, anyway, it appears to be more practical than the cumbersome arresting gear which requires considerable time for rewinding the tons of cable and restoring the gear for use—a process sufficiently complicated to force the closing of the runway over a two- to four-hour period.

The net or gear concept could have saved lives in the past. One example was the crash of an Air France 707 at Orly Field, Paris, June 13, 1963. The jet failed to get airborne on takeoff, overran the runway and burst into flames. One hundred and thirty persons died, including many prominent residents of Atlanta, Georgia.

Gear proponents point out that the device has been used at many military fields, saving hundreds of lives. This is true, but the Air Force and Navy use arresting gears largely for fighters with high landing speeds. They have never installed hooks on their large bombers or transports, relying instead on long runways and adequate overrun areas—something, again, which airline pilots prefer to arresting devices.

The FAA, airlines and most safety experts agree, feeling that the funds necessary for gear or net installations would be better spent in such areas as overrun and undershoot "buffer" zones, longer runways, grooved runways and post-impact fire suppression systems.

A possible compromise might be the installation of arresting devices on the shorter runways which, for reasons of cost or geography, cannot be lengthened or protected by overrun real estate. Runway length can be misleading, as a matter of fact, because the full length is not always available to pilots. A runway at Boston's Logan International Airport, for example (one which has had several overrun accidents) is ten thousand feet long—ostensibly more than adequate. But the glide path used by pilots flying instrument approaches to this runway takes them to a touchdown point more than thirty-four hundred feet from the threshold—leaving them just under sixty-six hundred feet for the roll-out.

Runway length, of course, is a vital factor in another type of airport crash—the takeoff accident. This category has accounted for about 5 per cent of fatalities in the jet age's first decade. While occurrence is far less frequent than that of landing and approach crashes, the results can be just as bad and the cures just as obvious. If a runway is too short for any out-of-the-ordinary landing, to a somewhat lesser extent it may be too short for a takeoff that goes sour.

The critical $V_1$ speed condition already has been explained in this book. If any engine fails during the takeoff roll, a pilot must stop before he reaches $V_1$. Beyond $V_1$ there is no choice: the pilot must continue his takeoff and get airborne on his remaining engine or engines. The $V_1$ of every jet is computed carefully before every takeoff, because it varies with aircraft weight, outside temperatures, the height of the airport above sea level and the length of the runway.

One classic example of a takeoff accident was the crash of a TWA 707 at Cincinnati on November 6, 1967. The jet began to roll with its crew unaware that a Delta DC-9 was stuck in the mud, off to one side of their assigned runway. The jet was still short of $V_1$ when the pilots spotted the mired Delta plane. It appeared uncomfortably close. As the TWA jet screamed by, its pilots were startled by a loud noise, a kind of boom. Their immediate reaction was that they had collided with Delta—the TWA copilot, who was at the controls, shouted, "Good God, I hit him!"

Actually, there had been no collision. The loud boom had come from an extremely infrequent type of engine backfire at the precise moment the 707 was passing the DC-9. But thinking a collision had occurred, the TWA crew instantly aborted the takeoff, applying brakes and going into full reverse thrust.

Their runway was seventy-eight hundred feet long. Their $V_1$ speed was one hundred and thirty-two knots. At the moment they decided to abort, they were at least several knots below that speed. Yet their jet failed to stop at runway edge and plowed into a field, catching fire. Thanks to swift and efficient emergency procedures, all aboard got out safely, but with a mystery in the wake of their successful escape—why had the aborted takeoff failed?

In theory, it should have been routine. Boeing's and the FAA's certification tests showed that a 707 grossing the weight of this TWA jet and aborting below one hundred and thirty-two knots on a seventy-eight-hundred-foot runway should have stopped in time. That it didn't takes us back to the shortcomings of the certification process. Dave Hoffman of the Washington *Post*, in a well-written analysis of the Cincinnati crash, succinctly explained the difference between certification tests and actual emergencies, emphasizing that the average pilot has only four seconds to recognize the nature of the emergency, decide what action to take and then take that action. In four seconds, a jet will have eaten up another thousand feet of runway and continued to accelerate another twenty knots—in which time $V_1$ may well have been exceeded. Added Hoffman:

"To determine the 707's runway length requirements, Boeing used a team of crack test pilots. It gave them a brand-new 707 with brand-new brakes. The 707's tires, fresh from the factory, were perfectly round and had deep, finely grooved treads. Installed on the 707's instrument panel was an oversized airspeed indicator that registered velocity in fractions of knots.

"Instead of staging the tests on a runway slickened by engine oil and jet exhaust particles, the pilots used a long stretch of dry, clean concrete. But more important, the men knew what lay in store as they sped down the runway."

In 1963, the FAA proposed a new regulation which in effect added eight hundred feet to $V_1$ runway margins; i.e., if a jet grossing a certain weight was supposed to be able to stop, say, in not more than seven thousand feet, the new allowable stopping distance would be only sixty-two hundred feet. The airlines and manufacturers protested, the former on the grounds that the rule would impose heavy economic penalties and the latter with the argument that test data plus certification standards were more conclusive safety evidence than fears expressed by a handful of airline pilots.

Increasing the so-called "accelerate-stop distance" could only have been accomplished by reducing jet pay loads at a number of cities. The airlines asserted that millions of safe takeoffs and scores of successful aborts negated the danger signals raised by some pilots on the basis of infinitesimally few unsuccessful aborts. The FAA scrapped its proposed regulation. There is room for debate on its wisdom, but here again is a situation where a stiffer rule would be unnecessary if runways were adequate.

The fact that the airlines objected to a rule which admittedly would have provided an extra safety margin may prompt the layman to believe the oft repeated criticism that the industry invariably puts economics ahead of safety. This is hogwash. Without safety, airline profits would nose-dive faster than a stalled jet. It is true that on occasions the airlines have made woefully wrong decisions involving economics-vs-safety. As an industry, the airlines originally fought mandatory installation of weather-warning radar, and fortunately they lost the fight. A handful of carriers, led by United, supported such a regulation, and UAL, in fact, equipped its entire fleet with radar long before the FAA got around to making it mandatory. It is to the industry's credit that every airline later admitted that United and FAA were right.

Nor is the industry's balking on some safety proposals a legitimate indication that profits are being put ahead of safety. The airlines have a very logical right to ask whether a safety recommendation actually enhances safety to a degree that warrants huge expenditures. For every indefensible airline objection, such as rejection of storm-warning radar, one could find a half-dozen objections which were justified because they were raised against safety ideas that were not thoroughly tested, that were premature or that created new problems even as they solved an old one.

One also could find a myriad of instances where safety advances have been generated to a great extent by the airlines themselves. Nowhere is this more true recently than in the area of "the last two miles" and the prevention of bad-weather accidents. In the past three years, there have been incredible strides toward fulfillment of aviation's fondest dream—the ability to operate safely and without undue delay under zero visibility and ceiling conditions, or the kind of weather "in which even the birds are walking." Much of the research, testing and funding has come from the FAA, but what progress has been made never would have gotten off the ground without airline enthusiasm, support and technical cooperation.

There are obvious economic benefits to be derived from making the last two miles a lot safer. In this case, however, economic and safety benefits are synonymous.

A prime example of airline-fostered safety action is the battle against one of the airman's oldest enemies—fog.

The first attempt to dissipate fog artificially occurred during World War II when the Air Force burned high-octane gasoline at English air bases so bombers could land after missions. The technique was successful and further experiments were conducted in California after the war, but the gas-burning method proved too expensive to be practical.

On December 26, 1963, a small plane flew over the fog-choked Salt Lake City airport and dropped pellets made of dry ice.

The plane had been chartered by United Air Lines, which had a jetliner grounded by the fog. UAL officials were waiting for just such a moment to test a fog-seeding technique in which they had become intensely interested. As soon as the Salt Lake City airport was closed to all airline traffic, they called Intermountain Weather, Inc., a local cloud-seeding company that UAL had retained for the winter.

Intermountain put eighty pounds of crushed dry ice into a Beech Bonanza and circled the airport. The ice was dropped through a temporary slit in the plane's belly, using an ordinary fertilizer spreader. In less than ten minutes, the fog began to lift and visibility increased to a half mile, allowing the United jet to take off. The pellets continued their dispersal effect for nearly four hours.

The next night, fog again closed down the airport and United ordered another seeding "raid." Twenty minutes later, the fog had lifted enough to reopen the field and permit takeoffs by five flights. The experiment was tried a third time on December 30 when a United jet flying in from the East Coast was unable to land because of heavy fog. Once more the pellets were dropped and the jet landed safely.

United spread the word throughout the industry. The three "raids" saved this one airline thousands of dollars by preventing cancellations or delays that would have affected two hundred and twenty-six passengers on seven airplanes, not to mention the safety aspects.

UAL was understandably cautious in its optimism. The type of fog prevalent in the Pacific Northwest is known as the "super-cooled" variety—it occurs in below-freezing weather. The dry ice seeding works only with this kind of fog. When the pellets contact the fog, a chemical reaction takes place which causes water particles to change to ice crystals. This results in an extremely fine snow that releases moisture and dissipates the fog.

In the winter of 1964, United "bombed" seven more Pacific Northwest cities afflicted with super-cooled fog—Seattle/Tacoma, Portland, Spokane, Reno, Pendleton, Medford and Boise. The technique was used on fourteen separate occasions. The accumulative results: the pellets evaporated fog sufficiently to allow takeoffs or landings by thirty flights carrying more than seven hundred passengers.

To the communities involved, United had given this argument in support of its contention that fog dispersal is an airport responsibility, the same as runway maintenance and snow removal. Said United, in effect:

"Try the experiment at your own airports. Fog seeding costs money [$65 per flight in the original Salt Lake City experiments]. But you'll get it back and maybe more through landing fees. If planes can't land, you don't collect anyway. At airports like Medford and Pendleton, where landing fees are based on scheduled landings, United and other airlines will underwrite the cost."

United picked these airports, plus Salt Lake City, on the basis of an unpublicized five-year study by UAL meteorology experts. They found that supercooled fog prevailed an average of two hundred and eight hours at Medford, one hundred and forty-nine at Spokane, one hundred and eight at Pendleton, ninety-six at Boise, sixty-five at Salt Lake City, forty-six at Reno, thirty-one at Portland and twenty-five at Seattle/Tacoma.

United wanted a concerted government-industry effort to continue the tests on a wider scale. The FAA, concentrating funds and talent on electronic all-weather landing systems, didn't show much interest. Other airlines, while impressed, pointed out that seeding supercooled fog would be of benefit mainly at airports on UAL's Pacific Northwest routes and would be of little use at cities on their own systems. How about warm-air fog, they asked—which is the culprit at 95 per cent of the nation's airports?

Late in 1967, the Air Transport Association plunked down $100,-000 for a new series of tests, these to be aimed at the more prevalent warm-air fog. The city picked for the experiments was Sacramento, California, where this type of fog persists throughout the winter months. On the average, fog shuts down the Sacramento airport more than forty hours during December alone.

The ATA project utilized a variety of new chemicals for the seeding. In charge was W. Boynton Beckwith, chief meteorologist of United, assisted by weather specialists from several other carriers. It would have been more spectacular if the defogging technique was tried at a huge airport like O'Hare or Kennedy, but this was impractical because of their heavy traffic. Besides, Sacramento is peculiarly susceptible to fog conditions which even resist the usual dissipation under morning sunlight—"a very persistent type," Beckwith explained.

The ATA tests ran from November 15, 1967, to March 8, 1968. In that period, the Sacramento Municipal and Metropolitan Airports were shut down by fog on forty-nine days. A total of thirty-six seeding flights were made on twenty-six days, but only twenty-seven of these flights were evaluated in terms of whether they achieved the standard of a successful seeding—namely, opening up an airport that had been closed because of fog. The other nine were practice or "warm-up" missions.

Of the twenty-seven flights, nineteen were successful or partially successful—or 70 per cent of the total. There were four failures and four flights judged to be inconclusive. The four "flunked" operations included one flight in which the chemicals had been diluted, one in which the control tower couldn't see the runway although pilots reported it had been cleared, one in which wind carried the chemicals away from the runway and opened up a hole over the city itself, and one in which the seeding aircraft had to abandon the test because the tower had conflicting traffic.

ATA said a study of climatological data showed that the nineteen successful flights resulted in opening the airport two to four hours earlier than would have been possible through natural fog dissipation.

Delays and cancellations due to fog cost the airlines an estimated $75 million annually; fog is responsible for most of the sixty-one thousand flight cancellations that occur in an average year. ATA believes a nationwide artificial fog dispersal program would cost about one fifth that amount—and the financial penalty of fog does not include the cost of aircraft which have been wrecked in fog accidents. There will be no nationwide adoption of seeding warm fog, however, until the technique has been fully perfected. The Navy found out the hazards of premature assumptions when it dropped ammonium nitrate into thick clouds in a related cloud dissipation experiment.

The chemical burned holes through a low cloud layer three thousand feet thick, enabling aircraft to descend through the holes and land. This was according to plan. What was not planned was the effect of ammonium nitrate on aluminum! For the chemicals also burned holes through aircraft skin and all the test planes had to be repaired with fresh skin patches.

"Bombarding" fog from the air, of course, has its own weather hazards. The ATA-financed tests are largely to evaluate the effectiveness of various chemicals; more practical fog dispersal methods probably will involve application on the ground instead of from the air. One device to be tested is a series of long tubes containing compressed air, and located alongside the runway. With the touch of a button, the tubes could blast chemicals into the air above the runway. ATA has been testing a modified orchard sprayer equipped with a one-hundred-foot tube that propels dispersing chemicals another one hundred feet into the air. Technicians have dubbed it "the jolly green giant."

Government-funded research has been trying out a means of utilizing ordinary table salt as an anti-fog weapon. Scientists mount an airplane propeller on the floor of a big flatbed truck. The prop blows the salt three hundred feet into the air, and two hundred pounds of it theoretically is capable of devouring a mile-long patch of fog the width of a runway. Laboratory tests have been encouraging and experiments at an actual airport were scheduled by the Cornell University aeronautics laboratory near Buffalo, New York.

The chemicals used in the ATA tests are expensive—four dollars a pound. A single big airport like O'Hare or JFK would require tons at an estimated cost of $2 million a year for total defogging. Whether special chemicals or common salt is employed, the principle is identical: fog is nothing but drops of water fused together in a kind of cloud. The chemicals merely attract water, turning the closely packed moisture into bigger raindrops.

German scientists have been experimenting with a huge vacuum cleaner which sucks the fog inside, drains the moisture and emits dry air from the other end. The Russians are working on ultrasonic vibrations that break up fog moisture into rain, although this technique has one large disadvantage: the vibrations are said to be extremely annoying to human ears.

Fog dispersal is just one area in which aviation science is trying to achieve all-weather operations. Even more dramatic and positive is the progress made toward virtually automatic, "look, Ma, no hands" landings. The work dates back nearly four decades; it was on September 24, 1929, when an Army pilot became the first man to land an airplane solely by use of instruments.

He was in a single-engine military trainer. His cockpit was covered by an opaque hood which prevented any outside vision, and he flew toward a radio signal being beamed from Mitchell Field, New York. At two hundred feet altitude, he lined up his plane until a special cockpit instrument hooked onto the beam. Then he followed the beam down to what he later described as a "sloppy" landing. It may have been sloppy, but it was eventful. The pilot who wrote this Braille-covered page into aviation history was Jimmy Doolittle.

Contrast that heroic but crude accomplishment with a scene that took place at Dulles International Airport on December 8, 1964.

A twin-engine United Air Lines Caravelle was making its final approach to Dulles. In the cabin sat some forty nervous reporters watching what was going on in the cockpit via two big closed-circuit television screens.

That's why these observers were nervous. Nothing was going on in the cockpit. The captain calmly poked at a couple of buttons, leaned back in his seat and took his hands off the controls and

throttles. The jet dropped lower and lower toward the runway
while a UAL technician supplied a play-by-play.

"We're leaving sixteen hundred feet . . . autothrottles are engaged . . . flight director is centered . . . glide slope and deviation
indicators are centered . . . rate of descent five hundred feet a
minute . . . throttles commanded to one hundred and thirty-four
knots . . . indicated airspeed one hundred and thirty-four knots
. . . horizontal and vertical ILS indicators centered . . . we're down
to six hundred feet . . . down to five hundred . . ."

The throttles and yoke were moving as if manipulated by the
hands of an unseen ghost.

". . . down to four hundred . . . three hundred . . . flare light
on . . . flight director bars are centered . . . throttles commanded
to one hundred and ten knots . . . all indicators centered . . .
radio altimeter shows fifty feet . . . ten feet . . . five feet . . . we
should be on the ground."

They were. A slight, almost imperceptible bump, and the Caravelle rolled smoothly down the runway. Only now did the captain
touch the throttles, pulling them back into reverse thrust. The reporters, stalwart exponents of questioning cynicism though they
were, burst into spontaneous applause.

This was a perfect demonstration of AWLS—an all-weather landing system. The litany of the United "announcer" was a recitation
of the technical operation of an AWLS, in this case developed
jointly by Lear Siegler of California and Sud Aviation of France.
The principle is virtually identical for all such systems, with only
a few variations. An AWLS engages the airport's regular instrument landing system, coupling the ILS beams to the automatic
pilot and throttles and literally turning the aircraft into an airborne
puppet guided by invisible electronic strings.

To understand better the device and its importance, it is first
necessary to understand the operation of ILS, which has been the
airman's primary aid for weather landings since the late 1930s.
There have been numerous refinements but basically ILS works
the same as it did thirty-five years ago. It projects two radio beams
to a cockpit instrument. One signal is the localizer beam, keeping
the pilot on course toward his assigned runway. The second signal
is the glide slope beam, which provides him with the correct angle
of descent. The localizer beam appears on the ILS dial as a vertical bar; the glide slope beam is a horizontal bar. When the pilot

gets both bars to form a perfectly-centered cross, he knows he is heading straight for the runway and on the proper glide path.

The only drawback to ILS is that its pin-point accuracy, so obviously essential to safety, deteriorates below two hundred feet. At this altitude, pilots must take over and land visually. A handful of airports are equipped with an improved ILS that under certain conditions will permit landings with a one-hundred-foot ceiling, but the general limit is two hundred feet and visibility of a half mile.

AWLS is a means of guiding pilots safely and accurately through that final and most critical two hundred feet. The Lear Siegler system, first to receive FAA certification, is capable of steering a jet through an electronic "gate" only forty-six feet wide and twenty-six feet high, guaranteeing touchdown within twenty feet from the runway center line and two hundred and fifty feet either side of the ideal touchdown point. Other systems, such as one developed jointly by Bendix and Boeing, have demonstrated equal precision. Most have a sensor device mounted on the wings which measures the angle of attack—the gliding attitude of the plane—as it engages the ILS beams and sends signals to the throttles and controls. Another major component is an extremely accurate radio altimeter. Every system can be overriden instantly by the pilot, a feature demanded by U.S. airmen, who fear total dependence on any little "black box."

The FAA has established five present and future categories governing the conditions under which an airliner is allowed to land in bad weather.

Category I is the present rule. It permits approaches down to a ceiling of two hundred feet and half-mile visibility on runways equipped with ILS. If RVR (runway visual range, which electronically measures visibility by feet) is available, the visibility can be reduced to twenty-six hundred feet.

Category II, now in partial use, permits approaches down to an RVR reading of only twelve hundred feet and a "decision height" of one hundred feet, at which altitude a pilot must establish visual contact in order to make a conventional manual landing. This is the first category to require use of an approved AWLS.

Category IIIA will permit automatic landings in zero ceilings, but the RVR must indicate at least seven hundred feet forward visibility.

Category IIIB also will involve automatic landings, but with RVR minimums reduced to one hundred and fifty feet.

Category IIIC will be a true zero-zero operation, entirely electronic, with no visual guidance even during roll-out and taxiing— or, as one Pan American official put it, "Category IIIC is when you can't see the terminal building after you shut down the engines."

The airlines already are at the Category II stage and nibbling at Category IIIA. On July 7, 1967, a Pan Am 707 made a fully automatic approach and landing at London with one hundred and twelve passengers aboard—the first such operation in a jetliner carrying paying passengers—using the Boeing/Bendix system. It was a proving demonstration rather than a landing under actual zero-zero conditions, for the weather was clear when Pan Am accomplished its "first."

But much experience will have to be gained under Category II before the FAA allows the airlines to enter Category IIIA and beyond. As of this writing, the industry is in a kind of Category IIA stage—a decision height of one hundred and fifty feet and RVR minimums of sixteen hundred feet. ALPA is urging caution before proceeding to the real Category II stage, a one-hundred-foot decision altitude and RVR minimums of twelve hundred feet. The pilots' union, which believes the industry should accumulate more experience with Category IIA, claims the airlines are rushing too fast into all-weather operations.

ALPA wants a "head up" display (HUD) in every cockpit equipped with AWLS. A HUD installation would involve a kind of small, transparent screen roughly resembling a TV screen and connected to the airspeed indicator and altimeter. Readings on the latter instruments would appear on the HUD, which would be located almost at eye level; this provides the captain with vital speed and height data, plus his position relative to the runway, and at the same time allows him to look directly ahead out of his cockpit windshield. Without HUD, a pilot conceivably could have trouble watching his regular instruments during the termination phase of a Category II approach and landing—that stage at which a captain has only one hundred feet of airspace left between him and the ground and about six seconds in which to decide whether a visual landing should be made or abandoned.

HUD is no theoretical designer's dream by any means. Members of an ALPA All-Weather Flying Committee have test-flown a DC-9 equipped with a head-up display system and were enthusiastic about its performance. The HUD program, however, has evoked little interest among the airlines and even less in FAA—apathy which pilots cannot understand because they think HUD could provide greater safety in ordinary landings, let alone Category II.

Whether the "rushing" charge is justified remains to be seen; ALPA has adopted a resolution "strongly recommending" that its members refuse to make landings with less than a one hundred and fifty foot ceiling and sixteen hundred feet visibility, even when the FAA approves an airline for the full Category II stage. This could culminate in an ALPA-airline fight, for a number of carriers are operating right now under first-step Category II and virtually all are training crews for full Category II with certification applications already submitted to FAA. The airlines point out that AWLS research has been going on since 1961 with approximately thirty-five thousand test landings made in complete safety.

The airlines were ready for Category II before the FAA was. United, American, TWA, Eastern, Delta, Western and Pan Am alone by the end of 1967 had trained and qualified more than six thousand pilots to make Category II landings. They also are equipping virtually their entire jet fleets with the necessary electronic gear. The other trunk lines and the local service carriers are not far behind.

FAA opened the doors to Category II in 1964, advising the industry that it would permit such operations using only specially trained crews at airports with Category II ground equipment. The latter includes improved ILS and vastly superior runway lighting. The airlines prepared their pilots faster than the FAA prepared the airports, with new runway lighting a prime bottleneck mainly because FAA revised its standards in this area. Some airports already had installed previously approved Category II lighting when the FAA decided it was not sufficiently bright and issued new standards which ran into development, testing and manufacturing delays. As of August 1, 1968, the airlines had equipped more than nine hundred jets for Category II at a cost of $37 million, while the FAA's own program lagged.

But gradually, all the obstacles are being overcome and it is safe to predict that by the end of 1969, about a dozen of the nation's major airports should be handling Category II as routinely as they have conventional ILS operations. For the airlines, virtual all-weather flying will mean even higher dependability performances and corresponding financial benefits along with increased safety.

The need for anti-weather weapons such as AWLS and fog dispersal is starkly illustrated in reciting the circumstances of just one fatal jet accident, the crash of a Canadian Pacific Airlines DC-8 at Tokyo's Haneda Airport on March 4, 1966. The flight, operating from Hong Kong to Tokyo, arrived at Haneda around 7 A.M. but was stacked up to await the lifting of heavy ground fog.

The big jet circled for an hour and the captain had just decided to try for an alternate airport when the Haneda tower informed him that visibility had improved to three fifths of a mile. This was above landing limits so the captain started his letdown, under the watchful eye of airport radar. The jet was still a mile from touchdown when the radar controller noticed that the target blip had slipped far below the proper glide path. He advised the flight to abandon the approach but even as he warned the crew, the DC-8's undercarriage snagged on the approach lights. The jetliner flipped against a concrete retaining wall at the edge of the runway, bounced over the wall onto the runway and burst into flames.

Sixty-four persons died, including the captain, who was blamed for the accident in the Japanese government's investigative report issued two years later. The report accused him of poor judgment in attempting a landing under weather conditions that had forced other crews to continue their holding patterns or proceed to other airports.

Perhaps he *was* guilty of bad judgment; the facts, however, indicate he also might have been a victim of the booby traps so frequently implanted over those "last two miles"; possibly the tendency of altimeters to lag at low altitudes, questionable visibility reports, and the sins of omission by others that so often lead to sins of commission by pilots—in plain words, the long delays in perfecting such tools as AWLS and fog-dispersing methods despite research that started almost with the birth of the jets.

Altimeter trouble, either a malfunction or a misreading, could have been a factor in this accident and it may have played unsuspected roles in other crashes blamed on everything but the altimeter.

This instrument, in a technical sense, is nothing more than a close relative of the common aneroid barometer used in many homes. The aircraft altimeter does not really measure height;

it merely measures the weight of the air, and translates that weight into terms of feet instead of pounds per square foot. Air decreases in weight as it goes higher. Thus, the altimeter gives a pilot a scale in feet corresponding to the average weight of air at a particular height.

It is a simple, usually accurate device, but it is capable of errors and it also is capable of being misread by a busy pilot. An aircraft entering a low-pressure pocket of air, for example, could have an erroneous altimeter reading ranging from a few feet to a couple of hundred feet. Some altimeters stick or lag, recording a height after the plane has left that height. Lagging is due to some malfunction, but there are other sources of altimeter error which leave behind no clues that would clear a dead pilot of blame. Airmen are convinced that many accidents attributed to navigation mistakes or plain carelessness were due to faulty or misread altimeters. The Air Force once admitted that between 1953 and 1958 there were thirty-three crashes involving military aircraft in which various altimeter deficiencies were either proven or suspected to be causal factors.

The newly developed radio altimeters (they project a signal toward the ground and record in terms of feet the time it takes for the signal to bounce to the plane) which are part of AWLS possess far greater low-altitude accuracy than the aneroid type. But while they appear to have licked the altimeter problem, the hazard of misreading this instrument persists.

In 1967, a Convair 880 clipped a ninety-foot-high power line *located forty-five miles from the airport for which the jet was heading!* At about the same time, a jet making an approach to Kennedy was reported seen at an altitude of only two hundred feet when it was *ten miles* from its assigned runway. In both cases, pilots apparently had misread their altimeters, which may seem impossible to any passenger who has not experienced the occasional difficulty of obtaining data from a rapidly unwinding instrument, while concentrating on a dozen other cockpit duties. There have been similar incidents, which will be discussed in a later chapter on the Boeing 727; for now, it is sufficient to say that the use of AWLS probably will be accompanied by adoption of some kind of altitude warning device. It would enable a pilot to pre-set the warning for an altitude below which he does not want to descend during various stages of letdown and final approach.

The FAA, in fact, will require all U.S. civil jets to carry altitude alerting systems by 1971, and at least two airlines already are experimenting with test devices.

December 8, 1963.

On that date, death came to all eighty-one persons aboard a Pan American 707 in a disaster which, by conservative estimates, had no better than a one-in-50-million chance of ever happening.

Pan Am Flight 214 was in the final portion of a scheduled trip between San Juan, Puerto Rico, and Philadelphia, with a single stop at Baltimore. The jet left Baltimore Friendship Airport at 8:25 P.M., cruising at five thousand feet for what normally would have been not more than a twenty-minute flight. A rare winter thunderstorm was lashing the Philadelphia area, however, and Flight 214 along with other planes wisely chose to circle at its assigned altitude until the storm passed out of the way.

A thousand feet above 214 was National 16, a DC-8, also circling cautiously while the squall line vented its fury.

The Pan Am crew advised Philadelphia Approach Control: "We're ready to go," meaning they were ready to land anytime they received permission.

"Clipper 214, stay in pattern," Approach Control advised. "I'll pull you away as soon as I can."

"Roger, no hurry," 214 replied cheerfully.

Approach Control was a hectic place on this stormy night. Several other flights on 214's frequency were demanding undivided attention. An Allegheny pilot complained he was getting kicked around by turbulence and was guided to another area. National 16 reported he couldn't hear Approach Control very well because of "snow static or something."

The controller patiently acknowledged all complaints and requests. After the squall line had passed the airport, he cleared an Allegheny flight and a small private plane for landing. National 16, still experiencing communications difficulties because of storm static, asked Approach Control to repeat a previous transmission.

"You're third in line for landing," the controller repeated.

"Okay," National 16 acknowledged.

"And how's the turbulence in your area now, National 16?" the controller inquired.

National never had a chance to answer. The next message Approach Control received was a death sentence for eighty-one persons.

"Mayday . . . Mayday . . . Clipper 214 out of control . . . Here we go . . ."

The stunned controller couldn't believe what he had heard.

"Clipper 214, did you call Philadelphia?" Approach Control asked.

The answer he got was not from Pan Am 214 but from the captain of National 16.

"Clipper 214 is going down in flames," he reported incredulously.

One thousand feet below him, a jagged bolt of lightning had cracked into the 707's left wing, followed by an explosion that tore off the wing. The jet began spinning toward the ground, on fire. It fell into a cornfield near Elkton, Maryland, close to the Maryland-Delaware state line, missing a house by one hundred feet. One piece of wreckage dug a crater fifteen feet wide and six feet deep in a paved road next to the cornfield.

Six thousand feet above the crash site was National 16, still circling and now receiving a lightning strike of its own.

"Ah, Philadelphia," the shaken captain paged Approach Control, "we'd like to get up to the New York area . . . we'll continue to Newark or Idlewild."

The controller said fine, but he had traffic holding at six thousand feet between Philadelphia and New York and he'd have to try to get National 16 a higher altitude.

"We don't want to stay here," National responded tartly.

"Roger. Understand, National 16. Ah . . . turn right . . . take a one-eight-zero heading out of the New Castle area . . . this could put you into a possible smoother area."

"It's smooth enough here," was the reply. "We're just getting lightning."

National 16 banked away. Approach Control made one last effort to raise Flight 214.

"Clipper 214 . . . are you still on this frequency?"

It wasn't. Clipper 214, ironically the first production model of the Boeing 707 to come off the assembly line and thus the first U.S. jet to go into scheduled service, was the victim of a fate the experts considered virtually impossible. Not in all the years man had flown metal transports had lightning ever been an instrument of destruction. The only suspected exception was a TWA Constellation which crashed during an electrical storm at Milan, Italy, in 1959. Investigation disclosed that a static discharge, built up by the plane as it flew through the electrical storm, ignited gasoline fumes in an empty wing tank. The explosion blew off a wing.

Static discharge, however, is not the same as lightning. It is what you experience when you walk over a rug under certain temperature conditions and then touch a metal doorknob. On an aircraft, static discharge is electric energy generated by the aircraft itself as it flies through electrically charged clouds. Lightning, on the other hand, is electric energy built up outside the aircraft. Both were regarded more as annoyances than menaces. Because an airplane in flight is never grounded, and thus is a fine electricity conductor, an electrical charge merely passes through the aircraft.

The TWA accident was considered a freak, but the FAA awarded Lockheed a contract for a study of both static discharge and lightning effects on transports, as they related to possible ignition of fuel. In May of 1963, Lockheed turned in a report which said it *was* possible for lightning or static discharge to ignite fuel fumes under extremely rare circumstances. FAA scientists were still studying that report when lightning destroyed Flight 214.

Had the FAA been slow in reacting to Lockheed's findings? No fair-minded person could say this. Lockheed's own engineers had admitted that not only was a lightning-induced explosion a one-in-50-million shot, but it was not quite certain what could be done to make a rarity an impossibility. Furthermore, the chances of lightning endangering a jet seemed even more remote than with prop-driven planes. FAA statisticians reported that jets were far less likely to be hit, for several logical reasons.

As of December 1, 1963, according to FAA's figures, piston-engine planes were being struck by lightning on the average of once every twenty-five hundred hours; propjets once every thirty-eight hundred hours; pure jets once every ten thousand, four hundred hours. FAA also discovered that 75 per cent of lightning strikes occurred at altitudes between five thousand and fourteen thousand feet, considerably below jet airways. And jets, the FAA learned, were less prone to suffer static discharges because their outer surfaces are smoother than the fuselage and wings of older planes.

So there seemed to be no urgency in the Lockheed research

report, which was more in the form of a theoretical warning than a loud alarm bell. FAA *was* considering stiffening the regulations covering lightning protection for jets before the Elkton crash, but in reality it was uncertain in which direction to move. Even long after December 8, investigators were unable to determine exactly how lightning could have knocked Clipper 214 out of the sky.

That lightning was the murderer there was no doubt. The CAB found seventy-two witnesses who saw lightning around the plane, seven who actually saw a bolt strike the jet and twenty-seven who observed fire on the 707 seconds after seeing the lightning.

On December 13, the CAB issued a cautiously worded statement hinting for the first time that lightning might have caused the accident.

"Investigators have found physical evidence indicating a fuel-air mixture [explosion] in the left wing fuel tanks," the CAB announcement said. "The physical evidence of the explosion is in the form of wreckage deformation in the area of the left wing fuel tank. Also Bureau of Safety investigators have found pronounced burning and pock-marking of the left wing tip, indicative of a lightning strike."

But lightning cannot ignite fuel itself. Some air must be present to vaporize the fuel first, or the fuel tank must be empty or almost empty with a residue of fuel fumes. Had Clipper 214 been afflicted with a slight fuel leak, possibly a loose rivet, which allowed fuel vapors to escape and become exposed to lightning? Another unknown factor in the deadly chain of circumstances was the outside temperature. Lockheed's research had shown that fuel vapor ignition by lightning required a certain temperature before the vapors could become combustible. Jet fuels increase in volatility as temperatures decrease.

Not for more than sixteen months did the CAB issue a report on Clipper 214's fate, and the report was an unusual admission of partial defeat. Lightning was blamed, but the CAB said "the exact mechanics of ignition" remained a mystery with further research warranted. The Board said the Boeing 707 met all FAA lightning protection requirements and that while additional protection obviously was needed, the "current state of the art does not permit an extension of test results to unqualified conclusions of all aspects of natural lightning effects."

The CAB report noted that various experiments conducted in

connection with the Pan Am crash paid off in at least one area. Tests showed that direct lightning strikes on certain fuel tank access plates and caps can produce sparks inside the tank. This research led to development of a practical means of eliminating this potential danger.

But on Clipper 214, there was no physical evidence of ignition-producing sparks inside the left wing tip, even though there was plenty of strike evidence on the outside. Nor was there any sign of electric arcing inside the wing. The lightning damage nearest the fuel tank outlet on the outer left wing, where the bolt apparently penetrated, was nearly a foot from the vent edge. The vents are necessary to equalize air pressure in the fuel tanks as altitude changes.

Shortly after the Elkton tragedy, the FAA, airlines and manufacturers agreed on additional precautionary measures. Static discharge eliminators were installed on early model 707s which lacked this device. Static discharge eliminators are tiny metal-impregnated wicks placed on the trailing edges of wings and tail stabilizers. Their main purpose is to drain off electrical discharges that accumulate when an aircraft passes through electrically charged clouds and cause interference with radio reception. They are not intended to ward off lightning, although they are a kind of miniature lightning rod. Clipper 214 was one of ninety-seven Boeing 707s flying at the time which had wicks on the horizontal stabilizers but not on the wings.

Another step was to thicken the skin covering jet wing tips, where lightning strikes were known to occur with by far the most frequency. Access plates in the wing surface were modified to ensure adequate electrical "bonding" or contact with the wing to prevent sparking. Meanwhile, continuing research, although it failed to produce conclusive evidence that the bolt which killed Clipper 214 penetrated to fuel vapors via a vent outlet, convinced scientists this is what probably occurred.

On September 5, 1967, the FAA ordered certain models of the 707—those whose vent outlets are placed near the wing tips—equipped with one of two new safety devices. The order affected the majority of 707s and 720s. One device, designed by Fenwal, Inc., of Ashland, Massachusetts, is a flame and explosion suppression system that prevents any flame propagation through the vents. It detects a flame as it enters the fuel outlet and automatically discharges an extinguishing chemical. The alternate device ordered by FAA was an auxiliary vent tube that provides a continuous flow of air in through the regular vents and out through the auxiliary tube, thus preventing any accumulation of ignition-prone fuel vapors.

One other aftermath of Clipper 214's death is of interest to those who believe the airlines always wait for a government air safety order before acting on a major problem. TWA worked closely with Fenwal in developing a new lightning protection system, distributed the research results to all airlines—foreign as well as U.S.—and began installing the system on *all* its Boeings, at a cost of $6.5 million, before the FAA order became mandatory.

United, it may be recalled, did the same with airborne radar. American equipped its entire jet fleet with DME (distance-measuring equipment), a new safety-enhancing navigation device, months before the FAA made DME mandatory. The industry often takes an undeserved rap for apathy and lethergy in safety; in a few instances, it has been guilty of slowness or indifference, but many more times it has led rather than followed.

And sometimes, the aviation community—airline, manufacturer and government alike—has been innocently unaware of potential hazards that existed, despite mutual devotion to safety. Even in an industry where accident prevention is a religion, not just a policy, it is unfortunately possible to make certain false assumptions and to take some things wrongly for granted—which can prove, on rare occasions, fatal, like germs hidden in a blood stream waiting for the body resistance to lower.

This was the story behind the misfortunes of the Boeing 727, the jet that turned out to be almost too good.

# 5

## THE 727—THE LIBELED AIRPLANE

The "Baby Boeing" they called it—the first American three-engine transport to carry passengers since the days of the famous Ford Trimotor.

It was quite a baby, starting with what it cost to design, build, test and produce it in quantity. Boeing, already swimming in red ink, as were all airframe manufacturers in the jet age, gambled no less than $1 billion that the 727 would be a commercially successful airliner.

It was conceived initially in 1956, two years before America's first scheduled jet transportation and while Boeing was immersed in the vast test program for its mighty 707. Just a few preliminary sketches at first, a total of nearly forty projected designs for what Boeing figured the airlines needed—a jetliner capable of operating economically and efficiently over both short and medium distances and at airports incapable of handling the big jets.

By early 1958, when Boeing engineers were assigned the task of actually designing a short-to-medium-range transport, the 707 itself still was five months away from airline operation and the 727 was an uncertain gleam in the eyes of only a handful of Boeing officials. The airlines knew what they wanted and needed, but how to achieve it was another matter. There were almost as many views on the right design as there were airlines. The majority leaned toward two power plants, with some support for four.

United in particular was suggesting a scaled-down 707, retaining the considerable safety margins of four engines. Other carriers rejected the higher operating costs of a smaller four-engine transport with limited capacity. TWA and then Eastern suggested the possibility of three engines but Boeing officials themselves were lukewarm toward the massive technical problems involved—not the least of which was where to put the third engine.

And there was competition. Douglas was toying with an idea for a small DC-8 with four engines to be called the DC-9 (the DC-9 is flying today, a highly successful transport but with two engines). Britain's de Havilland already was well along with design plans for a three-engine jet known as the Trident. The two-engine French Caravelle was flying all over Europe and there were rumors U.S. carriers were interested (United turned out to be the only purchaser, buying twenty Caravelles, with TWA ordering ten but later canceling the contracts).

Boeing's own economists were telling the engineers they could foresee a market for one hundred and eighty jets of the 727 type through 1965, provided the price was kept down to $2 million. The engineers greeted this forecast as they would welcome dismissal notices on Christmas Eve. Their estimates of design, test and production costs showed that the 727 would have to cost at least $3 million per aircraft and even at that price Boeing would have to sell at least two hundred just to break even. The first 707s and DC-8s were woefully underpriced even at around $5 million, due mainly to production cost inexperience with transports of their size. And the airlines, as traditionally price-conscious as a bargain-hungry housewife, seemed to present no market at all for a smaller jet carrying a proposed price tag of more than $3 million.

To keep said tag down to the lowest figure possible, Boeing seriously considered settling on a two-engine design, the power to be of the new fan-jet type in which the engine thrust is increased by fans driving an extra supply of air through the turbine gases. But United, the most interested potential 727 customer, still insisted on four engines along with economy guarantees that were impossible to achieve with then available turbine power plants.

At this point, most of Boeing's technicians still regarded a three-engine 727 as an aeronautical monstrosity. But TWA said "no thanks" to the two and four versions and Eastern joined TWA in expressing real interest in three, mainly because of the added safety needed for its considerable overwater operations. Boeing went to work in earnest on solving the design problems of a three-engine model—the ideal compromise for the potential market.

How the design problems were solved is a story in itself. Typical was the first question all the engineers asked—where do you hang that pesky third engine? They tried mounting it between twin tails, a design resembling the old B-25 and B-24 bombers of World War II. They fooled around with a V-shaped tail that would handle both rudder and stabilizer functions, like the tiny Beech Bonanza. Boeing even tested a weird-looking design in which two engines were mounted in pods under the wings while the third was hung on one side of the aft fuselage. All these proposals were discarded for aerodynamic and safety reasons, with Boeing finally settling on burying the third engine inside the rear fuselage and putting the air intake for the power plant on top of the fuselage, below a high T-tail.

That key decision was made in September of 1959. For other major 727 design characteristics, Boeing frankly credits United with a co-development role. United's specifications were reflected in the tri-jet's length, wing area and potential performance. But Boeing made another prime decision fairly early in the design game which contributed mightily to the 727's airline popularity—the fuselage was to be the same width as the plane's big sister, the 707, providing six-abreast coach seating and increasing the 727's load capacity far beyond the originally projected sixty-five seats.

United's contributions were typical of an aviation fact of life seldom understood or appreciated by the traveling public—the extent to which the design of a new airliner depends on airline suggestions, advice and criticism. Eastern, for example, dictated the 727's unusual wing configuration by insisting that the jet be capable of utilizing New York's LaGuardia Airport, where runway lengths are cramped and the shortest strip is less than five thousand feet long.

The result was the 727's new system of triple-slotted wing flaps, achieving the near-impossible task of turning a wing swept back thirty-two degrees for high-speed cruise into a wing with a 25 per cent greater area for low-speed approaches. To this concept Boeing added forward-edge flaps as well, thus prompting one airline captain to comment with more affectionate awe than concern, "On this bird you don't lower the flaps—you disassemble the whole damned wing."

As do virtually all airplanes, the 727 took on more weight and size than the original concept called for. Merely choosing a big Pratt & Whitney fan-jet engine for the basic power plants meant not only a heavier aircraft but a larger one—which added $250,000 to the price.

Design problems kept popping up. An unexpected headache

was the landing gear, which had to be changed completely after eighty planes had been ordered by several airlines. Nearly fifty engineers were assigned solely to the task of working out a revised track mechanism for the movement of the wing flaps after the original version proved unsatisfactory. They developed six separate systems before arriving at the final choice. In all, Boeing had more than one thousand men in the design section alone, working overtime on some sixty-seven thousand individual blueprints that covered everything from a cockpit coffee holder to the giant wing spars.

Ninety per cent of the 727 was standardized—in other words, identical to every customer. The other 10 per cent may have seemed minute, but it added up to approximately twelve hundred separate items per airline. The plane required fifty-five thousand individual tools. Wind tunnel tests consumed almost six thousand hours.

One of the most dramatic moments in the entire development program came when a full-size 727 was deliberately destroyed on a torture rack known as the major static test. This involved progressive increases in loads applied to key structural areas, the wings in particular. The stress placed on the 727's wings exceeded 10 per cent of the intended breaking point. In fact, the wing tips were deflected an incredible ten feet beyond their normal plane before the tormented, protesting metal surrendered to the inevitable and cracked with a frightening shriek.

The jet's greater-than-hoped-for strength was not the only unexpected bonus. Test flights showed the 727 a full fifteen knots faster than wind tunnel tests had predicted. The external noise level was far below even what Boeing prayed it could achieve. Fuel consumption was 3 per cent less than what Boeing had guaranteed the airlines and over-all operating costs a whopping 10 per cent under estimates—so vital to an industry where the difference between red ink and black ink is often the altitude at which a captain chooses to fly. And getting back to the greater strength—not only in the wings but in the vulnerable horizontal stabilizers and vertical fin that composed the tail section—this dividend added up to a transport that could carry more passengers, cargo, baggage and mail than Boeing had promised.

The first 727 was rolled out of Boeing's Renton, Washington, factory on November 27, 1962. As of that date, five airlines had ordered one hundred and twenty-seven tri-jets—United, TWA, American, Eastern and Germany's Lufthansa. A 727 dispatched on a series of national and world demonstration flights covered ninety-five thousand miles without an iota of mechanical or other troubles. On one occasion, the new Boeing jet was stopped in fifteen hundred feet after touchdown—on a rain-slick runway. Airline observers in the cabin burst into admiring applause.

Applause was about the only word that described the aviation community's reaction to the 727. The airlines applauded it for its economy, efficiency and reliability. Passengers applauded it for its speed and quiet comfort—while even veteran jet travelers got a kick out of the 727's swift, effortless climb ability which made the older jets seem stodgy and slow by comparison. Pilots loved the new bird for its easy handling, responsiveness and enormous reserve power—plus its amazing ability to squat down easily on runways that for the big jetliners were invitations to overruns and undershoots.

"The 727," marveled one captain, "makes a five-thousand-foot runway look like it was ten thouand feet long." He wasn't kidding. On a dry strip, the "baby Boeing" could be brought to a full stop from touchdown in one thousand feet.

Eastern was the first airline to carry paying passengers on the 727—February 1, 1964. In the next eighteen months, nearly two hundred of the new tri-jets were operating over the routes of sixteen airlines and Boeing's backlog of orders amounted to more than two hundred additional planes. The 727 was an unqualified success in every respect for carrier, passenger and pilot alike. It was significant that the latter group included Lockheed Electra captains, literally infatuated with the four-engine propjet, but who fell for the 727 even harder.

"I thought there would never be another airplane as easy to fly, as responsive, as totally dependable and strong as the Electra until I started flying the three-holer," commented one American Airlines captain.

Pilots traditionally fall in love with new planes, swearing undying allegiance in the same manner as they would repeat the marriage vow. But not all planes earn such loyalty from *all* the men who fly them. Even the beloved DC-3 had its early detractors. The first real exception to qualified affection was the Electra. Not even the Electra's mysterious flutter weakness, which caused two fatal crashes before it was solved and corrected, could shake pilot faith in the airplane. The second exception was the 727.

As with every new transport introduced into service, the 727 was examined carefully by a committee representing the Air Line Pilots Association and the Allied Pilots Association, the group being chosen from crews flying for airlines that had ordered the new plane.

The committee's final evaluation, after several special test flights, announced that the 727 "constitutes a major advance in aircraft design which will significantly enhance air carrier operations." No higher praise could come from professional airmen. The only other airliner to earn such unstinted pilot support was evaluated by an ALPA committee in these warm words:

"The committee is more than reasonably confident that the manufacturers, the operators, the pilots and the public will be satisfied with the record of safety, efficiency and economy which will be achieved."

The plane they were talking about was the Electra.

And on August 16, 1965, there began a series of tragic events that were to challenge airmen's faith in a proud new airliner just as the Electra's troubles had tested their devotion five years before.

One of the passengers who boarded United Air Lines Flight 389 on that August 16 was Clarence N. Sayen, who headed the Air Line Pilots Association for eleven years until he voluntarily left office in 1962.

Articulate, erudite and distinguished-looking, he was largely instrumental in raising ALPA from its original status as a young, sometimes ineffective union to a powerful voice in aviation policy. "Clancy"—no one called him anything but that nickname—succeeded in giving ALPA a double image, not only that of a tough labor union but also that of a respected professional organization.

A crusader for greater air safety, he had testified before scores of Congressional hearings and technical meetings. It was irony in the most infinite sense that he was about to take, along with twenty-three other passengers, his last flight. Flight 389, bound from LaGuardia to Chicago's O'Hare Airport, never reached its destination.

The smell of rain was in the air when a lifeguard, walking along the shore of Lake Michigan with a friend, looked up with a start

as he saw a tremendous fireball split the dark curtains of night.
The flash was accompanied almost simultaneously by a muffled roar.
The time was 9:21 P.M. CDT. Clancy Sayen, his fellow passengers, three flight deck members and three stewardesses were dead.
And Flight 389, a Boeing 727 delivered to United only eleven
weeks before the crash, had disintegrated into hundreds of pieces
under two hundred and forty feet of Lake Michigan's cold waters.

The first fatal crash of any new model transport raises immediate fears of mysterious, unsuspected "bugs." But the 727 had
relatively few teething troubles, in fact amazingly few in view of its
radical design and many new systems. Yet some kind of major,
hitherto unrevealed flaw was still a prime target of suspicion in the
early investigation into the fate of Flight 389. The location of the
wreckage did not help matters any. The Civil Aeronautics Board's
accident investigators (they are now part of the Department of
Transportation) dread more than anything else a crash in deep
water where wreckage recovery cannot only be difficult but sometimes impossible. Significantly, of the half-dozen unsolved airliner
crashes that have occurred since 1938 when the CAB began in-
vestigating accidents, four involved wreckage lost in water. When
there is no corpus delecti, so to speak, the mystery is likely to
remain unsolved. And it looked very much as if the first 727 crash
was going to be included in this frustration category.

There was no hint of forthcoming tragedy and sudden death.
Captain Melville W. Toule, who flew for Capital until that carrier
was absorbed by United in commercial aviation's biggest merger,
was a competent, careful veteran. O'Hare radar picked up the
flight routinely as it descended toward final approach.

First Officer Roger Whitezell had just signed off a position and
altitude report, along with a laconic "Roger, United 389" acknowledgment of approach clearance from fourteen thousand to six
thousand. The 727's last supposed altitude was the assigned six
thousand feet, just below a cloud base. Weather was clear with no
reported turbulence.

Flight 389's watery graveyard was searched by an army of scuba
divers, Coast Guard cutters and fishing boats using every means
of detection from shrimp nets to sophisticated sonar and underwater television cameras. Even a two-man diving bell was utilized,
along with huge grappling irons. A scuba diver found the first piece
of wreckage. After three months, searchers had managed to

raise forty-five thousand pounds of twisted metal—about half the
727's weight. Dredged out of the lake's icy waters were sixty-five
of the ninety-one seats, a twenty-foot chunk of fuselage skin, nine
windows, a six-thousand-pound piece of the tail, a pitiful collection
of shattered cockpit instruments, most of the left engine, much of
the center engine, parts of the right engine, two window escape
hatches and twenty-one of the thirty bodies.

The salvage operation at this point had cost the CAB and
United a half-million dollars with no productive results. The recovery work went on through the cold fall days and nights,
sometimes amid high waves and winds that on one occasion almost capsized a salvage barge anchored above the crash site.
By mid-December, all thirty bodies had been recovered along
with approximately 80 per cent of the wreckage—enough to give
the CAB some inconclusive clues as to Flight 389's fate.

Actually, what was found merely eliminated some areas of
suspicion without providing a probable cause. Sabotage, for example, was ruled out. Autopsies disclosed that all fatalities resulted from impact injury. There was no indication of explosive
residues on metal or in the bodies or on the clothing of the
victims. Nor was there any evidence of a mid-air breakup. The
fireball seen by so many witnesses, the CAB felt, must have been
produced by the 727's exploding as it struck the water at high
speed. In fact, the majority of investigators were and still are
convinced that for some unknown reason, the jet was flown into the
water—the pilots apparently unaware of their proximity to the
lake as they descended.

This would be an incredible explanation, yet it would not be
beyond the realm of possibility. Overwater approaches at night
are known to involve a visual phenomenon known as "sensory
illusion," causing pilots to believe they are flying higher than they
actually are. In transferring from instrument flight to visual flight
under these conditions, more than one pilot has been trapped
into a false sense of security by relying on his eyes after he stops
using his altimeter. Compounding this hazard, in the case of the
United crew, could have been a faulty or misread altimeter.
While it is virtually impossible for both altimeters to be in error,
only one of the two pilots monitors this instrument during final
approach and perhaps the altimeter being read by the pilot not
flying Flight 389 was the culprit.

A misread altimeter was more of a possibility. This blooper, while extremely rare, is neither unlikely nor unheard of. In 1967, a DC-8 carrying nearly two hundred passengers was en route from Hawaii to the West Coast on a night flight. The copilot was flying the plane and the captain, busy with communications, did not notice their altitude until he happened to glance at his altimeter. He yelled "Pull up!" and it was a good thing he did. The DC-8 was *less than one hundred feet from the ocean*—the copilot had misread his own altimeter by ten thousand feet and at the time the captain spotted the error, the descending jet was only seconds away from disaster. While the incident never made the newspapers, it was widely circulated among the airlines and corrective measures taken promptly by every carrier in the form of more frequently required altitude cross-checks.

Federal investigators, in fact, eventually listed a misread altimeter as a possible cause of the Lake Michigan crash. It was established that the copilot probably was flying the 727, because the captain's voice was identified on the air traffic control tapes. It is customary for the pilot who is not at the controls to handle radio communications, and the investigators speculated that the copilot might have misread his altimeter, while the captain was watching for other traffic and/or completing a checklist.

Buttressing this theory was a puzzling element. Flight 389's last definitely established altitude was twenty-six thousand feet, at which time the crew reported it was descending to fourteen thousand. Two minutes later, ATC cleared the flight to six thousand feet, at which level it was supposed to hold. Radar later observed the aircraft at a position about four miles from where the aircraft crashed, and a reconstruction of the final flight path showed the 727's speed at the time was about two hundred and sixty miles an hour.

But if the flight actually *had* leveled off at six thousand as required and was still at six thousand at the time of the final radar and voice communications contact, it could not have flown the last four miles to impact point at two hundred and sixty MPH and struck the water at the established impact time *unless its descent rate was averaging nine thousand, four hundred and thirty feet per minute.* Furthermore, the plane hit the water in an almost level attitude, which would have been impossible with such a high rate of descent.

Thus it was obvious that Flight 389 was below its assigned altitude of six thousand feet, for reasons undetermined and for which the National Transportation Safety Board frankly offered "no reasonable explanation." Moreover, the last communication from the flight involved altimeter setting—the pilot read back the setting incorrectly and the controller corrected him. The pilot then read it back correctly. Never reported officially was the fact that the Air Defense Command's "SAGE" system recorded the flight at two thousand feet while the plane was supposed to be not lower than six thousand feet.

The aircraft's altimeter was of the "three-pointer" type which pilots acknowledge is the most susceptible to misreading. In trying to establish the likelihood of a misread instrument, the Board came up with a finding that under certain conditions it was theoretically possible to misread the altimeter by ten thousand feet—in this case, to mistake six thousand feet as sixteen thousand feet. The Bureau's findings noted that from its cruising altitude of thirty-five thousand feet, Flight 389 was cleared to several lower altitudes in such rapid succession that the crew never leveled the plane or held any one altitude for any length of time. In a continuous descent, the three pointers on the altimeter would have been in continuous motion and the chances for a continuous misreading would have been enhanced.

While the Board's final verdict was of the rare "for reasons unknown" category, it tended to absolve the 727. There was no evidence of pre-impact difficulties, no real evidence of a malfunctioning altimeter and no conclusive evidence that an experienced copilot like Roger Whitezell (he had nearly eighty-five hundred hours of flight experience, almost four hundred of them in the 727) had misread the altimeter.

Recovery of most of the engine components eliminated an early theory that the middle engine, buried in the aft fuselage, might have tossed a turbine blade, causing structural failure of the tail. This had happened to a 727 shortly after the tri-jets had entered regular service, while the plane was on the ground. Damage to the tail section was considerable. But this failure led to extensive power plant modification by Pratt & Whitney and furthermore there was no sign of blade failure in the UAL plane.

The precious flight recorder was never found. It would have given valuable data on the plane's final path, including its rate of descent—a vital factor in subsequent 727 accidents. When the Board's report on Flight 389 was issued early in 1968, excessive rate of descent was discarded as playing a role in the accident. So was the possibility of a low-altitude stall—which was suspected by some experts in the early stages of the investigation. This was a hypothesis stemming from serious stall hazards encountered in the test flight program of Britain's new BAC-111 jetliner.

The "deep stall" was the technical moniker placed on the potential danger by aeronautical engineers. An airplane stalls when the airflow over the wings diminishes to the point where lift cannot be maintained. The resulting rapid loss of altitude causes the airflow to strike only the underpart of the wings. With no airflow hitting the leading edge of the wings, the nose will pitch up sharply, forward speed is deteriorated further and the descent continues even faster until the loss of airflow is extended to the elevators. This is the deep stall, and the final stage in this fatal chain is the tendency of the elevators to trail upward, causing complete loss of control.

On a straight-wing aircraft, loss of airflow creates a stall condition over the entire wing area which merely results in loss of altitude and can be corrected with relative ease. But on a swept-wing plane, the loss of airflow and the resulting stall condition concentrates first on the wing tips before spreading to the rest of the wing. If you gently held a model airplane by the tips of its wings, it would tend to flop tail-first, nose-up. This is precisely what happens to a jet in the deep stall, particularly to the tail-heavy rear-engine jetliner. The wing tips stall first and the nose goes up sharply. Elevator control diminishes immediately and effectiveness continues to evaporate to the vanishing point. It requires a tremendous forward push on the control yoke to get the nose down and come out of the stall—and it should be remembered that the aircraft has continued to fall with the nose up. One test showed that a rear-engine jet, deliberately exposed to the deep stall, required twelve thousand feet for recovery.

In October of 1963 a British crew was putting a new BAC-111 through its fifty-third test flight. The program on this particular day involved a series of stall tests under various flap settings. Recoveries had been made successfully from four stalls. On the fifth test, with flaps set at only eight degrees, the twin-engine jet was throttled down to a deliberate stall. The 111 kept going down with the crew frantically but vainly applying power. It hit the ground at a flat altitude like a runaway elevator with its cables snapped, and all aboard were killed.

On rear-engine jets with the so-called "T" tail (horizontal stabilizers placed almost to the top of the vertical fin) loss of stabilizer-elevator airflow can be even quicker and more critical than on aircraft with conventional tails because the aircraft is inherently tail-heavy, increasing the tendency for nose pitch-up, and because the higher stabilizer location eliminates any aid from wing airflow. Even before the BAC-111 test accident, Boeing had engineered deep-stall hazards out of the 727, mainly through the shape of the leading wing and elevator edges and by providing extremely efficient stall warning plus a simplified, direct connection between the cockpit control yokes and the elevators. The latter enabled pilots to compensate for any tendency of the elevators to swing up in a stall condition.

Similar improvements were made in the BAC-111 after Boeing made available to the British Aircraft Corporation all wind tunnel and test flight data relating to the deep stall. And while a few officials continued to suspect a stall as the killer of Flight 389, there was absolutely no evidence to back this up. In fact, all the evidence pointed against it. Considering Captain Toule's experience and skill, as well as the 727's more than adequate stall warning, it was inconceivable that the jet had simply been allowed to quit flying.

There was no solution to the fate of Flight 389, no positive or even plausible explanation. A grim, unanswered question mark hung over the 727 and grew larger at 8:02 P.M. EST, November 8, 1965, when a second tri-jet crashed, killing fifty-eight of the sixty passengers and crew members aboard.

It had taken Dan Teelin a full ten years to rise from a rookie first officer, hired by American Airlines in 1946, to the four stripes of captain.

In that decade, he had accumulated many thousands of hours of flight time, a host of friends who liked him for his warm, friendly personality, and a reputation for falling enthusiastically in love with whatever new plane American added to its fleet.

He also acquired a reputation as one of American's superior pilots, skilled enough to warrant promotion to a 727 check captain after winning his own rating on the new jet. It was this duty that assigned him to Flight 383, non-stop LaGuardia–Cincinnati, on the evening of November 8.

The pilot whose performance Teelin was monitoring was Captain William J. O'Neill, a qualified four-striper on piston-engine equipment but now in the process of being upgraded to captain on the 727. Flight 383 was to be his seventh qualification flight, the previous six having been conducted under the same check pilot.

The flight departed LaGuardia at 5:38 P.M. EST, twenty minutes behind schedule. All was routine as the swift tri-jet flashed over the Pennsylvania countryside at thirty-five thousand feet. At 6:57 P.M., the crew already had commenced the letdown and notified Cincinnati Approach Control it was leaving five thousand feet for four thousand. Approach Control acknowledged and cleared 383 "for a visual approach to runway one-eight, precip [rain] lying just to the west boundary of the airport . . ."

One minute later, Approach Control advised Teelin and O'Neill that radar showed them six miles southeast of the Greater Cincinnati Airport.

"Cincinnati Tower, it's American 383, we're six southeast . . ." That was Teelin, handling the radio.

Tower: "American 383, Cincinnati Tower. Runway one-eight, wind two-three-zero degrees five, altimeter three even."

383: "Roger, runway one-eight."

Tower: "In sight. Cleared to land runway one-eight, American 383."

383: "We're cleared to land, roger."

Only one second later, Teelin asked: "How far west is that precip line now?"

Tower: "Looks like it's just about over the field at this time, sir. We're not getting any on the field, however."

383: "Okay."

Tower: "If we have a windshift, I'll keep you advised as you turn into final."

383: "Thank you very much, we'd appreciate it."

Tower: "American 383, we're beginning to pick up a little rain now."

383: "Okay."

Tower: "American 383, you still got the runway okay?"

383: "Uh, just barely. We'll, ah, pick up the ILS here."

Tower: "American 383, approach lights, flashers and runway lights are all high intensity."

383: "Okay."

That one word was the last anyone heard from Dan Teelin and Flight 383. The time was one minute and twenty-two seconds after 7 P.M. Exactly five seconds later, the plane that Teelin had recently told a fellow pilot was "the greatest thing ever put into the air" crunched into a wooded hillside two miles north of Runway 18 and seconds later burst into devouring flames.

Sitting in the most forward window seat of the first-class section was Elmer Weekly, an American captain riding on a non-revenue pass. The impact threw him to the floor. Stunned, he extricated himself from a pile of debris. He saw flames coming from the rear of the cabin. He stumbled forward and, still dazed, noticed that the entire cockpit area had disappeared, leaving him a miraculously open exit. Weekly stepped out of the wreckage to safety just before the flames from exploding fuel swallowed what remained of the one hundred and thirty-four foot fuselage.

Also forward, sitting in her assigned jump seat prior to landing, was twenty-five-year-old stewardess Toni Ketchell. The impact hurled her out of the seat and the plane itself, thus saving her life but inflicting multiple internal injuries, including a crushed pelvis and legs so badly broken that at this writing—more than two years after the crash—she still is undergoing therapy treatments in hope that she will be able to walk again someday.

The two other lucky survivors were passengers in the rear tourist section. When the jet hit the ground, they were hurled out of breaks in the fuselage wall. Neither they nor Miss Ketchell ever remembered getting out of the plane. Weekly, however, was able to testify at the CAB hearing on the accident. He told investigators that the en route flight was routine, but that the initial descent into the Cincinnati area seemed rapid.

He saw the lights of the city to the north as the 727 leveled off. The next time he looked out the window, "It seemed like we were very low . . . I sat there unconcerned and it seemed like we were on approach, after I looked out the window, and yet it seemed we had started another left turn and we were in maybe a ten- to fifteen-degree bank . . . I heard what I thought at the time to be hydraulic flap motors actuating, unwinding toward the rear of the airplane, and it was just immediately after this that we made contact with the ground . . ."

From the professional but naturally hazy testimony of Captain Weekly, the CAB could derive only an infinitesimal guess as to what had transpired in the cockpit of Flight 383. But the tiny, one-inch-wide aluminum foil taken from the plane's flight recorder told them far more than any shock-affected human mind ever could. As the CAB reconstructed the accident from that recorder, the story of Flight 383's final six minutes was a deadly combination of poor judgment, overconfidence, understandable but wrong assumptions and just bad luck.

The CAB's "probable cause" finding was a sharp indictment of the two pilots, not the airplane—"failure of the crew properly to monitor the altimeters during a visual approach into deteriorating visibility conditions."

Behind that seventeen-word verdict of pilot error, however, was a careful, sober analysis of what must have been the circumstances that led to pilot error. Because a dead airman cannot defend himself, explain or alibi, part of the CAB's analysis had to be speculation and surmise. Certainly it would seem almost unbelievable that two such experienced captains (Teelin had more than sixteen thousand hours in the air and O'Neill in excess of fourteen thousand) "could spend almost two minutes descending below 1,200 feet at night, under adverse weather conditions, and not properly monitor altitude." That was the Board's curt phraseology, and to many pilots the only answer is that two such captains never would make so massive a mistake. Yet even airmen who defended the two American pilots conceded that the circumstances and the available evidence hinted strongly at a fatal sense of overconfidence in the 727 itself.

There was no doubt, for example, that an excessive rate of descent was allowed to take place in the final stages of the approach to Runway 18. That rate was about twenty-one hundred feet per minute, far above established maximums for low altitudes. The alleged failure to monitor the altimeters could have been nothing more than a culmination of the error in judgment that permitted the plane to descend too fast. Swept-wing aircraft tend to sink fast anyway, and the 727 has an even higher sink rate in order to accomplish short-length landings.

Having presumably painted themselves into a corner by coming down too fast, the crew could have increased their own workload to the point where other mistakes were almost inevitable—such as not watching the altimeter. The CAB said there was considerable evidence that the pilots maintained such relatively high airspeed and descent rates during the approach, there was little time in which to complete the changes in flap settings and other landing checklist items required in the final approach stages.

Compounding this situation was a sudden deterioration in visibility. Recall Teelin's remark to the Cincinnati tower when the latter asked if the runway was still in sight: his answer was "just barely." It should be pointed out that Flight 383's approach to the assigned runway involved a base leg pattern, roughly comparable to a dogleg on a golf course. In other words, after turning into the base leg and throughout the descent, the airport was always on the left side of the plane. To keep the field in sight, the pilots could look only to the left.

Here was another unsuspected booby trap on the way to what the investigators termed pilot error. The terrain directly to the left of 383's flight path was a river basin about four hundred feet lower than the ground over which the aircraft was passing, or the ground to the aircraft's right. Rising steeply from the river to the same level as the airport was an unlighted, wooded hillside. Only a few residences lined the riverside, providing little or no terrain definition. In the dark, with visibility conditons poor at best, the crew easly could have mistaken the lights in the river valley as being at the same elevation as the terrain on which the airport was located. These lights were all the pilots and flight engineer John LaVoie could see out the left side of the cockpit.

True, both Teelin and O'Neill had flown in and out of Cincinnati many times—in fact, Teelin had check-ridden the other pilot over the route only four days before the accident. But night flight in limited visibility can contribute to what the CAB itself termed "a sensory illusion of adequate altitude," and the Board's report admitted that this could well have been a major causal factor.

All this would not explain why two skilled veterans did not consult their altimeters in a bad-weather approach at night. The CAB said bluntly this apparent failure was "difficult to reconcile." It offered two possible explanations:

—The plane was equipped with a "drum" type altimeter, accurate and reliable but one that requires two separate readings to obtain altitude. First a pilot must glance at a vertical indicator mounted on a revolving drum that measures altitude by each thousand-foot level. Then he glances at a radial pointer to obtain the hundred-feet indication. To quote the CAB report: "At stabilized altitudes or at low rates of climb/descent where the drum [vertical indicator] is moving slowly or not at all, the pilot must be certain to associate the proper thousand-feet indication in relationship to the hundred-feet reading."

For example, an altimeter presentation of nine hundred feet would show the "1" (thousand feet) slightly above the thousand-feet index on the drum, while the radial indicator would be pointing at the nine on the outside dial. All a pilot would need to misinterpret his altitude would be erroneously to associate the radial pointer reading with the "1" slightly above the horizontal index, instead of the zero below the index. This would give him an altitude of nineteen hundred feet instead of nine hundred feet—or an altitude one thousand feet in error. Recalling the DC-8 incident cited earlier, there is considerable support for this hypothesis.

—The investigation showed that when the flight turned into the final approach course, it was only two and a half miles from the runway. At that distance, the jet should have been trimmed and configured for landing with airspeed and rate of descent stabilized well within established limits. Yet examination of the wreckage disclosed that when the turn was being completed, the flap extension was only twenty-five degrees and the landing gear was still retracted.

Routine landings are not made with flaps set at twenty-five degrees. It was obvious that the airspeed on final approach was too high to permit the necessary configuration of thirty- or forty-degree flaps for landing. This left an abnormally long list of incompleted items on the before-landing checklist, with touchdown only two and a half miles away and the distance dwindling every second. The crew, the CAB noted, must have been extremely busy. Teelin, as the check pilot riding in the right seat, probably was trying to keep the airport lights in sight while at the same time handling radio communication, extending the flaps and performing the landing checklist. Remember, the airport was off to the left. To keep the runway lights in sight, he had little time to look back at his own instruments on the right side of the cockpit—including his altimeter. Rather, it is conceivable that he checked the captain's altimeter instead—misreading it from a side angle just as a person in the right front seat of an automobile invariably misjudges the speedometer reading in front of the driver as higher than the actual speed.

(Several American pilots have a theory about the Cincinnati crash which apparently was not investigated by the CAB; at least there was no reference to this possibility in its report. Controllers at most airports tell approaching pilots to stay above fifteen hundred feet before intercepting the glide path on a final approach. But Cincinnati is one of the rare exceptions; it is customary, or was at the time of the accident, to allow descents to one thousand feet before glide path interception.

("When they turn you loose for an ILS at Cincy," one captain told me, "it's possible for you to be so used to that fifteen-hundred-foot minimum you forget you're at one thousand."

(If that were the case with Teelin and O'Neill, they could have been at one thousand as they started their turn into base leg, at right angles to their assigned runway. Normally, they would have lost about five hundred feet in that turn, heading for the terrain that murdered their ship. The hill they struck was two hundred and twenty-five feet *below* the elevation of the airport itself. But according to the theory of their fellow pilots, by thinking they had one thousand feet of sky left when they entered base leg, in actuality they had only five hundred feet, which was insufficient to clear the hill.)

The CAB reasoned that Teelin and O'Neill, who had flown together on many occasions, each assumed that the other was following normal procedures. In the CAB's own words:

"It is possible that the check captain, confident in the other pilot's ability to operate the aircraft safely, would assume that the altimeters and other flight instruments were being monitored and could therefore concentrate on maintaining visual contact with the airport. Moreover, it is possible that the captain being observed was secure in the knowledge that a well-qualified check captain was in the right seat performing copilot duties. He could therefore, in view of the rapidly decreasing visibility, concentrate on keeping the airport in sight, depending on visual reference to ground lights for altitude guidance, with the assurance that the

check captain was monitoring the flight instruments and would alert
him to any unusual contingency."

In one word: overconfidence.

But there might have been an additional element of overconfidence, too. Overconfidence in the plane both pilots not only respected but loved. That would be the sole explanation for the
excessive rate of descent, particularly when Flight 383 was so
close to the airport and over hilly terrain. An almost blind feeling
of trust in a well-designed, beautiful-flying piece of machinery, as
responsive and mercury-quick as a fighter plane.

That element was not recognized at first. But it became a definite
part of the 727 story only three days after American 383 crashed—
on the night of November 11, 1965, when a third 727 went down
while landing at Salt Lake City in almost perfect weather.

The jet age was not kind to Captain Gale Kehmeier.

He became a United Air Lines pilot in 1941 and successfully
qualified on the DC-3, DC-4, DC-6 and DC-7 in quick order.
He was good enough, in fact, to earn his captain's stripes in less
than four years, which was relatively fast in those days. But when
United began transitioning its pilots to the jets, Kehmeier—as
did some other airmen—found it hard to adjust to the new planes.

In 1960 he began DC-8 training. His ground school grades
were average and the same was true of simulator training. In
DC-8 flight school, he was judged only marginally average and
he flunked an oral session. The failure caused his removal from
flight training and he underwent three weeks of additional ground
school.

This time he passed the oral examination but when he was returned to flight training, he did worse than before. A United
instructor requested that Kehmeier be given a special check ride
by a management captain. The latter observed Kehmeier's performance and recommended that his DC-8 transition training be
ended.

"A review of Captain Kehmeier's record still indicates unsatisfactory performance in the areas of command, judgment, standard
operating procedures, landing technique and coordination," the
check captain wrote.

Kehmeier returned to DC-6 schedules and had no further
trouble until he tried again to switch to the higher-paying jets—

this time to the Boeing 720. His progress through 720 ground, simulator and flight training was satisfactory but he still was required to spend additional time in a Boeing cockpit simulator after he failed to recognize a compass failure warning. An FAA inspector who gave Kehmeier his 720 rating commented that the captain had a tendency to "deviate from accepted procedures and tolerances."

Kehmeier's line performance in the four-engine Boeing was rated "creditable" but in 1964 he failed a routine instrument proficiency check. The check captain criticized his ILS approaches, go-arounds and landings with 50 per cent power. Specifically, Kehmeier was flunked for being too high on the glide slope on two approaches under minimum conditions, slow to add power on the first go-around and for selecting full flaps too early in a simulated two-engine approach. Two days later he took another check ride and passed.

In January of 1965, Kehmeier started 727 training, where he was judged satisfactory. His final type rating check flight, conducted by an FAA inspector, was called "a little below average." However, he received an en route proficiency check about six months later and was given an above-average grade.

His spotty and rather inconsistent record was to become a disturbing part of the investigation into the last flight he ever commanded—UAL 227, LaGuardia to San Francisco via Cleveland, Chicago, Denver and Salt Lake City. Kehmeier took over the flight at Denver where a crew change was made and flew the 727 to Salt Lake City, accompanied by First Officer Philip E. Spicer and Second Officer (Flight Engineer) Ronald R. Christensen.

Spicer was flying the aircraft on the Denver–Salt Lake City leg, under Kehmeier's supervision. The thirty-nine-year-old copilot had only eighty-four hours on the 727 and the older captain was monitoring his performance. The flight was routine until it was cleared for final descent into the Salt Lake City airport traffic pattern. When a controller requested 227's current altitude, Kehmeier's reply was: "Okay, we're slowed to two-fifty [knots] and we're at ten [ten thousand feet] . . . we have the runway in sight now . . ."

It was only too apparent, then and at the subsequent accident hearings, that having the runway in sight while the plane still was at ten thousand feet would require a rapid descent for final approach.

And the descent *was* rapid. The jet's flight recorder established a descent rate of more than two thousand feet per minute in the last minute and thirty seconds of the flight, and twenty-three hundred feet a minute in the final sixty seconds. That was almost *three times* the recommended rate of descent for a landing approach. United's own 727 operating manual called for a maximum descent rate of between six hundred and eight hundred feet per minute on landing approaches. Further, United's procedures called for pilots to monitor their descents with their ILS glide slopes even when an instrument approach was not being made. Flight 227 passed over the airport's outer marker (a radio beam indicating proximity to the runway), less than six miles from touchdown, a full two thousand feet above the normal glide path.

What was transpiring in the cockpit at this time was to become a matter of heated controversy. But there was no doubt that the 727 was coming down fast—far too fast—and the sink rate was further increased when the flaps were lowered to a full forty degrees for landing in Flight 227's final ninety seconds of life. The only way to halt a high sink rate at low altitude, with flaps full, is to increase power.

One and a half minutes away from touchdown, Spicer—still flying the ship—reached for the throttles. Kehmeier brushed the copilot's hand away from the thrust levers.

"Not yet," the captain said.

Those two words doomed Flight 227.

A long thirty seconds went by. The 727 continued to sink. Again Spicer reached for the throttles and moved them halfway forward. When he started to apply full thrust, Kehmeier himself suddenly took over the controls and was shoving the throttles to full forward.

The 727's wheels touched down, but not on the runway. They hit with a tremendous thud three hundred and thirty-five feet short of the runway threshold. The main landing gear, stressed to absorb an impact velocity of twelve feet per second, which is considerable force, collapsed. The right gear was driven into the belly of the fuselage, severing fuel and electrical lines. As the 727 skidded on its stomach toward the runway itself, the spewed fuel caught fire immediately.

The plane continued its deadly slide for nearly three thousand feet—the length of ten football fields. Survivors said later that the fire broke out not more than two seconds after impact, concentrating in the cabin itself as the flames from the rent belly licked through the cabin floor. Two minutes is the theoretical maximum time in which anyone exposed to smoke and flames can escape from a burning aircraft. The long roll of the United jet, nosewheel still down and intact, prolonging the fiery slide, robbed the occupants of at least a minute of precious survival time.

As the shattered, flaming plane skidded to a stop, stewardess Victoria Cole tried to open the main cabin door located on the left forward side of the aircraft. But a flood of panic-stricken passengers, several shouting or screaming, headed for the exit simultaneously. She was pinned against the door until Flight Engineer Christensen—following his assigned duty of going back to the cabin in a crash to aid the stewardesses—shoved the mob away and opened the door.

The emergency slide inflated immediately and passengers began to jump—taking with them, in their rush to safety, stewardess Cole, who literally was knocked into the chute. She bravely tried to get back into the burning plane but was held back by a passenger.

Kehmeier and Spicer evacuated through the sliding cockpit windows. All cabin emergency exits were used—unusual in an accident—but by the time they were opened, many passengers already had been overcome by the thick smoke and raging fire. Stewardess Annette Folz, the most junior cabin attendant, with a little more than a year's service, was occupying a jump seat attached to the door leading to the ventral stairway. She opened the door to determine if those rear stairs could be used as an emergency exit. Two male passengers went through the door before she could stop them and started down the stairs ahead of her.

The extended nose gear and the sheared main landing gear had left the jet in a nose-high attitude that prevented the rear stairs from opening more than six inches. Stewardess Folz and the two passengers started back up the stairwell to the cabin but were blocked by the rapidly developing fire. Frightened and almost resigned to certain death, they huddled together at the foot of the stairwell. Finally, the stewardess suggested they pound on the fuselage to attract the attention of firemen who by this time had arrived on the scene.

Their pounding and yelling went unheeded and unheard. Miss Folz squeezed her arm through the six-inch opening and began waving. A rescue worker running by spotted her frantic signal for help and a hose was passed through the narrow stair aperture. The water kept the flames away from the trapped trio, but ironically it was fire that eventually saved them. The flames burned through the rear cabin wall and left them a large enough hole through which they were dragged to safety.

About twenty-five minutes had elapsed between the crash and their rescue, which the CAB labeled "unprecedented." That was a beautiful way of understating what was more of a miracle. But there were no miracles available for forty-one of the eighty-five passengers aboard, all of the fatalities due to smoke, intense heat, burns or a combination of the three. Two survivors died later of burns. Subsequent autopsies on all the victims showed not a single fatal traumatic injury, which meant the accident should have been 100 per cent survivable. The reason it was only about 50 per cent survivable was to be dealt with later. The first question to be answered was why the crash occurred in the first place.

Three months after the accident, the CAB opened hearings in Salt Lake City. Captain Kehmeier's allegedly hot-and-cold flying history was duly introduced into evidence, via a four-and-a-half-page summary of various below-average and unsatisfactory verdicts by instructors and check pilots, much to the annoyance of his fellow airmen and United itself. They felt that the unfavorable comments amounted literally to quoting out of context. A UAL report on the accident, submitted to the CAB for consideration, had this to say about Kehmeier's airmanship reputation:

"The impression created by the use of . . . every instructor and check pilot comment made with respect to below-average performances throughout a twenty-five-year professional airman's career seems patently unfair to the airman, his employer and the Federal Aviation Agency, which granted him the license to perform as a transport pilot. A review of any airman's file in the industry will indicate that below-average performances are to be expected from time to time, especially during training and checking, and that instructors and check pilots are models of silence with respect to comments concerning average or better performances, and quick to comment concerning less than average performance in a certain area. The system would be valueless otherwise. But to isolate twenty-five years of such comments in four and a half pages of a summary report is, indeed, to create a biased and inaccurate impression."

United, naturally, was trying to erase the implication that it allowed a marginal captain with a poor record to command one of its jets. But the CAB let the implication stand. In its final report on the Salt Lake City crash, it declared that Kehmeier's training history "indicated a pattern of below-average judgment, as well as a tendency to deviate from standard operating procedures and practices."

"Indeed," the CAB added, "it is significant that in this case the history not only reflects an apparent indifference toward adhering to acceptable procedures in general, but specifically during the landing or ILS approach phases of flight.

"The aeronautical knowledge and skill levels required for an airline transport pilot may be determined through testing, but the less tangible aspect of mature judgment may not be so readily measured or determined . . . safety in air transportation requires the air carrier . . . to identify those pilots who are marginal or who have demonstrated a failure to adhere to proven procedures and reassign them to duties compatible to their capabilities and limitations."

Whether Kehmeier should have been placed in command of a fly-her-by-the-book jetliner will always be a matter for debate. What helped "hang" Kehmeier was testimony by his own crew. In one vital area, their testimony collided head on with his defense and explanation of his actions.

Kehmeier testified that when Spicer tried to add more power, the 727 was at an altitude of sixty-five hundred feet and that this was the point at which he stopped the copilot from advancing the throttles. He said Spicer did add power fifteen to twenty seconds later, at fifty-five hundred feet, with no response from the engines. Kehmeier said it was then that he took over, shoving the thrust levers to full or takeoff power. He estimated that he assumed control of the aircraft when the flight was one and a quarter miles from the runway at an altitude of one thousand feet, at least thirty seconds before the impact with the ground. He insisted that the engines still refused to respond.

Spicer's story, however, contradicted that of his captain in one key respect. He said Kehmeier didn't apply full power until at

least five and no more than fifteen seconds before the plane struck
the ground—his best guess being about ten seconds. Flight Engineer
Christensen went even further in a sworn deposition (he did not
testify in person). He said full thrust was applied only seven or
eight seconds prior to impact and, he added, "the descent was
extremely steep and made me uneasy during the last twelve hundred feet."

The pertinent point concerning the amount of power response—
Kehmeier's chief defense—produced mixed testimony. The captain
said there was no response, although he admitted he could not
remember actually reading the engine instruments. Spicer said he
neither heard nor felt any engine response. But the flight engineer
testified that he heard the turbines respond normally and he was
backed up by many survivors, including two stewardesses who were
in the rear cabin. In fact, several survivors testified they heard
the engine noise increase sharply only three to five seconds before
impact.

The engine "spool-up" actually was moot. More to the point was
all the evidence that Kehmeier had let the 727 establish a sink
rate far in excess of recommended limits. There would have been
no need of an emergency power application if the flight had been
making a normal approach descent at the proper glide slope. Assuming that the copilot and flight engineer were more accurate than
the captain in estimating when full power was applied, Kehmeier's
delay was merely a final mistake that made a crash inevitable. The
727's Pratt & Whitney engines will accelerate from idle to half
thrust in only five seconds, and from idle to full or takeoff thrust
in six to eight seconds. Kehmeier claimed he had thirty seconds
in which to avoid disaster, but that the engines let him down. His
crew said he had no more than fifteen seconds and possibly as
little as seven. The CAB provided the hearing with testimony that
there was absolutely no indication of engine failure, and that "all
engines were found to be capable of producing rated engine power
prior to impact."

The Board's "probable cause" determination was "failure of the
captain to take timely action to arrest an excessive rate of descent
during the landing approach."

The CAB went an unprecedented step further in its indictment
of Captain Kehmeier.

"The Board is concerned," the report continued, "that the pro-

cedures for pilot testing prevailing at the time of this accident were
such that an individual with the pilot behavioral characteristics of
the pilot in this case could qualify and be retained as pilot-in-com-
mand of a B-727 aircraft."

On April 6, 1966, Gale Kehmeier resigned (he says he was given
a choice between resigning or being fired) from United Air Lines.
He received a $45,000 cash settlement in severance pay plus his
regular lifetime pension.

At the time of the Salt Lake City accident, he was forty-seven
years old. In 1967, approximately two years after the crash, he
appeared on a television panel show discussing air safety problems.
On the screen he appeared to be a man in his late fifties or even
sixties.

The Salt Lake City hearings were held in the wake of the fourth
727 fatal crash.

On February 6, 1966, an All-Nippon Airways tri-jet on a flight
from the island of Hokkaido to Tokyo crashed into Tokyo Bay six
miles from the Tokyo Airport. All one hundred and twenty-six
passengers and seven crew members were killed.

The accident was a virtual carbon copy of the first 727 crash at
Chicago. An approach at night, with the crew apparently flying
the jet right into the water. Recovery of the flight recorder and
other evidence, however, also showed a disturbing similarity to the
known common denominator at both Salt Lake City and Cincinnati—an excessive rate of descent. This, plus the probability of
nighttime sensory illusion concerning altitude over water, made
the All-Nippon accident less of a mystery than a national tragedy.
For by this time, air safety experts had cleared the 727 of blame
after a controversy whose bitterness can only be compared with
that involving the Electra.

The Salt Lake City crash already had touched off the battle
of the 727. Recalling the black eye given the Electra, one sees it
as history repeating itself. The new Boeing had been in three
accidents killing one hundred and thirty-one persons over a three-
month span.

At least three travel agencies notified airlines operating the tri-
jet to cancel all 727 bookings.

About a half-dozen major corporations ordered their employees
to stay off all 727 flights.

While some cities reported little or no adverse reaction, others said hundreds of passengers were either canceling their reservations or requesting space on flights utilizing different equipment.

One airline reported typical passenger remarks to reservation agents: "Not a 727, I hope," or "Is the 720 different from the 727?" One frequent question: "Haven't they been grounded yet?"

Business secretaries in one city specifically inquired about the type of plane being used when requesting space for their bosses, and a great number rejected space on 727s.

An airline called a competitor to ask if it had any overflow on a certain flight, explaining: "We can give them protection on ours —it's a 727 and we've got plenty of space."

One airline sales manager in a large Midwestern city admitted that "We're losing fifty passengers daily from 727 flights."

And the final irony came from an airline which operated both Electras and 727s. It said many passengers were asking to be switched from 727 flights to the older, once maligned propjet.

It was the Civil Aeronautics Board which helped contribute to the 727's black eye, only slightly lighter in hue than the one suffered by the Electra. Shortly after the Salt Lake City crash, undoubtedly pressured and influenced by public and Congressional concern, the CAB disclosed it was asking the FAA to make certain modifications in the Boeing tri-jet—corrective steps based on the Utah accident. Unfortunately for the 727 and for the airlines operating it, the CAB's recommendations—all of them deserving serious consideration—became ammunition for that irresponsible handful of Congressmen who demand air safety reforms before anyone knows what needs reforming.

As was the Electra before it, the 727 was a prime target for rumors and scare talk even without the CAB's suggestions. What the CAB unwittingly and innocently did was to provide all the rumors with a cloak of authenticity. The Board's Bureau of Safety first suggested that the 727's fuel lines be relocated so they pass through the fuselage floor beams near the centerline of the aircraft. The fuel lines themselves, the Bureau said, should be made of stainless steel with thicker dimensions. Finally, the electrical generator leads—their severance in the Salt Lake City crash was one of the two probable sources of fire—should be rerouted to provide maximum separation from the fuel lines and placed in a separate plastic conduit for greater strength and flexibility.

The Bureau also urged changes in the 727's emergency lighting system, which on the UAL plane had failed to illuminate the emergency exits. And the CAB, again through its Bureau of Safety, noted that current FAA tests had disclosed "a number of deficiencies" in the materials being used in aircraft interiors. Such materials, the Bureau felt, could be capable of producing toxic gases as well as thick, blinding smoke.

"Preliminary information [from the Salt Lake City investigation] indicates that the interior furnishings contributed greatly to the spread of fire and the emission of heavy black smoke, both of which contributed to the fatalities," the Bureau advised the FAA.

Before the FAA or anyone else could act on the CAB's recommendations, a Texas Congressman named Henry Gonzalez marched on stage with all mimeograph machines whirring. Gonzalez had been feuding with the FAA ever since that agency, under Najeeb E. Halaby, shut down the San Antonio Traffic Control Center in a general consolidation of such centers for greater safety and efficiency. Almost every fatal air accident has an inevitable aftermath —a statement by Gonzalez blaming the FAA.

The Congressman needed only one look at the Cab's recommendations before he immediately demanded that the jet be grounded as unsafe. He used the CAB's suggested improvements as a basis for charges that the tri-jet was poorly designed and an actual menace to every passenger who boarded one. Because he was a Congressman, no FAA, CAB or airline official challenged these exaggerations and what might be charitably interpreted as an overhasty appraisal of the situation.

He charged, for example, that the 727 had idiosyncrasies in handling with an "abnormally" high sink rate and should not have been certificated for passenger travel. This was pure malarkey, as any 727 pilot or aeronautical engineer could have told Gonzalez and the few Congressional colleagues who joined him in a grounding demand. The tri-jet's sink rate *is* high, particularly when the flaps are lowered to landing configuration. But this is normal, not abnormal, for the very purpose of a jetliner like the 727 is the capability of landing in shorter distances at airports that cannot handle bigger jets. This short-field ability is a safety measure in itself. At the time Gonzalez was denouncing the 727's "abnormally" high sink rate, the Boeing plane had made more than six hundred thousand landings in its first three years of service—which seemed to indicate that when the 727 is flown by the book, it presents no problems.

The Congressman went on to cite "deficiencies" in the tri-jet's design, such as "defects in the fuel lines, generator leads and landing gear." The CAB made no such charges of design deficiencies. It recommended modifications because of experience gained in an unusual accident under unusual circumstances. If the 727 had been test-flown for ten years before it was allowed to carry a single passenger, that decade of experimental flights probably would not have disclosed what the Salt Lake City accident did in a few terrible seconds. As a matter of fact, there is a great deal of available evidence that the CAB's proposals concerning relocation of the fuel lines were on the wrong track.

FAA and industry experts, after studying the CAB's recommendations, pointed out to the Bureau of Safety that the 727's fuel lines actually were placed in the safest location possible—in such a way that they were surrounded by the heaviest structure available. If the fuel lines were moved inboard as the Bureau suggested, they would be subject to rupture by items in the cargo compartment in case of a belly landing—far more expectable in emergency landings, which are more frequent than the type of landing experienced by the UAL jet. The FAA did agree that fuel lines could be strengthened. Yet a few weeks after the United crash, the main landing gear of an Eastern 727 collapsed on landing in what could have been a repeat tragedy. The belly structure held and there was no fire.

The FAA acknowledged that the main gear itself could be strengthened and Boeing agreed to make engineering changes on every 727. But this was not an admission of a design failure. The impact suffered by Flight 227 would have smashed the landing gear of any airplane. The gear modification was a precautionary safety bonus, not an admission of faulty design.

Gonzalez, other Congressmen and a few newspapers made much of the CAB's criticism of materials used in the cabin. But the CAB found out later that it was wrong in assuming that "current" FAA tests already had found such materials hazardous and that safer upholstery and cabin linings were readily available. Actually, the FAA's Aircraft Development Service was then in the process of completing those tests. Upon completion, the Agency informed the CAB of the results of those tests. The verdict: cabin materials used in the 727 and other jetliners as well were "the best the current state of the art produces." That judgment was reached after exhaustive fire tests showed that the maligned materials actually had significant fire-extinguishing capability.

Since those tests were made, in March of 1966, further research has produced even better cabin materials. But at the time Gonzalez leaped so eagerly on the CAB's admittedly premature criticism, the terminology "deficient materials" was grossly unfair and even libelous. As for the possibility that upholstery and cabin linings might produce toxic smoke, the FAA's tests demonstrated a need for further research in a tricky, little-explored area, and such research is now in the process of some promising developments.

It should not be assumed from the foregoing that the government, the airlines and Boeing kissed off Salt Lake City as just another case of a pilot goofing. The FAA summoned every U.S. airline operating the 727, plus foreign carriers as well, to a conference on what—if anything—was wrong with the airplane, with operating techniques or with training procedures. There were no punches pulled at this session, either.

At the same time, the CAB organized a special "Flight Control and Performance Characteristics Group" which was assigned the task of reviewing the 727's airworthiness, aerodynamics and over-all flight behavior under all possible circumstances. The CAB also conducted a survey among members of the Air Line Pilots Association and Allied Pilots Association. Its purpose: to determine if pilots themselves were aware of any hazardous or undesirable features of the 727, any marginal performance or unusual flight characteristics experienced in actual line operations.

The National Aeronautics and Space Administration, at the request of the CAB, reviewed all Boeing 727 research data for the slightest evidence of unusual difficulties.

The FAA itself re-examined the 727 flight training programs of every U.S. airline.

All this technical soul-searching produced nothing but an absolute "not guilty" verdict for the tri-jet. The FAA, following its "what's wrong with the bird" meeting with seventeen airlines, pronounced the 727 "completely airworthy" and added that this opinion was shared unanimously not only by the carriers but also by their pilots.

"We have found nothing to indicate that the 727 is not completely airworthy and properly certificated," an FAA official told newsmen after the conference. "We found no cause to be suspicious of the 727 as an airplane."

That FAA announcement was followed one month later by a special CAB report which also exonerated the tri-jet. The Board called the 727 a safe plane representing an advance in aeronautical design. It said the 727's performance and flight characteristics were "excellent and representative of an advance in the state of the art."

This report, prepared by CAB technical experts, dwelled heavily on the Board's survey of 727 pilots. It noted, for example, that American's crews regarded the 727 as a "pilot's aircraft"—an expression, the technicians observed, that was an accolade "often used by pilots to designate an aircraft with superior qualities." Other "exceptionally favorable" comments quoted in the report included such praise as "finest airplane I've ever flown" and "best commercial jet transport."

This enthusiastic exoneration, however, was by no means a whitewash job, a sweeping-under-the-rug of responsibility. After all, there *had* been a pattern to the four crashes which took two hundred and sixty-four lives, with charges of pilot error involved in three and possibly all four accidents. All four had occurred in the landing or approach phase. Was there any common denominator in pilot error itself? Was there any explanation for the excessive rate of descent present in three of the crashes? Was there any reason why skilled, dedicated airmen should make the same mistake?

The NASA report to the CAB pretty well pinpointed the real reason for at least three of the four tragedies—failure in airline training programs to emphasize the *virtues* of the 727 as a potential hazard. Namely, that its ability to make short landings could also be a booby trap for any pilot who does not fly the 727 by the book. NASA informed the CAB that close-in, so-called "unstabilized" approaches with high rates of descent, were being conducted more often in the 727 than in any other jet transport.

A stabilized approach requires a pilot to position his aircraft no higher than five hundred feet after he passes the runway outer marker (about six miles from the runway threshold) and the inner marker (about four miles). This is to assure a gradual descent. All airlines demand that their crews make stabilized approaches whenever possible, but the 727 tragedies showed that not all carriers

were emphasizing this rule in training or on check flights. To quote
the CAB's report on the Cincinnati crash:

". . . consideration must be given to the fact that the 727 does
have highly responsive and versatile flight characteristics and that
these *favorable* [author's italics] characteristics may be misleading
to the pilot, or are presenting the impression that greater liberties
may be taken with the aircraft in normal operating situations, especially in the approach/landing regimes."

In plain and simple language, this amounted to pilot overconfidence in a brilliant airplane. The airlines, in their operating
manuals, *had* warned their crews of the 727's high sink rate in full
(forty-degree) flap configuration unless power is applied to counter-
act the high drag. The major reform stemming from the four 727
accidents was a unanimous airline promise to re-emphasize this
hazard in all manuals and on all check rides—literally, a flat order
to make stabilized approaches at all times. Further, the FAA now
requires all carriers to include a demonstration of a low-altitude,
high rate of descent maneuver as part of their training programs.
And some airlines no longer will let pilots even use forty-degree
flaps at any time—a ban which Northwest and later TWA instituted
even before the first 727 accident.

The final stigma against the 727 was erased early in 1968 when
a Salt Lake City court dismissed five liability and damage suits
filed against Boeing after the United crash. The court held that
there was insufficient evidence of negligence in the design or manu-
facture of the plane.

There were two more lessons to be learned from the story of
the doughty three-holer. The first was that an air crash warrants
concern but not hysteria—certainly not frantic demands for grounding, loud cries for corrective action without knowing what, if anything, needs correcting, and damaging accusations that a certain
type of aircraft is unsafe. The 727 literally was a libeled airplane.

The second lesson, however, was the direct result of the Salt
Lake City accident—the tardy realization that passengers need
better odds for getting out of a theoretically survivable crash.

# 6

## HOW DO YOU WALK AWAY?

On April 9, 1964, one hundred and seventy-four persons got a pretty fair idea of what it was like to be in an airliner crash.

Or perhaps the word should be written "crash."

Because this was an emergency evacuation demonstration conducted by United Air Lines. At the time, United was being pressured competitively to add more seats to its DC-8 jets on the San Francisco–Hawaii run. The airline was resisting on the ground that raising the seating capacity from the then current one hundred and fifty to one hundred and seventy-four involved a safety problem—namely, could you get that many passengers out of a crashed plane in sufficient time?

The demonstration was staged in a United hangar at O'Hare Airport. Parking a DC-8 in the safe confines of a cavernous hangar in broad daylight may not seem like a realistic emergency test, but UAL provided more realism than its guinea pigs bargained for. The passengers were mostly UAL employees and their families, including children as young as six and a few elderly persons ranging up to their mid-sixties—in other words, a typical and representative passenger load. Also present were a few reporters, indulging in typical wisecracking as newspapermen will, until they were suddenly converted into swift believers in evacuation problems. This conversion included me.

No one was briefed on what was to happen, not even the four stewardesses who were summoned to the airport for what they thought was a special flight. Windows were covered with heavy cloth to simulate a night takeoff. Every seat was filled, causing one United official to comment wryly, "it looks like wall-to-wall people."

One of the stewardesses gave the usual "welcome aboard" announcement and the so often ignored suggestion that passengers read the little seatback cards "containing the location of emergency exits." Inevitably, not one out of ten paid any attention even though the "passengers" knew by now that they were about to take part in an evacuation test.

The cockpit-cabin PA came to metallic life, the voice of a captain pleasantly announcing, "Good evening, we have been cleared for takeoff."

A tape recording produced the sound of screaming jet engines in a realistic crescendo. There was no sensation of motion, of course, but the sound seemed to press most of the occupants back in their seats as if there were actual acceleration. I noticed that a few people even clutched their arm rests.

Suddenly, the engine noise ceased. A stewardess yelled, "Brace . . . we're crashing!"

There was a scattering of nervous giggles. But then came new taped sounds. Metal scraping raucously on concrete and then ripping. Unnoticed, a UAL official hidden in a rear lavatory stepped out and began pumping non-toxic mineral oil smoke through the cabin by squeezing a bellows attached to a small tank.

In less than ten seconds, the entire cabin was so full of thick, blinding smoke that it was impossible to see more than a few inches in front of my face. A child began crying in real panic. Nobody had been told there would be smoke.

In the front of the plane, a stewardess started to open the main cabin door. The handle came off in her hand. United had loaded the dice for realism by making four of the eight exits inoperative but not warning the cabin attendants in advance which ones could be used. In a real crash, it is only too likely that airframe damage could warp windows and doors and make them impossible to open.

"Unfasten belts and head for the nearest exit," a stewardess shouted. "Women, take off your high-heel shoes."

As one of those one hundred and seventy-four guinea pigs, I unfastened my belt and started stumbling through the smoke toward the rear—where I remembered boarding. (My reaction was typical of the majority of all airline passengers; I instinctively headed for the door through which I boarded, even though there was an emergency exit much closer.) The heavy smoke, weirdly foglike in its intensity, filled me with almost real fright as I groped toward the sound of a stewardess's voice. That voice was all that guided me. Not until I neared the rear cabin door did I catch a hazy glimpse of a blue uniform. By this time, I was roughly shouldering slower passengers out of the way, and with no thought of anything but an intense desire to get out of the plane. I knew it was nothing but make-believe, yet that logic was buried under actual panic.

As I reached the rear exit, I stepped on somebody's foot and heard an elderly woman grunt in pain. I still didn't stop. I kept heading for that blessed, comforting figure in blue. The stewardess was shouting, "Jump and sit! Jump and sit!" She half shoved me out the door. I jumped—into the inflated chute. I sat and slid down to the hangar floor eighteen feet below.

Coming out of the smoke into reassuring daylight was like awaking from a nightmare. I looked back at the DC-8 and watched fellow passengers still jumping. Those leaving by the wing exits were caught by United mechanics standing next to big mattresses. These occupants nervously dropped from the trailing edge of the wing—far slower than those jumping down door slides. Even with the mattresses waiting for them, they obviously were hesitant. If there had been a real fire, there would have been less delay but it was only too apparent that the relatively narrow window exits over the wings are not the acme of efficiency. Squeezing through them was rather laborious and traffic bottlenecks formed quickly.

Stop watches clicked as the last passenger evacuated, followed by the four stewardesses—four minutes and fifty seconds from the first yelled command of "Unfasten belts and head for the nearest exit." A UAL official shook his head.

"Nearly five minutes," he murmured. "If it had been a real crash, we would have lost at least two thirds."

Almost five minutes. Three minutes beyond the allotted maximum time in which smoke and fire can fill and burn human lungs. Three minutes—the length of a round in a prize fight. This was a demonstration, of course. Just practice. And this was in 1964, long before the Federal Aviation Agency required the airlines to prove that any aircraft they operate can be emptied in two minutes using only half the exits, and with the evacuees including women, children and the aged. But to the reporters observing and participating, it was a grim lesson in the problems of emergency evacuation.

And if this simulated crash was a frightening experience, ponder the emotions of passengers exposed to a real accident. Such as the UAL 727 crash at Salt Lake City mentioned in Chapter 5. That tragedy was a classic example of how death can come so unexpectedly regardless of superbly trained cabin attendants— United has no peer in emergency procedures training for its stewardesses—and in a crash where the airframe stays relatively intact.

Those passengers at Salt Lake City consisted of sixty-six adult males, sixteen adult females, an eleven-year-old boy, a six-year-old girl and one infant. Four couples were traveling together. Included among the males were three FAA employees, one member of the Salt Lake City fire department, five Air Force and three Navy personnel. Among the female adult group was a uniformed stewardess deadheading to San Francisco and an elderly lady who was boarded at Denver in a wheel chair.

Before the takeoff from Denver, the usual pre-flight emergency admonitions were given. Mention was made of the oxygen masks and how they were to be used if cabin pressure dropped abnormally. Attention also was called to the seatback cards containing location of emergency exits. Later many survivors admitted to investigators that they paid little or no attention to this briefing. The majority never looked at the emergency cards.

There was no time whatsoever for special instructions from the stewardesses. The first mistake committed by scores of passengers was their refusal to stay in their seats until the plane stopped skidding along the runway, despite shouted warnings from the stewardesses. Some could not stay put because their seats caught fire. But a great many simply left their seats and were moving toward exits when the jet suddenly veered to the right, throwing them off balance and causing injuries as well as hampering the evacuation flow when the plane did stop.

The noise of the crash impact and general confusion—including screams and panicky shouts—prevented many from hearing any stewardess instructions. In fact, only seven of the forty-eight survivors said they heard anything. One was in the forward cabin. He remembered the stewardess on the front jump seat yell "Stay in your seats." The other six were in the rear cabin, just ahead of the point where fire first broke out.

Fire propagation was rapid, some survivors testifying that flames erupted only one or two seconds after initial impact. The fire came up through the cabin floor, one survivor reporting that the flames then "shot backwards and forwards . . . it was in my seat and all around me."

C. Hayden LeRoy, an investigator for the CAB's Bureau of Safety, later did a thorough and valuable analysis of the evacuation flow, as well as other survival aspects of the UAL accident. His study provided an interesting correlation between the seat locations of surviving passengers and the exits they used. The majority followed an escape route toward the entrances used when boarding. In some cases, this contributed to the fatality toll because a number of passengers were overcome by smoke and flames before they could reach exits at the opposite end of the plane.

LeRoy also recounted the experience of a male passenger in a forward seat who released his belt and dropped to the floor to escape the rapidly increasing smoke. He started to crawl between the legs of fellow passengers who were blocking the aisle leading to the main cabin door. Absorbed with his crawling, he actually went past the door and found himself in the unoccupied cockpit. He futilely tried to kick out a window, never noticing that both sliding windows were open. Again he dropped to the floor and crawled back through the cabin, over several bodies and past the open galley service door until he reached the left window exit. He climbed out of this, having by this time ignored four other exits already opened and available for use.

Although this accident occurred on an airport runway, with fire and rescue equipment alerted only seconds after the first flames were seen, the equipment saved pitifully few lives. LeRoy reported that all but three survivors were out of the burning jet before the first fire truck arrived—three minutes after the crash. The three exceptions were the stewardess and two passengers trapped in the ventral stairway.

Of the forty-one who perished in the cabin, sixteen were found in the aisle between the forward main door and the galley service area in the middle of the cabin. The body of one woman passenger was found in the cockpit. Eight bodies were in the aisle between the galley and the rear lavatories. Eight more were still in seats, although only two were in the seats they had occupied during the flight. All other bodies were recovered from between the seats.

The unbelievable deadliness of the smoke-fire combination is underlined by the results of autopsies on the bodies of ten victims found in locations where they might have blocked an exit or lay in the path of other victims trying to escape. Not a single autopsy disclosed traumatic or impact injuries. There were no hemorrhages, bone fractures or any evidence of other internal injuries. All died from smoke inhalation, burns or a combination of the two.

There was not the slightest doubt that this was a survivable accident. Except for the collapse of the landing gear and the subsequent damage to the fuel lines and belly, there was only small structural damage. The impact force was severe enough to fail the gear, but forward speed was relatively low, resulting in mild deceleration. All of this added up to the fact that there should have been ninety-one survivors instead of forty-eight. Fire and smoke were the killers, as they have been in the overwhelming majority of airline crashes involving mostly intact aircraft structures.

This was the second accident which led to reforms in evacuation procedures and rules. The first was the July 11, 1961, crash of a United DC-8 at Denver (it was ironic that UAL, whose emergency training has been admired and in many cases been copied by other airlines, happened to be the carrier involved in both cases). The jet was making an emergency landing because of hydraulic failure. The malfunction itself did not cause the crash, but it triggered a deadly chain of events that demonstrated how a relatively minor difficulty can mushroom into tragedy.

First, the thrust reversers on the engines reacted asymmetrically (unevenly), causing the plane to swerve off the runway. This, too, presented no particular problem except that the swerving occurred just at the point where a truck was parked next to the runway. One wing collided with the vehicle, a fuel tank burst open and the fuel ignited. Contributing to the tragedy was the fact that despite the hydraulic trouble, the crew had managed to lower the landing gear in a down and locked position, leading the captain to believe that the landing would be normal. He even advised the passengers of this, and the first warning of potential danger did not come until the wheels had touched down and the jet began to swerve. There was no time for any precautionary measures, such as would have been taken in a so-called planned emergency.

There was little hysteria aboard the aircraft but confusion arose as the passengers headed for the exits. One woman carrying a child started toward an exit, reversed course and blocked an aisle. Another passenger, with good intentions and admirable courage, yelled "Everybody stay calm and keep in your seats!" His advice cost at least a few lives because the plane had stopped and there was no time to "stay calm and keep in your seats."

Of the seventy-nine passengers in the coach section (the rear), fourteen went forward and used the exits available in the first-class cabin. One rear exit was useless because the collision had warped it structurally. There was little use of window exits. This left only one rear emergency door and sixty-seven persons tried to get through it. Sixteen did not make it, perishing from the effects of smoke. Later it was disclosed that many passengers were unaware of the forward emergency exits. A stewardess saved a paraplegic passenger by picking him up in her arms and carrying him to a slide.

The accident prompted an intensive study of emergency evacuation problems by the FAA, CAB and the airlines. Here was a prime example of fatalities occurring in a crash where the plane itself remained virtually intact. Out of the study came such improvements as better marking of emergency exits, more extensive oral briefings of passengers by stewardesses, and the required use of placards by every seat illustrating exit locations—with the oral briefings calling attention to these instructions.

The FAA also ordered the airlines to demonstrate, under simulated but realistic conditions, that every transport they operated could be emptied in not more than two minutes using only half the available exits. The evacuations were to be conducted with a full load of "typical" occupants, including women, children and elderly persons.

In ten months, the FAA monitored more than three hundred test evacuations involving more than twenty-five thousand "passengers" who propelled themselves out of aircraft windows and doors, skidded down chutes and descended ropes. To many airlines, the tests were rude eye-openers. They believed that their emergency equipment was efficient and their cabin attendants well trained. The early results jolted them out of their complacency.

In the first two months, the failure rate on the required two-minute evacuation deadline was well over 20 per cent. Some of the evacuation times were horrendous—four and even five minutes. To their credit, the airlines that flunked did some hasty soul-searching. Marked improvement resulted, particularly in the installation of better evacuation chutes. All airlines operating jets switched to a door-mounted chute ready for the first evacuee in not more than ten seconds; the older models took as long as forty-five seconds for inflation.

Stricter maintenance was another reform. Too many of the initial tests went over the two-minute mark because chutes were improperly installed. One airline conducting an Electra evacuation found the stewardesses unable to break open the rear lounge slide. A supervisor discovered that the pin securing the slide was made of unbreakable steel. The same thing then happened in another Electra evacuation demonstration. Further investigation disclosed that the rear lounge slides in *every* Electra the carrier was operating were secured with the same unbreakable pin—and a subsequent probe of this mystery revealed that the part numbers for the unbreakable component and a frangible or breakaway pin were identical—a million-in-one maintenance freak that could have cost lives if any of the Electras had been involved in a survivable accident.

Of three hundred and eight demonstrations, one hundred and forty-four were simulated aborted takeoffs, one hundred and six were simulated gear-up crash landings, and fifty-eight were simulated ditchings. From these the FAA recorded seventy deficiencies during fifty-five separate demonstrations, of which twenty-three had to be repeated.

Of the seventy deficiencies noted, fifty-nine involved failure of evacuation slides traced to design faults, improper maintenance, lack of crew training or a combination of the three factors. Typical examples included slide straps not attached to ceilings or straps which were crossed when installed and inflation release cables which became disconnected. Shrouds were discovered entangled, slide storage doors malfunctioned, slide inflation valves failed to work and, finally, there was too much time required to install and inflate slides. Also reported were cases of stuck cabin doors, jammed overwing exit windows, exits blocked by malfunctioning crew seats and—infrequent but still inexcusable—inadequate crew training.

FAA inspectors reported twenty-one deficiencies in ten of the fifty-eight simulated water ditchings, three of them requiring a repeated test. Twenty of the twenty-one deficiencies involved malfunction of rafts or their stowage compartments, and the twenty-first was a case of poor crew training.

"A few airlines scoffed at the demonstrations but they got

converted in a hurry," one FAA official commented. "At first we experienced resistance and even indifference on the part of some carriers and crew members. Once they got interested, though, they went beyond mere compliance.

"Some carriers voluntarily began experimenting with new types of emergency equipment, like chemically treated tape on the sides of a chute that glows when it's exposed to air, or a new kind of completely fireproofed chute. And when a pilot or stewardess become believers, they turn into worse martinets than any FAA inspector."

The reforms accomplished much but not enough, as the Salt Lake City crash was to prove. One prime source of difficulty was the ineffectiveness of passenger briefings through the use of seat placards. There was, *and still is,* no way of making sure that passengers read and digest the cards. Part of this has been due to the reluctance of some carriers to get the message across, their stewardesses delivering the "read the placard" admonition in such mild terms that the majority of passengers could be forgiven for ignoring the whole thing.

Several airlines prepared "canned" cabin PA announcements in which their stewardesses advised the customers to "read the cards at your leisure." Inasmuch as a crash could have occurred on the subsequent takeoff, seconds after this pablum-worded announcement was made, such a warning was useless. In other instances, economy-minded airlines put evacuation instructions for all types of aircraft they were operating on a single card. Not all passengers know what kind of plane on which they're flying. And in virtually every case, the placards themselves failed to impress passengers with the need for knowing how to get out of a burning plane— the wording generally was more reassuring than stern. United, again ironically, for years was one of the few airlines which didn't sugar-coat its placard phraseology, as the following direct quote will indicate:

"For your safety *know how to move out of this airplane fast* [italics United's]. There is fire danger any time a landing is other than normal—particularly when the airplane structure is damaged. Below is a floor plan of the plane you are in. Familiarize yourself with the location of the exit nearest you. Study how they are opened and also the protective position you should assume during an emergency landing. When leaving, move to the exits immediately . . ."

After Salt Lake City, it was apparent that more reforms were needed. Obviously, it was one thing to give crew members better training but another to guarantee the instruction of passengers. In the Salt Lake City crash, passengers opened five of the six exits and fumbled with three of them before getting them opened. Even presumably experienced passengers are not always prepared —in one technical report on Salt Lake City, an expert declared that among the cabin occupants were an FAA inspector and a deadheading crew member who "were not properly oriented to the airplane."

Conversely, there is considerable evidence that passenger knowledge can save lives. One of the survivors in the crash of a TWA Convair 880 at Cincinnati late in 1967 testified later that "If I hadn't read that seat placard, I never would have gotten out."

There is even some evidence that passengers resent messages aimed at their own safety. A couple of years ago, United pilots— with the airline's blessing—began urging passengers to pay strict attention to the emergency briefings and cards. They had to discontinue this campaign because too many customers complained the announcement frightened them.

A great many stewardesses are disturbed over the lack of attention paid to oral and written emergency instructions. I know several on one large airline who go beyond their mild "canned" announcements on the seat placards and admonish passengers to "please take them out and read them right now."

One stewardess got tired of observing passengers who buried their faces behind newspapers or magazines during the oxygen mask demonstration, paying absolutely no heed to instructions that could mean their lives. The next time she delivered the mask announcement, she risked her job but proved a point.

". . . and when the mask drops down," she intoned with a straight face, "attach it to your navel and breath normally."

Not a single passenger looked up and not a single one realized what she had said. One might alibi that the overwhelming majority of passengers already have heard the oxygen briefing. True, but there are forty thousand brand-new airline passengers every day and if there is only one such newcomer on every flight, the announcements are necessary.

A safety-minded American stewardess once decided to conduct an informal spot check of how well the seat cards are read. She picked as her subject a frequent traveler, one of American's most loyal customers and a man who had flown with this particular stewardess many times. He was sitting in 8B, directly across from the 727's galley, which is a primary emergency exit and plainly designated as such.

"Just for fun," the stewardess said to him about thirty minutes after the usual emergency instructions had been voiced, "if something happened when we landed at Chicago, what exit would you use?"

The passenger looked around him, and nodded knowingly in the direction of the nearest window exit—six rows in back of him and approximately seven yards farther from him than the galley exit.

Obviously, there is considerable "it always happens to the other guy but it could never happen to me" thinking on the part of the public or, for that matter, even on the part of some crew members. This ostrich attitude could be placed in the same category as smoking three packs of cigarettes daily or driving a car at sixty MPH after downing five martinis. It is a foolhardy attitude because no one can predict an accident and no one, even more significantly, can predict his own reactions if an accident occurs.

A training instructor for a major airline put the problem in plain words while addressing a group of pilots and stewardesses and urging them to *know* their emergency procedures as the only protection against unexpected self-panic:

"Who knows what he really will do when the occasion arrives? Every soldier is faced with this question before battle in wartime; a battle for lives during an airline accident is not really different. CAB accident investigation experts have established during their researching that there is little foreknowledge of what a crew member will really do when he or she faces his emergency procedures blindly. Will he forget that he ever learned any, or will he cut and run?

"One fairly recent crash landing brought forth examples of all of the above. One girl connected the evacuation chute, inflated it as trained, then was the first to slide to safety. Another wandered around the airplane helping where she was told, but forgetting what she had been trained to do. Another worked steadily, in her own section of the plane as well as others', saving many lives, until she was forced to leave the burning structure by one of the male crew members, who also was doing what he was trained for and was expected to do. Other male crew members on this occasion did not do what was expected of them.

"Every publicized air accident brings forth its heroes and heroines. Usually they are surviving crew members just doing their jobs; but often they are outsiders who rush in where aviators fear to tread.

"We all feel proud when a fellow professional pilot does a textbook job of ditching, or a hostess evacuates a hundred passengers safely before the fire spreads, or makes any difficult decision quickly and correctly. Some of it rubs off on all of us.

"Likewise, we all hate to hear of the incorrect, fateful decisions, the botched approaches and the ignorance which kills. Our noses are rubbed in this."

Those sobering words were directed at airline personnel, but they also could have been aimed at passengers who fail to realize that their own knowledge—rudimentary and hastily acquired as it may be—could save their lives. Such as, for example, knowing how to open an exit, or the location of the exits. No one can predict his or her reaction in an emergency. One possible result is what evacuation experts term "negative panic"—the frequent tendency of passengers to remain in their seats, frozen with fright, and actually refusing to follow evacuation orders.

In the crash of a DC-6 some years ago, twenty passengers perished—all from smoke inhalation—even though the cabin was only slightly damaged by impact and the fire itself took several minutes to reach the interior. Some of them, incredible as it may seem, were sitting next to emergency exits which they made no move to open.

Probably one reason for so-called negative panic is that aforementioned belief by so many persons in the unsurvivability of a crash—in other words, the conviction that nobody walks away from an airplane accident. As is stated elsewhere in this book, this belief simply is not true. A great many *do* walk away. True, not as many as should be able to, partially because of a strange paradox involving the superbly designed jets.

It is one of the rare inconsistencies of the jet age that in some respects, survivability is less in a modern jetliner than in older transports. The DC-6B, an airliner dating back to 1951 and carrying as few as sixty passengers, has ten exits. The Boeing 727, which can carry up to one hundred and thirty, has six, not including the rear ventral stairs, which are not really considered an emergency exit. And five of the six exits are concentrated in a six-row area of a twenty-one-row aircraft. (The stretched version of the 727, however, has eight exits, an admirable improvement.)

The Boeing 707 and DC-8, capable of hauling nearly two hundred persons, have eight each. In these latter two jets, six of the eight exits are located from midway over the wing to just behind the cockpit. This leaves two exits—the rear boarding door and rear galley door—the only exits in an area comprising almost two thirds of the fuselage length, and this same area is composed exclusively of six-abreast seating with comparatively narrow aisles. There actually are more available exits proportionate to the passenger load in the ancient DC-3 than in jets.

As a matter of fact, it could be argued that such giants as the 707 and DC-8 actually have only four real emergency exits, rather than eight. For on both planes, four of the eight exits are removable windows over the wings. These have two major disadvantages —they are too small for easy and quick egress, and they are located over the wings in the most fire-vulnerable area of the aircraft.

J. H. Grant, safety expert for Australia's Qantas Empire Airways, told a 1966 FAA conference on evacuation problems that the escape facilities on jet transports were apparently designed for rare ditching emergencies instead of the more frequent crashes that occur on land. Grant warned that too much reliance is placed on the overwing exits which are extremely efficient if a plane comes down in water, but inherently hazardous in a land crash because of proximity to the fuel stored in the wings. The Australian urged that more emergency exits be provided away from the wings, either forward or aft but preferably aft. He also remarked that passengers and crew might be made aware of the hazards of opening wing exits—which often are fire-blackened so that fire cannot be seen.

The airlines' successful demonstrations of emptying a fully loaded jet in two minutes or less (ninety seconds is the new standard) would seem to indicate that emergency facilities are adequate. They are, but only in a theoretical sense. No two crashes are alike. There has been 100 per cent survival in some landing or takeoff accidents, for example, but fatalities occurred in other low-speed crashes almost identical in circumstances. Much depends on the speed of whatever fire develops, although even this is an uncertain criterion.

How totally unpredictable survival chances can be in a jet accident is shown by comparing the 1964 crash of a TWA 707 in Rome with that of a BOAC 707 at London four years later.

In the latter case, one engine of the BOAC jet caught fire immediately after takeoff. The pilot turned around and landed even as flames enveloped one wing and spread to the fuselage. One hundred and twenty-one of the one hundred and twenty-six persons aboard got out safely; the five fatalities, all sitting in the rear, succumbed to smoke. The evacuation time took a full three minutes, one minute over the maximum survival deadline. An interesting sidelight was the behavior of some passengers using window exits over the wings. They reached the trailing edge, balked at the foreboding distance to the ground, climbed back into the cabin and evacuated through door exits, their hesitation costing them at least a minute of survival time. They can be classed as just plain lucky.

The TWA 707 at Rome aborted a takeoff and rolled to a stop on a hard runway with the landing gear intact, and no injuries or even shaking up of passengers. Unfortunately, just before the plane stopped, the right outboard engine hit a steam roller parked close to the runway. Fuel ignited. In not more than *twenty seconds*, the jet was demolished by a series of violent explosions.

There were twenty-three survivors—all of them getting out of the plane within those first twenty seconds. But forty-nine persons still inside the aircraft died from burns or smoke inhalation. As if the swiftness of the devouring flames was not bad enough, the main escape chutes (they were the old style, mounted in the ceiling instead of the doors themselves) proved difficult to operate, and one of them actually was installed backward, requiring consumption of precious seconds to get it into place. The rear galley exit proved unavailable because the fire already had seared a deadly path almost to the tail. The four window exits were blocked by flames as the wing tanks exploded progressively and with incredible speed.

There is no intention to put an onus on TWA for this particular tragedy and the circumstances which turned what should have been a totally survivable accident into a tragedy. TWA was unlucky, for if virtually any other airline in the world had been exposed to the same set of conditions at the time, the results probably would have been identical. The truth is that under some circumstances, jet emergency evacuation facilities are marginal, although new advances have been made in the form of even stricter FAA regulations and requirements instituted in September of 1967.

The new rules require the airlines to demonstrate they can empty any transport currently in operation in not more than ninety seconds, using only half the available exits. They also require:

—All passenger seatbacks to be in the upright position for takeoffs and landings (a reclined seat subjected to violent deceleration exposes the occupant to severe back injury, because of the body's position and the reduced restraint of the seat belt; reclining also would interfere with the passenger behind the seat in an evacuation).

—Cabin attendants to occupy regularly assigned seats, uniformly spaced near emergency exits, during takeoffs and landings.

—Evacuation briefing cards applying only to the aircraft being flown, not to an airline's entire jet fleet.

—No carry-on luggage permitted that cannot fit under seats.

These were regulations which went into effect almost immediately. In addition, the FAA gave the airlines from one to two years for compliance with other new rules. These include installation of improved, self-supporting and instantly inflatable slides at all doors more than six feet above ground level, rupture-proof fuel lines that are located in aircraft bellies (an offshoot of the Salt Lake City crash), more efficient emergency lighting and replacement of present cabin lining materials with those having better self-extinguishing properties.

The industry winced at a regulation calling for removal of seats in the immediate area of emergency exits. The loss of a single seat in aircraft being flown nine to fifteen hours a day can add up to hundreds of thousands of dollars in reduced revenue over a long period. The FAA-ordered modifications will cost the airlines 4 per cent of their currently available seating capacity. All in all, the Air Transport Association—which represents the scheduled U.S. airlines—estimated originally that the new rules would cost at least

$1.3 billion and as high as $2 billion in overhaul costs and lost revenue. The figure has been scaled down to $75 million, which is still a considerable chunk of cash. The industry successfully fought several proposed rules, such as the one which would have required stewardesses to hand out individual emergency instructions of the throwaway variety to every passenger that boarded—a little item that would cost approximately $1 million annually with still no assurance that passengers would read them, and presenting an additional interior fire hazard.

If anyone thinks the airlines were being overly economy-minded, we might examine just one regulation—the requirement of new door-mounted slides on all primary exits, which the airlines, incidentally, supported despite the expense. On some aircraft—the Electra, Convair 880, Convair 990 and one model of the 707—exits were not designed to use automatically deployed slides. Their doors either are not capable of accepting the additional weight of the slide, or the added weight itself would make the door extremely difficult for a stewardess to handle. Now the doors must be redesigned, at a cost of $50,000 per door.

The airlines' motives in opposing some of the new regulations or at least requesting a delay in compliance were not entirely based on economics. Cost was an important factor, naturally, but there also was a strong feeling that adoption of all the rules would not increase safety to the extent of warranting massive modification expenditures on current aircraft. Many airline safety experts held that the reforms were aimed at increasing survival chances in crashes involving fire, without attacking that major source of fatalities itself. In brief, they argued that if more energy, effort and financing were devoted to prevention of fire on impact, there would be no need for expensive cabin modifications or regulations which create a certain amount of inconvenience for passengers themselves.

This is not to say that the industry resisted all of the proposals. Some of them were backed or even originated by the airlines even though they involved some passenger inconvenience and inevitable complaints from the public, which naturally tends to blame the airline and not the federal government for such items as limitations on carry-on luggage. Early passenger resentment might have been reduced if the airlines had frankly told their customers the "why" instead of merely posting coy notices that the ban against most carry-on baggage was "required by the federal government," in a kind of "don't blame us, blame Uncle Sam." As in the case of sugar-coated instruction placards, the airlines sometimes are too loath to call a spade a spade. This is even more regrettable when the industry's over-all concern for and dedication toward safety is considered. The airlines have an unhappy tendency to apologize or remain speechless for the very achievements they so constantly make in the field of air safety. It was an airline idea, not the FAA's, for example, to lower the maximum evacuation time from two minutes to ninety seconds.

Many passengers still do not know that the new carry-on luggage regulation was purely a safety measure. They do not realize that luggage can turn into lethal missiles in sudden deceleration. To give one example, two passengers boarded a plane with bags too large to stow under any seat. The stewardess asked them to check the luggage and they refused. The aircraft later encountered turbulence. The bags, placed behind the last row of seats, flew out and injured two occupants painfully. Even bags stored under seats can be dangerous, which is why a restraint system will be required in the near future.

Likewise, there was no real attempt to explain to the public why seatbacks should be upright during landings and takeoffs— so that they won't interfere with the passenger behind you if he has to get out in a hurry, and to prevent injury in sudden deceleration. Six months after the rule went into effect, stewardesses were having to explain it to irate, balky passengers.

There is no quarrel with the FAA's "bigger stick" insofar as future airliners are concerned. The agency ruled that new aircraft must have their emergency exits uniformly distributed, with a minimum number of exits (of greater width) in ratio to the passengers carried. Boeing's mammoth 747, the so-called "jumbo jet" with a passenger capacity of nearly five hundred, will be the first transport designed with an evacuation *system* rather than the past method of installing exits almost as an afterthought with seating capacity and cabin service taking priority in aircraft design.

On the 747, for example, the main doors are forty inches wide, twice the size of the 707's doors and permitting two six-foot passengers to evacuate simultaneously via a double-size chute—which not only speeds up evacuation but provides a psychological boost for those who fear jumping alone into a chute or slide. The 747 chute inflates in five seconds. The jumbo has ten exits, only two of them over the wings. The window exits themselves are almost as big as the main doors on present jets and the cabin aisles even in the coach section are wider than those in first-class compartments on current jetliners. At least four exits are plainly visible from every seat in the plane. Finally, Boeing has designed power-operated doors that will be easier for stewardesses to open—a necessity because the 747's cockpit is not on the main cabin level, and flight deck members are not likely to be available for help in opening exits. Every door is identical in operation.

The 747, the Boeing supersonic transport and the new so-called "air buses" like the Lockheed 1011 and McDonnell-Douglas DC-10 all will have cabin walls and ceilings made of self-extinguishing plastics or fibers, such as DuPont's remarkable new Nomex. This is a honeycombed form of fiber glass that is almost as fire-resistant as asbestos. Nomex, which costs about $6 a pound, is one of several new materials which became available only about a year ago in purely experimental form—just about the time several Congressmen were attacking manufacturers and the airlines for not installing safer cabin interiors. Boeing even then was buying every conceivable kind of fabric, plastic and fiber being produced and testing them for possible use in cabins. At one time, it was even considering fireproofed toilet paper, towels and sanitary napkins!

"Hell," says one Boeing engineer, "some of the fabrics and fibers were so new nobody even knew how to process it so it could be put into an aircraft interior."

The FAA timetable calls for various safety retrofits, like improved linings for walls and ceilings, on older planes as well as requiring adoption of the new equipment on future transports. For example, interior lighting must be modified so that if a fuselage splits open, 75 per cent of the interior lighting must continue to function in both sections. All fuel and electric lines must be flexible under severe impact forces. Power cables will have to be isolated from fuel lines. All airliners will be required to carry exterior lighting so evacuated passengers can see when they get outside—there is a tendency to pause in going from a lighted interior into darkness.

All these federal regulations, plus all the new safety gimmicks such as improved slides and more informative briefing cards, are

pretty useless without the real catalyst in an airliner emergency—
the stewardess. One of the surprising developments in modern
commercial aviation is the increasingly important role of cabin
attendants in providing greater air safety.

As recently as ten years ago, some of the smaller airlines permitted a stewardess to handle a load of passengers on a DC-3
with only a single day's training. These same carriers now require a minimum of three weeks' training, approximately one
third of it spent on emergency procedures and other items directly
or indirectly related to passenger safety. The bigger carriers, with
more elaborate cabin service requirements, put their girls through
a five- to six-week course with at least one full week devoted to
emergency training—sometimes nearly two weeks.

It would provide a lot of reassurance to passengers—and an eye-
opening to the cynics who sneer about stewardesses being
glamorized cocktail waitresses—if they could actually witness today's cabin-attendant training.

Take the biggest carrier, for example—giant United. Its stewardess training center in Chicago includes mockups of every
type of plane UAL operates, and these make-believe cabins are
not for teaching meal service or how to mix cocktails. They are
solely for instruction in emergency procedures. The training includes sound effects of a crashing plane, smoke and a few other
items designed to provide maximum realism for young girls who
before they were accepted in stewardess school didn't know an
escape chute from a wing flap. A typical evacuation session will
find some girls wearing signs proclaiming "invalid" or "blind passenger"—to make sure the trainees know how to handle special
cases. It is somewhat disconcerting, as a matter of fact, for a visitor
to see a couple of trainees sporting placards that read: "PREGNANT."

The training is deadly serious. Movies of actual crashes are
shown—the FAA's hair-raising Phoenix crash tests being a frequently used visual aid. Instructors frankly discuss past accidents
and the lessons learned from them. There is a surprising and
healthy amount of sharing such information among the airlines.
Two days after a TWA 707 crashed at Cincinnati following an
aborted takeoff, details of how all the passengers were evacuated
safely were being discussed at an American Airlines stewardess
refresher course in Washington.

There has been, in the past, too wide a variance in the quality of stewardess emergency training. Some carriers paid only lip service to truly adequate education. The Training Committee of ALPA's Steward and Stewardess Division a few years ago surveyed cabin attendants of two major carriers engaged in overseas operations, delving into the quality of their initial ditching instructions. The comparison was interesting, as you can see.

| AIRLINE I | AIRLINE II |
|---|---|
| 1. Training provided explicit directions for operation of all survival equipment. | For operation and use of survival equipment, cabin attendants were told to read the directions on the container after entry into the raft. |
| 2. Thorough discussion of raftmanship. | Told to read the booklet on raftmanship contained in the storage compartment of the raft. |
| 3. Practical demonstrations of employing the raft evacuation of the aircraft plus the operation and use of survival equipment all took place at sea under realistic conditions. | Employment of the raft took place in a swimming pool. The only operation of equipment in the raft was installing the canopy. |
| 4. Designation of special duties for each crew member during evacuation was discussed thoroughly. | Designation of crew duties was not mentioned in class. |
| 5. All questions were answered and clarification made when requested. | When the instructor was asked a question, frequently he would answer "You needn't worry about that." |
| 6. Considerable time was spent on the emergency duties of flight deck members, including frequent references to available rescue facilities and navigation problems, in the event cabin attendants would be the only crew survivors in a ditching. | No time was spent on the subject with cabin crew trainees. |

The combination of FAA prodding (and the FAA admittedly was late itself in doing the prodding), some of the bitter lessons learned in accidents, and the examples set by the more enlightened and conscientious airlines brought the entire industry to the realization that inadequate training in emergency procedures bordered on criminal negligence. The jet age was a major spur, for when even the small airlines began flying bigger planes, procedures and techniques permissible in DC-3 days obviously were as outmoded as the DC-3 itself.

Even the local-service airlines today have emergency training comparable in thoroughness to what the major trunk carriers offered only five years ago—and in the important respects, it is equally thorough to the quality of instruction given by the trunk airlines. It has to be, for an airline's size does not exempt it from the FAA's insistence that all planes must be proven to be totally evacuable in not more than ninety seconds. The small carrier may lack some of the more sophisticated training aids, such as cabin mockups, but anyone sitting in on the emergency procedures course of any airline would be impressed with the curriculum.

Few passengers realize—and few airline critics bother to notice —that stewardesses are subject to the same frequency of refresher training as pilots. Twice a year, every scheduled carrier must put every stewardess through recurrent training. Usually, this takes place in the spring and again in the fall.

A typical spring session involves the actual operation of emergency equipment, from fire extinguishers to the opening of all emergency exits and activation of slides. The stewardesses themselves must go through test evacuations. One of these sessions lasts as long as six hours. The fall session is mostly a verbal briefing on new or improved procedures, a review of old ones, and a stiff written test—approximately fifty questions. If a stewardess misses only seven questions, she takes the test over again until she passes —or she is grounded for individual reinstruction.

TWA invested several hundred thousand dollars in a "safety school on wheels"—a mobile classroom transported by trailer truck to the airline's hostess bases at Los Angeles, San Francisco, Chicago, Boston, New York and Newark, for recurrent training sessions.

The classroom van is fitted with doors and overwing exits from every type of aircraft TWA operates, plus ceiling life rafts from

Boeing 707 overseas equipment. There also are seven rows of seats and a large screen for showing safety slides and movies.

Airline recurrent training usually is conducted in whatever lay-over aircraft are available, which means the sessions often are held after midnight when girls are likely to be tired and not as attentive. The mobile trainer concept permits the same training at better hours and with smaller groups at one time—advantages being examined by other airlines who may follow TWA's lead. Whatever the classroom or whenever the training is held, it is another good example of the "other two thirds of the iceberg" that the public never sees.

I went through a recurrent training course—this one happened to be American's—held in an FAA conference room at Washington's National Airport. Twenty of American's one hundred and five stewardesses based in Washington were attending this particular class. The other eighty-five would receive recurrent training over the next three days as they came off regular trips.

The instructor was Harriet "Clancie" Henderson, manager of American's stewardess service at the Washington base and one of the most effective teachers of "what to do when everything hits the fan" in the airline industry. It was Miss Henderson who provided one of aviation's classic lines when a young stewardess asked her why passengers couldn't use the cockpit emergency exits.

"Because when all hell breaks loose, they'll be full of pilot butts," Clancie explained logically.

On this occasion, she opened by distributing floor plans of the three aircraft types to which Washington-based girls are assigned —the 727, the BAC-111 and the Electra. (If any of these steward-esses were transferred to a base using different equipment, such as the 707 or Convair 990, they would have to be retrained before they were allowed to fly trips.)

"You all know why you're here," Clancie began. "To make sure you know what to do in a few minutes or even seconds to assure the safety of the greatest number of passengers possible. And I mean seconds. If something goes wrong with no warning, you won't have time to look up procedures in your manual. One year ago, when some of you attended a similar session, I reminded you we had two minutes to get everybody off your airplane. Now that survival time has been cut to ninety seconds.

"There will be a test at the end of our discussion. Don't panic.

It's not something to worry you, but to help you. To make certain you have a good feeling, a confident feeling, right in your guts. Just this morning, one of our 400's [American's designation of the BAC-111] had gear trouble coming into National. The boys had to crank the gear down by hand and even with the green lights showing, they weren't sure it would hold when they touched down. So the captain told the girls to prepare the passengers for possible trouble. These happened to be New York-based girls. But they could be any two of you going on a trip tomorrow morning.

"If you have any question, even if it seems stupid and you're embarrassed to ask it, go ahead and ask. It may save somebody's life someday. And remember, never has an American Airlines stewardess let the rest of her crew down in an emergency."

Miss Henderson, a tall, attractive brunette who flew the line for ten years before she became a supervisor, then reviewed the new FAA regulations regarding evacuation equipment and procedures. The revised before-takeoff cabin PA requiring the admonition that all seats must be upright ("We used to leave sleeping passengers alone," Clancie warned, "but now you wake them up if their seats aren't upright as required") . . . the new luggage carry-on rules . . . the forthcoming regulation requiring a small barricade underneath every seat to prevent baggage from sliding forward in a sudden stop . . . tie-downs for crew luggage ("Until these are installed, stewardesses must put their own suitcases under whatever seats are available").

Some of the items warranted brief discussion and questions. It was mentioned that if a passenger brings a dog aboard in a carrying case, the case must fit under the seat or the dog goes into the baggage compartment.

"Every cloud has its silver lining," Clancie chuckled. "American made some lovely pet-carrying cases available to passengers but now they're verboten because they're too big. So we're using them for storing ladies' wigs in the baggage bins."

From the new FAA rules, the class went on to the subject of emergency medical treatment for passengers. In the past eight months, Clancie told her girls, American flew eight million customers. There were one hundred and thirty-four slips and falls, thirteen of them inside the aircraft. Twenty passengers received burns, from spilled hot drinks or cigarette lighter flareups. There also were five fatal heart attacks.

"Be alert to potential troubles," Miss Henderson advised. "Such as telling people not to walk around in turbulence, or—and I'd like to have a dollar for everytime it happens—going to the lavatory just before landing."

Self-protection also was brought up. The instructor recited the sad tale of stewardess injuries during the same eight months—sixty-eight blocked ears ("Don't fly if you have a cold"), twenty-three hurt in turbulence, twenty-one struck by equipment (usually buffet), thirteen caught on equipment (again, usually buffet), five falls and four girls injured by lifting heavy items.

"Stewardesses are only nine per cent of American's total employees," Clancie noted, "but they suffer thirty-five per cent of employee injuries." (A recent industry survey disclosed an annual injury rate of 7 per cent among stewardesses.)

She recounted the various symptoms of ailments that may require emergency medical treatment by a stewardess—hyperventilation (too much oxygen), shock, diabetic stupors or comas, epileptic seizures, strokes, heart attacks and so forth—plus the required treatment. Samples:

"There is no way to stop an epileptic attack. Your only responsibility is to protect the afflicted passenger from himself. Keep him as secure as possible, because when he starts thrashing around in a fit, his strength is unbelievable. You may have to call on other passengers for help—if they will help. One of our own girls had a passenger go into an epileptic fit a few months ago and couldn't get anyone to help her. She did fine by herself but when it was all over and the victim recovered, another passenger came up, introduced himself as a doctor, and wanted to know if there was anything he could do. In addition to restraint, the most important thing to do is prevent the epileptic from swallowing his tongue. Put something in his mouth like a metal spoon wrapped in a towel or napkin . . .

"You may very well encounter a mental patient. Don't argue with one. Don't try to restrain him physically. Don't speak to him in harsh or authoritative tones. Make sure the cockpit is locked—that's a must, so some nut can't get into the cockpit. Do advise the captain what's going on. Treat the patient with respect, kindness and reassurance. Try to keep him from harmful acts. Be firm and positive, though—in other words, handle him as you would a drunk."

Miss Henderson got out a medical kit and removed each item,

explaining the function of every one. Then she went into planned emergencies—where cabin attendants get sufficient warning of trouble to prepare passengers for a possible crash landing. She drew laughs as she recalled the three rules of her own early days of flying—"check the lavatories, check your personal appearance and get out the passenger inconvenience forms." But then she became serious.

". . . if you have time to prepare for an emergency, if you know what you're doing and you keep calm, there is no reason for injury to a single passenger. Given sufficient time, everything is working for you and those in your trust. Our pilots are trained to bring your bird down in one piece even with no landing gear."

Now the training session got rougher. Clancie began firing questions. She had one stewardess read the required PA announcement prior to an emergency landing. The girl's voice was soft, hesitant and uncertain as she stumbled over obviously unfamiliar words.

"How many of you have ever read this PA aloud?" Miss Henderson asked.

No one raised her hand. Clancie shook her head.

"I cannot stress too often the importance of hearing your own voice under what might be emergency conditions," she scolded. "You've got to be loud and forceful. I'm not criticizing the girl who just read that PA. All of you admitted you've never tried saying it aloud, in practice. Lock yourself in your bathroom if your roommate laughs at you. Don't trust to luck in any phase of emergency procedures. The chances are that not a single girl in this room or this base will ever have to make that PA. But this doesn't mean you shouldn't be prepared to make it. Even a person accustomed to public speaking will stumble over unfamiliar words."

Another stewardess had to tell how she'd instruct a passenger on opening the main cabin door of a BAC-111. A third was told to make believe she was advising a passenger on the right way to open a window exit. Another simulated the briefing of a crippled passenger.

Now the class proceeded to unplanned emergencies and the questions came at the girls like machine-gun bullets.

How do you handle an incapacitated passenger in a crash landing? . . . What do you do in case of an in-flight cabin fire? . . . Where are the emergency stations for the first stewardess . . . second . . . third? . . .

Then came the written test. Questions like:

During your briefing for a planned belly landing in a 727, where would you tell a passenger sitting in 19A to try to evacuate first?

If there is a planned emergency on a fully loaded 727 and you are the fourth stewardess, where will you sit during the actual landing and state why you answered as you did?

On a 727, how many passengers will the third stewardess specifically brief on how to operate exits?

You notice a passenger in a stuporous, incoherent condition resembling intoxication, but he did not have a drink. What do these symptoms indicate and how would you apply emergency treatment?

If, during a briefing for an anticipated emergency landing, you find a child or woman sitting next to a window exit, what would you do?

What would your first action be if you suddenly felt your aircraft swerve off the runway during a routine landing?

What is the first command you give after a crashing aircraft comes to a halt and before evacuating the passengers?

Under what conditions will passengers be allowed to re-enter a disabled aircraft?

If time permits where would you seat incapacitated passengers?

What do you do if an evacuation slide fails to inflate?

And so on. Pencils and pens scribbled away. Clancie and another supervisor graded the papers swiftly. One girl got eight wrong answers, muttered "God, I'm stupid," and started taking the test all over again. The second time, she missed only two. Clancie went over the two wrong answers with her and pointed out her mistakes. The big conference room was empty by now, stale with cigarette smoke. The last stewardess left. Clancie slumped into a chair, lit a cigarette and sighed: "Well, tomorrow another batch. I'm tired, but it's so damned important that they learn."

The class started at 1 P.M. The time was now 6:25 P.M. Outside, jet engines spooled up as planes waddled away from the ramp area.

The chances were good that the stewardesses aboard those planes, fresh-faced kids so saucy in their stylish uniforms, knew what to do if "everything hits the fan," as Clancie Henderson likes to put it. The record of the stewardess profession in actual emergencies is a proud one, and includes more than one instance in which stewardesses have sacrificed their lives to save passengers.

The interest of cabin attendants in air safety, particularly in such areas as better evacuation methods and equipment, would astound the average passenger. The stewardess division of the Air Line Pilots Association, for example, has a separate air safety forum held in conjunction with the pilots' annual safety meeting. The girl's sessions include films, lectures on safety problems, discussions of latest safety developments and—most important—a sharing of information that transcends the natural rivalry among airlines and their personnel. Sample: a United training official delivering a thirty-minute talk on UAL's training methods to stewardesses representing not only United but Braniff, Western, Allegheny, Mohawk, Air West and numerous other carriers.

The seriousness and dedication of the girls has impressed every government and industry official who attended their safety forum. In one of the 1968 sessions at Seattle, an FAA expert on cabin safety finished a lecture on the new regulations and asked for questions. For one solid hour, he was interrogated on such items as the questionable security of some stewardess jump seats, how does FAA think cabin attendants should handle the increasing number of pot-smoking hippies flying between Los Angeles and San Francisco, is the FAA enforcing rules requiring a minimum number of stewardesses in proportion to the total passengers carried, and the increasing propensity of passengers to stuff garment bags with heavy objects—thus making the bags potentially lethal objects when placed in overhead racks.

"I showed up expecting to teach these kids something," the FAA man said later. "I learned more from them than they did from me."

Curtis McKay, FAA air carrier operations specialist who has appeared at several stewardess safety conventions, wryly complained once that his attendance invariably results in an increased workload.

"As soon as their safety forum is over," he commented, "I go back to Washington and write twenty or thirty letters to carriers based on what the girls have reported, complained about or questioned. If anyone told me a stewardess was just a glorified waitress I'd belt him."

It also would reassure passengers if they were privileged, and the word "privileged" is used deliberately, to witness one of the

FAA-required demonstrations for ninety-second evacuation. They would be impressed with the thoroughness and seriousness of the tests. The shrill, almost grating orders of the stewardesses to "Jump and sit! Jump and sit!" The cameras recording the entire process, so airline safety officials can study the evacuation flow and correct any flaws. The debriefing session after the tests, where the cabin attendants are questioned politely but intently by airline and FAA personnel on what went right and what, if anything, went wrong. The solemn responses of the stewardesses, perhaps quietly but firmly questioning a technique or a certain piece of equipment that proved too hard to activate. The playback of tape recorders strategically placed in the cabin to judge passenger reaction—including the plaintive, rather chilling cry of an eight-year-old boy calling out, "Daddy, don't leave me!" . . .

The real Achilles' heel in crash survival today is not so much the cabin attendant or the aircraft itself, but the passenger. His frequent apathy plus his ignorance of apathy's consequences is something the airlines have yet to overcome. The next time you fly and the stewardess delivers her suggestion that the placards be studied, look around and see how many of your fellow passengers are following her advice. I've done this frequently on flights and never recorded more than two or three fellow passengers looking at the cards. Maybe it was a case of the majority knowing all about the exits and emergency procedures, but it would be a pretty good bet that not one passenger in ten or even twenty could pass any test on same. And some passengers actually resent the rules put into effect for their own safety. I saw one stewardess, at first politely and then firmly, ask a man to put his seat forward before a landing. He growled, protested and cursed and his seat went forward only when the stewardess pushed the button herself. As soon as her back was turned, he reclined the seat back a few inches in a childish gesture of independence. He got away with it, but if an FAA inspector has been aboard, the stewardess could have lost her job because of his stupidity and arrogance. And in an accident, he might have lost his own life and that of the person sitting in back of him.

Dr. Chator Mason, a University of Southern California psychologist who has made special studies of human behavior under panic, is one expert who devoutly believes in the importance of safety messages—even to the point of suggesting that stewardesses might have to jolt passengers into attention. He told the 1968 convention of ALPA's stewardess division about a cabin attendant who announced at the start of a flight:

"You've heard a lot of misinformation about air safety. Here is the right information."

"I don't think there was a person on the plane who didn't look up, and then listen carefully," Mason added. "The point is, she gave a different announcement. When people hear the same message over and over again, they not only will ignore it but they may even become hostile."

The arrogance of some passengers and their resistence to safety briefings, according to Mason, could well be a manifestation of inherent fear. He cited psychological research which established a definite correlation between anger and fear, indicating that the very passenger who sullenly resents or ignores the briefing is likely to be the one who will panic. Other Mason observations:

"If a stewardess encounters a balky, difficult passenger, the best weapon is to tell him quietly: 'Okay, it's your responsibility if something happens.'"

"The airlines must realize that their passengers have a built-in anxiety, the anxiety of just getting to where they're going, which isn't true of any other form of transportation."

"One problem stewardesses have to face is male ego. The average man is afraid to look scared, which means that in an emergency he'll just sit and wait for somebody else to act."

Mason's favorite stunt is to shock an audience into displaying unexpected fright. He did this at the 1968 stewardess safety forum; he was talking quietly about panic reactions when he suddenly pulled a gun out of his pocket and fired two blanks into the air. While the girls' heartbeats were returning to normal, he explained that their reaction was typical of human response to a fright stimulus.

"Your body make-up actually changed," he went on. "Physiological and psychological changes were involved to such an extent that in actuality, you were carrying around brand-new bodies. And this is what can happen in an aircraft emergency. When you are afraid, you literally get a new body trying to react to a new experience and the result can be entirely different or even confused reactions. Fear can restrict attention and even limit vision. This is why most people faced with panic need leadership. They

tend to fix their attention on one single means of survival even
though that means may not be the best one. This explains why
passengers in a crash landing often ignore open exits, or more
available exits than the exits they choose. Fear is a form of regres-
sion, a loss of adult reactions.

"Any person can panic, and the ingredients of panic are mostly
lack of information and where to go or what to do. People do
best in an emergency situation when they recognize reality, so
don't hold back information."

Apathetic passenger reactions to briefings that could save lives is
beginning to concern the airlines. Air Canada and Trans Carib-
bean have been experimenting with the use of forceful male voices,
recorded on tape, which seems to achieve the dual purpose of
delivering varied messages and attracting attention. National also
has been using recorded safety announcements, employing the
voice of the girl in NAL's television commercials ("Is this any way
to run an airline? You bet it is!"). National's stewardesses say the
gimmick has resulted in considerably increased attention because
the professional model used in the tapes has a distinctive, rather
loud and attention-getting delivery.

Air safety experts are encouraged by the record of passenger
survival percentages in jet crashes that have occurred over the
past two years. No conclusive figures are available, but there is a
general impression that the survival rate is increasing. Even so,
an examination of actual accidents tends to show that survival
can be a matter of luck as well as adequate facilities and superb
crew training. Typical was the crash of a U.S. jetliner on foreign
soil in June of 1968; the majority of those aboard got away safely,
but the margin for many was unpleasantly thin.

The accident itself stemmed from an erroneous altimeter setting.
The jet came in for a landing approach in bad weather about
five hundred feet lower than the captain thought it was, resulting
in impact short of the runway. The landing still might have been
made safely if it were not for a last-second lowering of visibility
in rain that wiped out the view of the runway.

The cockpit crew all suffered minor injuries (the captain sustained a broken back) mostly because they had neglected to
wear their shoulder harnesses.

In the first-class area, the senior stewardess waited until the
plane stopped rolling, then ran to the main entry door and opened

it with some difficulty. She heaved out the chute but did not inflate it, turning instead to aid a two-hundred-and-sixty-pound passenger who had been tossed almost into the cockpit when his seat belt failed. The burly man was only half-conscious, lying helplessly on the floor with numerous broken ribs, a broken leg and his pants hanging unceremoniously around his ankles.

The flight deck crew already had evacuated, jumping out of hastily opened cockpit windows into soft mud twelve feet below. The copilot and flight engineer staggered back to the main door and saw the uninflated slide. They shouted to the stewardess, "Pull the handle!" but she still was trying to tug the injured passenger out from under debris. The copilot climbed up the chute, hand over hand like a man going up a rope, but just as he got to the door the stewardess finally pulled the inflation handle. The slide ballooned out, knocking the copilot back into the mud.

The stewardess stationed by the forward galley door opened it quickly. The only passenger in sight was a young girl running back and forth in the first-class cabin, crying frantically for her parents. The stewardess grabbed the youngster and went out the main entry door. Meanwhile, the senior stewardess managed to pull the injured passenger to the same door and rolled him into the slide. She went back to the cabin, remembering that an infant had been in a bassinet hanging on the partition that separated the first-class and coach areas. Flames from the left wing started shooting through the cabin windows and smoke was filling the cabin. There was no sign of the baby (who already had been evacuated by his parents), so the senior stewardess jumped into the main-door chute.

Most of the passengers and two other stewardesses left the burning plane via one of the right-hand overwing emergency exits. The window exits over the left wing were unused because of the fire. The two stewardesses who went out through the right wing exit said later that when they decided to evacuate, with no more passengers visible, the cabin was in pitch blackness. They were unable to tell whether the emergency lights were knocked out or merely obscured by smoke.

A fourth stewardess, seated in the last row of the coach section, ran to the main rear entry door after the plane stopped. She could not move the door handle. A husky male passenger tried to help her but their combined efforts failed to budge the door.

Another passenger managed to open the rear galley door on the left side but flames blocked the way. The stewardess again tried in vain to open the main door on the other side. She then attempted to go toward the wing exits but the cabin aisle was clogged with seat cushions, debris from the overhead bins and other debris. A passenger grabbed her arm and literally threw her out of the rear galley door, which fortunately was only four feet above the ground. The stewardess and the passenger who tossed her out the door somehow found a way through the fire and ran to safety.

The senior stewardess was the last to leave the plane, the other fifty-five survivors evacuating before the fire ate into the cabin. Seven persons, including the purser, did not get out. Their bodies were found in the rear cabin. The victims either were stunned by the impact or were trapped by collapsed seats, a buckled floor or the considerable debris torn loose by the crash. They also might have been victims of panic or shock, although this was not likely in the case of the purser.

Despite the fortunately high survival percentage, this was not an example of a smoothly coordinated emergency evacuation. A single seriously injured passenger had distracted and occupied the attention of a stewardess to the point where she failed to perform a primary function: inflating a main slide. Significantly, this exit was used by only two persons—the stewardess and the injured passenger. The other main exit apparently had been deformed by impact forces and was useless. Only one of the two galley doors, also classed as main exits, was used and this by just two persons who jumped out of it in sheer desperation. If the right wing had caught fire as did the left, there is no telling what the death toll might have been; certainly it would have been much higher unless the passengers, by instinct or verbal direction, had gravitated toward the two main exits in the forward cabin.

Aside from demonstrating what can go wrong in an emergency, the accident also underscored the biggest factor in crash fatalities: fire, which is the major menace of them all. To quote Jerome Lederer, former director of the Flight Safety Foundation:

"Prevention of fire on impact deserves the same priority in aviation as did the Manhattan Project, which developed the first atomic bomb."

# 7

## FIRE AWAY

The problem is simple.

When a plane crashes, impact forces can tear open fuel tanks. The fuel thus is released in large quantities. This sudden and massive release results in rapid vaporization into a fine mist as the fuel instantly mixes with oxygen. All that is needed is an ignition source—and this is supplied with deadly ease. Just a spark generated by the friction of torn metal scraping a runway or other metal. Or the enormous heat from engines that have been operating at high temperatures, these white-hot components coming in contact with the fuel spray at impact.

It is the vaporization of the fuel into fine particles that creates the biggest hazard. It doesn't make much difference whether the fuel has low volatility. A static electricity charge has been known to explode wheat flour dust. To cite a further example, a fuel tank containing only a residue of fumes is far more vulnerable to lightning ignition than a full tank, which as far as anyone knows is lightning-proof. Powdered aluminum also burns rapidly in air.

The action of ignition on fuel spray is so instantaneous (it has been estimated at less than two tenths of a second) that the fire actually is more of an explosion. On one type of jet fuel (JP-4), which is now seldom used, the spread of flame after ignition was clocked at two feet per second.

Fire does more than sear. It creates heat and smoke—both killers. Tests by the Flight Safety Foundation and the Air Line Pilots Association a few years ago revealed that fire enveloping an airliner cabin can raise interior temperatures to two thousand degrees in less than three minutes.

The FSF experiment involved a deliberately crashed helicopter carrying only forty gallons of fuel. Within thirty seconds after impact, those forty gallons of burning fuel had raised the temperatures inside the helicopter fuselage from sixty degrees to nine hundred and fifty. In another ten seconds, the temperatures climbed to one thousand, seven hundred and forty degrees. This is sufficient to char the human lung into cinders with one whiff.

Heat propagation inside the more insulated cabin of an airliner would be less rapid, but not to any significant extent. The more recent ALPA tests, conducted at Cleveland, recorded 2000° F temperatures inside a transport-type aircraft, reached in less than two minutes.

The ability of the modern airliner structure to withstand severe impact exceeds the belief of most laymen. It is theoretically possible for the majority of passengers to survive the majority of crashes because the airframe stays relatively intact. And perhaps not so theoretically.

A special ALPA committee recently studied a total of six hundred and eighty-two accidents involving the five largest U.S. airlines between 1938 and 1961. The committee was surprised to discover that nearly five hundred of the crashes, or 73 per cent of the total, resulted in *no* fatalities even though the aircraft were substantially damaged or totally destroyed!

Add to those statistics the fact that most airliner accidents take place during the landing or takeoff phases of flight, occurring at such relatively low speeds that survival is possible. It cannot be repeated too often that fire is the murderer in otherwise survivable accidents.

The CAB's old Bureau of Safety once analyzed sixty-one landing and takeoff crashes involving airliners over an eleven-year span. The sixty-one crashes took two hundred and forty-five passenger lives out of the total of five hundred and forty-three aboard, or 45 per cent.

But of the two hundred and forty-five fatalities, two hundred and twenty-one died as the result of fire or smoke inhalation. Add this number to the 55 per cent survival total and the survival rate would have been a whopping 96 per cent! Only twenty-four of the fatalities were due to the force of impact, injuries from the collapsing aircraft structure, from the deceleration forces or from flying objects torn loose in rapid deceleration.

It is plain, therefore, that fire is the prime enemy of air safety and that prevention or suppression of fire after impact theoretically could have saved at least nine out of every ten lives lost in previous crashes. The figure for future accidents is something that can only be estimated, but it seems logical to assume that when the fire menace is reduced or even eliminated, fatality totals could be cut by anywhere from 50 to 90 per cent if the accident occurs at a low enough rate of speed to permit *any* survival.

It is to aviation's discredit—airline and government alike—that so little has been done in the past to conquer post-impact fire. Up until three years ago, there was very little research under way in this vital area. Most of it involved experiments in spraying hot engine parts with water or a fire-extinguishing chemical, the application being made automatically or manually on impact. The tests were mildly promising, but the so-called water inertia systems were like using aspirin against a major disease. For one thing, engines are not the only way of igniting spilled fuel. Also, the water inertia system contains an element of hazard on its own. Inadvertently activated, for example, the system could deprive a pilot of his power. Furthermore, such a system would be useless to prevent post-impact fire on the rapidly increasing family of rear-engine jets whose fuel is stored in the belly and in engine-less wings.

But if past research was dilatory, lackadaisical and even feeble, current efforts are not. There is almost as much attention being paid to the fire problem today as in prevention of air collisions. There has been no real break-through, but the outlook is promising and optimistic.

For a brief time, aviation authorities were hopeful that post-impact fires would be lessened considerably by the increasing use of jet fuel, which is supposed to be far less volatile than high-octane gasoline.

In a technical sense, it is. Most jet fuel is kerosene, which has a lower flash point than gasoline. But even with this lesser volatility, according to a military study covering ten years of crashes involving jet-powered transports, nearly 70 per cent of the accidents resulted in fire.

The sad truth is that while kerosene *is* less volatile than gasoline, once it is ignited the flame propagation is almost as swift. For some time, the airlines used a fuel that blended kerosene with gasoline, the type known as JP-4. The blend is considerably more volatile than kerosene and airline usage has dwindled almost to the vanishing point, partially because of a strong anti-JP-4 campaign waged by the Airways Club. This organization, composed of frequent air travelers, virtually lobbied JP-4 out of existence. Some of the airlines' ever ready critics charged that the industry used JP-4 for economic reasons, a ridiculous assertion because the fuel in reality was more expensive than kerosene. The chief reason for its widespread consumption was its availability in foreign countries, where JP-1 (also known as Jet-A or regular kerosene) was harder to obtain. Even the Air Force succumbed to the heat of the controversy, switching Air Force One (the Presidential jet) from JP-4 to Jet-A. In truth, there is very little difference between JP-4 and kerosene from a safety standpoint. Fire can start a little more easily with the former, and spread more rapidly, but not to any appreciable extent of increased survival time, which is the most important factor of all.

Irving Pinkel, a fuel expert with the National Aeronautics and Space Administration (NASA), addressed the 1966 ALPA Safety Forum in the middle of the JP-4-vs-kerosene battle and in so many words told the delegates that the controversy was ridiculous.

Pinkel conceded that a lower-volatility fuel might be a little harder to ignite and slower to spread. But he added that the severity of a post-impact fire depends largely on the size of the spillage pattern; any fuel, once ignited, burns fast.

The goal, of course, is to *contain* fuel in a crash—to keep it from mixing with oxygen and forming the deadly mist so susceptible to ignition. And containment research has been concentrated in two areas—prevention of spillage and prevention of the vaporizing that follows spillage.

A fuel tank virtually impervious to crash forces is not beyond the realm of achievement. Such tanks have been built and tested under the most severe conditions.

An Army-sponsored research program, for example, came up with promising developments in plastic-lined fuel cells. In one test, a C-45 was equipped with multi-ply nylon tanks bonded with polyurethane. The aircraft's wing struck a telephone pole at nearly one hundred miles an hour, the impact occurring directly at the center of the tank and compressing it to almost 50 per cent of its depth. Not a drop of fuel leaked. Nor did the same tank when it was placed in a helicopter deliberately crashed at forces exceeding one hundred Gs—almost ten times the maximum impact strength involved in landing or takeoff accidents considered survivable. The tank even resisted penetration by jagged metal.

The Army also tried out a similar material with a felt core and a surface of thermoplastic film that worked equally as well. In one staged crash, a full tank from a C-45 was thrown completely clear of its wing structure and landed six feet away, with no leakage. The Army then put a fuel-filled tank lined with the same felt core and plastic film on a helicopter, positioning it between a cargo floor load and large boulders attached to the bottom of the "chopper." The helicopter was then dropped from a large tower-structure with vertical crash forces surpassing one hundred Gs. Again, no leaks—and Army scientists estimated that even this severe crash environment utilized less than 20 per cent of the tank's crash-worthiness potential.

The Boeing SST probably will have the world's first ruptureproof fuel tanks. Boeing plans to line the inboard wing tanks—those closest to the fuselage—with a honeycombed surface made of a special plastic. This, combined with the fire-resistant qualities of titanium itself (Boeing tests showed that fire capable of burning through conventional aluminum cannot penetrate a titanium skin lined with plastic), should make the SST the ultimate in crash-worthiness.

The honeycombed fuel tank is another promising possibility—the same structural principle as an egg carton. The tank merely is strengthened by the addition of a honeycombed aluminum structure placed inside. The added weight penalty is only 2 per cent and there is surprisingly little loss of storage space. Flight Safety Foundation tests showed that a honeycombed tank resists impact damage and prevents fuel spraying to a dramatic extent, but with one big disadvantage. This type of tank structure seems to be a breeding ground for bacteria and fungi which can contaminate fuel and cause hazardous loss of power. The latter problem could be licked by a special additive developed by the Phillips Petroleum Co. and now being used by both the military and commercial aviation in increasing volume.

But specially constructed fuel tanks are not likely for wide adoption because they probably would require expensive and difficult structural modifications to the current airline fleet. The jetliner has what is known as "wet wings"—meaning that the wings themselves are the fuel containers. There actually are no fuel tanks as such on jets like the 707 or DC-8. The so-called "tanks" are merely partitions in the wings themselves, and to insert actual tanks, cells or bladders inside the wings would mean the literal reconstruction of every wing, not to mention possibly severe weight penalties depending on the types of rupture-proof tanks used. It may seem callous to regard a weight penalty in the same breath as saving lives, but weight can be a hazard, too, as well as an economic factor involving pay load.

To a certain extent, the wings of the big jets are remarkably immune from impact damage. There are numerous cases on record where jets have crash-landed without fire developing, principally because of wing strength. At least two Boeing 707s have made wheels-up landings with no serious fire results. This is a strong testimony to the structural integrity of the wings, for on jets like the 707, whose engines are suspended *below* the aircraft's belly line, the engines must touch the ground when the landing gear is not lowered. At best, however, the ability of a jet wing to stay intact is relatively chancy, depending on the circumstances of the crash. In some accidents, fire erupts immediately; in others, the wing has stayed intact.

And this brings us to the most hopeful development of all in the field of fuel containment and fire prevention—the so-called gelling process.

The flammability of any petroleum fuel depends on two factors —the rate of vapor release and the size of the fuel's particles. Fuel gelling, which is simply the addition of a jelly-like substance to the fuel, controls both these factors by reducing the rate of vapor release and preventing the fuel particles from breaking down into a spray or mist.

Science has known for some time that either gelled or emulsified fuel has a drastically lower burning rate. Even raw JP-4, the most volatile of all jet fuels, has been kept under control by the addition of only 2 per cent gel. Higher percentages rendered the fuel almost impossible to ignite. To cite one experiment, addition of a 2 per cent gel reduced flame propagation by 90 per cent— from 1.22 feet per second to .11 feet per second.

The slow-burning quality of a gelled fuel is only one of its advantages. It also prevents the sudden release of fuel in large quantities that normally would form an instantaneous mass of spray as soon as it combines with oxygen. This was demonstrated dramatically in the second of the FAA's 1964 Phoenix crash tests.

On September 3 of that year, FAA and FSF technicians sent a four-engine Constellation speeding down a four-thousand-foot runway at Deer Valley Airport, the nose gear hooked ingeniously to a railroad track to keep the plane rolling straight. It smashed into a series of strategically placed barriers, crumpling the wings, buckling the fuselage in two places and draping the old airliner over a small hill like a gigantic beached shark.

The Connie had once flown TWA's world routes and cost the FAA $38,000. But when science executed this once proud queen of the airways, it was a well-spent $38,000. The plane itself carried only enough fuel (fifty gallons) to traverse the obstacle course. The two outer wing tanks were filled with colored water (yellow and green) simulating high-octane fuel. The two inboard tanks also contained water, dyed burgundy, but to which had been added a gelled substance.

When the two hundred and fifty test observers reached the aircraft's broken carcass, they saw plainly what the gelled water had achieved. Rocks and sand over a wide area were stained yellow and green and the right side of the fuselage was almost saturated with both colors. Yet the wine-colored spillage from the gelled tanks was in a relatively small area, confined mainly to the wings themselves and trailing behind the wreckage in a slim path. In fact, the left side of the fuselage was virtually free of any stain even though it was adjacent to a gelled tank that had burst open. If the water in the outboard tanks had been real fuel, there would have been an explosion on impact that would have engulfed at least one side of the cabin.

Impact occurred at one hundred and fifteen miles an hour. There were twenty-one adult dummies and three dolls aboard, the latter serving as simulated infants. Engineers who inspected the interior after the crash said only two of the large dummies and one doll would have been real-life fatalities. They were in an area immediately behind the cockpit, where the floor collapsed and drove their seats downward with violent force. (It is interesting to note that the fuselage buckled at precisely the two points predicted by engineers before the test; in fact, the night before the experimental crash reporters were handed diagrams of what the wreckage probably would look like the following day. The actual photographs of the crashed Constellation were perfect reproductions of the advance drawings.)

As has been the case with so many proposals for greater air safety, fuel gelling appeared to be the golden panacea for reducing or even eliminating post-crash fires. But it was quickly apparent that its adoption was not to be accomplished easily. While large quantities of jet fuel could be gelled almost instantly, its presence in a working turbine engine was the equivalent of putting large amounts of sugar into an automobile gas tank. The problem was how to gell fuel without causing at best drastically reduced engine performance, and at worst causing engine failure.

One method studied in early experiments was the installation of auxiliary tanks, the idea being that when a crash was inevitable, a pilot could initiate the gelling process by pushing a button or level. The gelling substance would then be injected into the fuel tanks. The obvious disadvantage was the necessary amount of complicated pumping equipment. As one expert put it sadly, "We'd need plumbing of the Rube Goldberg variety."

Another suggestion was to gell the fuel in the tanks themselves, but separate the gel from the fuel before it entered the engines. This, too, would require some intricate hardware beyond present technological means. The most recent experiments have involved gelling fuel in small enough proportions so that power input is not affected, yet retaining the control of volatility and the reduction of both spray and misting. Mostly, it is a matter of increasing the pressure that sends fuel from the tanks through jet injector nozzles into the engines.

Army experiments showed that a gelled fuel capable of resisting spray could be passed through injector nozzles with less than a 3 per cent increase in the pressure required for ungelled fuel. Jet engines of the type used on commercial planes have been ground-tested with gelled JP-4. FAA technicians reported no loss of power, although there was some rise in fuel temperature at various stages of compression. The FAA also has awarded research contracts for various fuel additives promising volatility control without changing the liquid state of fuel even infinitesimally.

Emulsified fuel may be even more efficient than the gelling process. The latter involves enclosing liquid fuel in a gel substance, while emulsification disperses one liquid in another, namely the fuel. An emulsified fuel does not require the higher pressure of

gelling, it is easier to make and it has even slower flame propagation than gelling. Monsanto and Esso tests have shown the propagation rate of an emulsified fuel to be one hundred and fifteen
times slower than that of JP-4. Emulsifying at present has two
major disadvantages, however: it reduces usable fuel tank space
by 25 per cent, and it would add at least $60 million a year
to airline fuel costs.

On February 22, 1968, the Army actually flew a piston-powered
helicopter using emulsified fuel and then deliberately crashed the
copter. The flight lasted only thirty minutes, which was not
considered long enough to determine the fuel's propulsion characteristics. In the remote-controlled crash, however, various fire-
resistant devices worked extremely well. The fuel itself was in a
nylon-lined tank and the fuel lines had special seals. The impact
was severe—about forty-five feet per second, which is survivable
but enough to result normally in post-impact fire. The fuel lines
were torn loose but not a drop of fuel leaked through the seals;
likewise, the tank did not break open. Further tests were planned
for helicopters not equipped with special tanks and fuel lines,
to see if the emulsified fuel would resist ignition and flame-spread-
ing.

Various types of foam have long been regarded as an anti-fire
device in aviation—the technique of foaming runways, for example,
in cases of wheels-up landings has been used many times. The
foam provides a kind of cooling cushion that prevents friction
between the aircraft's metal underbelly and engines and the runway
itself.

More recently there has been interesting and in some ways
promising research into the practicality of using foam as an interior
fire suppressor.

The foam method, as applied to cabin fires, is not new. Eastern
has a Bliss system installed at its Miami overhaul base, a roll-up
unit that can be connected instantly to a cabin. The foam is
forced into the interior through a chute. Eastern ordered the device
after a jet undergoing overhaul was ruined by a fire.

But the manufacturer, the E. W. Bliss Co., believes the system's
greatest utility would be its employment as a fire suppressant
in the event of a crash. In effect, the foam—released in an aircraft interior—traps existing cabin air into breathable bubbles and
thus theoretically increases survival time by several minutes or

more. The Bliss system would fill a DC-8 or 707 cabin completely in thirty seconds, ejecting its foam from a series of generators that shoot compressed air through a detergent solution carried in tanks.

Bliss, late in November of 1967, staged a demonstration of the system. Four employees sat in a 707 cabin mockup that was filled with foam. None of the four reported any discomfort.

"Breathing the stuff isn't pleasant," one of the participants added, "but it's better than breathing fire and smoke."

The foam suds wipe off easily, leaving only a small amount of dampness on clothing and skin. The foam also extinguishes fire, and in an actual crash it could put out flames near or around exits as it spilled out doors and emergency windows. A big jet would require several systems throughout its cabin and Bliss estimates the installation cost at between $6000 and $10,000 per aircraft for equipment that would weigh fifteen hundred pounds.

The foam system has one big disadvantage. The sudsy mixture is so thick that passengers could not see through it or even hear the evacuation instructions of stewardesses, which not only might create a safety problem but suggests possible serious psychological effects.

The Fenwal Company, an experienced manufacturer in the field of fire protection and detection, has an "explosion protection" system successfully used in a number of industrial facilities and which has been adapted to aircraft cabins. The Fenwal method is fantastically sensitive and fast. Its effectiveness can best be understood by remembering that an explosion actually has a beginning and an end. From the beginning (ignition) to the end (establishment of a flame front) there is a measurable time delay. Not much of a lapse—as little as 10 milliseconds, which is only a fraction of the time it takes to blink your eye—but enough for this protection system to go to work.

The system, in only five milliseconds, can (1) detect the beginning of the explosion, (2) discharge suppressants to halt combustion, (3) open vents in advance of pressure build-up, (4) inert adjacent areas to prevent secondary explosions, (5) isolate primary explosion area by activating high-speed shut-off valves.

The Fenwal system uses a fluorocarbon gas rather than foam as a suppressant. Toxicity tests were conducted on dogs and indicated that the mixture cannot harm a human being. The detectors and suppressors would be installed in various aircraft areas, including cabin, cockpit, baggage compartments and other sections. The rapid detection and activation capability results in total discharge in not more than two seconds. And the Fenwal cabin inerting system is regarded highly enough to have been offered tentatively as optional equipment on the giant Boeing 747.

At this writing it is difficult to say in which direction the airline industry will move—toward fuel gelling, protection of the tanks themselves, cabin suppressant systems or perhaps a combination. The successful application of any one method would make the others rather moot. But the goal is plain: fuel containment on impact, no matter how it is accomplished.

The FAA is evaluating a plastic smoke hood which is capable of providing enough breathable air and protection from smoke and flames for up to eight minutes, thus increasing survival time far beyond the usual ninety-second allotment. The hoods, which cost about $3 each, have a visibility drawback but the FAA thinks this disadvantage can be eliminated through a minor redesign. In evacuation tests with untrained volunteers, the time required to don and tighten the hoods added only a few seconds to total evacuation time.

The Vietnam war has produced one new product which is real off-the-shelf hardware rather than experimental. It is called Safoam, an inerting substance developed jointly by the Scott Paper Co. and the Firestone Tire & Rubber Co. Scott perfected the substance itself and Firestone worked out a means of using it in flexible fuel tanks. Safoam is 97 per cent void of volume and thus takes up not more than 3 per cent of tank capacity. Also, it is extremely light in weight. Combat experience amply demonstrated its ability to prevent fuel tank explosions and the FAA was sufficiently interested to fund a research project to determine whether Safoam could be used in airliners. The FAA in addition is testing a plastic foam that seems highly capable of slowing down fuel spillage from tanks broken open by impact. The polyurethane foam has the appearance of a rubber sponge but it does not absorb fuel.

It has been mentioned previously that the structure of a transport plane is amazingly strong and capable of staying intact under impact conditions that would turn an automobile into twisted junk. Yet ironically, there have been cases where the rupture of an aircraft fuselage actually saved lives instead of causing injury and death.

In each instance, the breakup of the fuselage provided impromptu emergency exits, wide enough for several passengers to go through simultaneously. This seeming incongruity has produced a technique of deliberate fuselage fracture, through a controlled explosion that literally blasts open a fairly large hunk of fuselage skin so that the fracture is turned into an additional escape hatch.

One company, Explosive Technology of Fairfield, California, has developed an explosive emergency exit system that deserves mention in any discussion of evacuation problems. It involves a relatively minor structural modification in which the chosen exit area is rectangularly framed with a light explosive material known as RDX. The explosive charge is triggered electrically and automatically by a pre-set impact force. The system can be armed only from the cockpit and the arming would be done before every landing or takeoff. Once safely airborne, the crew would disarm the system to avoid the somewhat embarrassing possibility that a section of the fuselage could blow out in flight.

The theory is logical and some airline pilots have expressed interest in the explosive emergency exit. Similar systems already are installed on military aircraft and spacecraft—most fighter planes, for example, are equipped with explosive charges that hurl the cockpit seat completely from the airplane when a pilot must jump to save his life. But many air safety experts look with suspicion on any system that has the remotest chance of inadvertent or accidental detonation. While the manufacturer insists the system can be foolproof and totally safe, adequate regular exits would be less expensive and even more foolproof. At any rate, development of a practical and efficient fuel-containment or fire-suppressant system would negate the need for anything as complicated as explosive exits.

If you were to witness a takeoff or landing involving Air Force One, the Presidential aircraft, you would notice the presence of a small helicopter hovering protectingly until the nation's most important airplane is either on the ground or climbing safely toward cruising altitude.

It carries specially trained firemen equipped for instant action if Air Force One should crash on takeoff or landing. Its pilots also are geared to hover their craft over the Presidential jet—using the rotor blades to fan any flames away from the cabin.

These Air Force fire-fighting 'copters are not for the exclusive protection of the President. Similar crash-rescue "choppers" are on alert duty at more than seventy-five AF bases throughout the world, and they have proved their worth on numerous occasions.

Typical was the day an F-105 fighter was landing at Seymour Johnson AFB, North Carolina. The landing gear collapsed, the fuselage broke in two and flames erupted from split fuel tanks. But the pilot had been experiencing some engine trouble and had radioed ahead that his landing might not be normal. Overhead, waiting for the crippled fighter, was a crash-rescue helicopter. The minute the crash occurred, the 'copter discharged via parachutes two firemen equipped with one thousand pounds of extinguishing foam. At the same time, the helicopter was maneuvered over the burning wreckage so that the rotor blast held back smoke and flames from the cockpit. In less than two minutes, the firemen had extricated the pilot, who suffered only minor burns.

Many safety experts would like to see such helicopters at every airport that handles airline traffic. The system is far faster than any ground vehicles, which are known to have been notoriously slow in reaching the scene of a crash. Furthermore, a takeoff or landing accident frequently occurs beyond the airport area itself, in rather inaccessible areas for ground equipment. The ubiquitous helicopter, with no such limitations, could reach with ease almost any crash scene in the vicinity of an airport.

The FAA has conducted experiments to see if the technique of fanning flames with 'copter rotor blades could increase survival time in a transport crash. Technicians set five old Boeing Stratocruisers on fire and then flew helicopters over the burning hulks. In one key test, the right wing of the Boeing was loaded with twenty-five hundred gallons of jet fuel. After the fuel was ignited, a chopper tried to fan the flames away from the fuselage. Instruments inside the cabin showed that the downdraft from the blades succeeded in reducing the heat and fire damage to such an extent that survival time would have been increased to an impressive *fifteen minutes*.

Not all the tests conducted on the five planes were this successful, but the technique has been proven practical by the Air Force and there seems to be no reason why it could not be adopted by civil airports. Helicopters *are* expensive, but so are fire engines and crash-rescue vehicles. A fire-fighting 'copter might well be as good an investment in safety as a ponderous piece of ground equipment which must be inevitably limited in its range. It appears to be a more economical investment than the runway arresting gear concept. And it would be good insurance at airports where fire-fighting equipment and personnel are barely adequate —a sad state of affairs at too many U.S. airports. At some airports, fire and rescue facilities are virtually non-existent. Only one airport, Baltimore's Friendship, has emergency hospital facilities— a two-hundred-bed unit.

The FAA, aware that few if any cities could muster enough ambulances to transport the more than four hundred passengers who might be injured in a 747 or supersonic airliner airport crash to downtown hospitals, looked with great interest at Baltimore's Friendship's hospital unit. It went so far as to suggest that mobile civil defense hospital units be stationed at major airports—a proposal that got nowhere with an indifferent Department of Health, Education and Welfare, which has jurisdiction over these units.

Post-impact fires have long since outstripped in-flight fire as a major aviation hazard. The latter, in fact, has almost been eliminated as even a minor concern, mainly because the jet engine itself is far less vulnerable to fire than the old pistons.

Pilots, as a matter of fact, regard false fire warnings as more of a problem than actual fires. There has been a notable reduction in false alarm occurrences on jets—from five for every one thousand hours of flight to one every seven thousand hours—but even the vastly improved fire warning devices occasionally malfunction. It can result in unnecessary engine shutdowns and even precautionary landings, which in turn cause inconvenience, annoyance and considerable extra expense for the airline if fuel is dumped.

It is hard to remember that pilots once dreaded in-flight fires in about the same proportion they feared fog, collision and thunderstorm turbulence. Improved extinguishing systems and the reliability of the jet engine put fire in flight far down on the list of major factors in causing fatal accidents—almost entirely off the list in the jet age.

All of which made the events of July 9, 1964, even more unbelievable.

At 6:10 P.M., EST, a United Air Lines Viscount—Flight 823

from Philadelphia to Huntsville, Alabama—was seen about forty miles from Knoxville, Tennessee, by a number of ground observers at a low altitude and trailing smoke. They estimated the plane's height at between two hundred and five hundred feet. Several eyewitnesses reported that a large black object (later identified as a passenger) dropped from the aircraft shortly before it nosed up, fell off on one wing and crashed into a rocky, wooded hillside near Parrottsville, Tennessee.

Flight 823 had made a scheduled stop at Washington, D.C., and would have made another stop at Knoxville before continuing on to Huntsville. Air Traffic Control communications with the plane were routine. Eight minutes before the accident, the Atlanta Air Route Traffic Center informed the crew the flight would be handed off to Knoxville Approach Control when it got a little closer and to stand by on the Atlanta Center's frequency.

"Okay," was the laconic acknowledgment—and the last thing heard from 823.

At 6:14 P.M., the Atlanta controller called the flight to report loss of radar contact. He got no answer.

The Viscount's unusually low altitude was the first thing to attract the attention of various witnesses, most of whom watched 823's death throes over a ten- to twelve-mile flight path. One woman located eleven miles from the impact point told investigators she saw a "violet red" light burning on the fuselage—and she said the plane was low enough so that she could read the word "United" above the cabin windows. She did not observe any smoke, but a ground witness about five miles from the impact site said that at this point "smoke was coming out of the tail part . . . and there were brown spots like the paint was off of it about halfway back on the body."

Witnesses even closer to the crash scene saw black smoke pouring from the four-engine propjet, the smoke coming from the fuselage near the wings. Those who saw the body fall said it was followed by dense black smoke and that heavy smoke continued to come from the plane until it struck the ground. Coincidental with the eyewitness reports of the falling passenger was a "bright object" which fell from the aircraft about a minute later. This was identified later as an emergency window exit located over the left wing. The majority of witnesses told the CAB they did not observe any flames, but a few said they saw fire in and/or on the plane.

There were thirty-four passengers, two pilots and two steward-esses aboard Flight 823. All died. One of the stewardesses had been flying less than four months.

Normally, a fatal in-flight fire is a comparatively easy case to solve because fire leaves voluminous clues as to origin. But the fate of Flight 823 was not only difficult to solve but impossible; it still is listed as an unsolved crash. Veteran investigators had never seen a previous accident to match these circumstances, nor has there been any subsequent incident aboard a Viscount or any other type of plane that would throw the slightest light on what happened to Flight 823.

At first it looked easy. Investigators combing through the wreck-age found severe fire damage in the electrical bay, that area con-taining the majority of a transport's wiring, generators and other electrical components. One of the first theories was that electri-cal arcing in a through-stud started a belly fire that burned through the cabin floor and got out of control. A through-stud is a tiny metal conductor which allows electric power to be brought through the fuselage of a pressurized aircraft without affecting the pressurization itself. If a stud becomes loose, arcing can spark and ignite either the fuselage skin or adjacent hydraulic lines.

But this explantion was discarded quickly. Stud arcing, traced to poor design, was the cause of all Lockheed Constellations being grounded in 1946. The Viscount's stud installations were designed to avoid any recurrence of the Constellation's troubles. In six mil-lion flight hours piled up by the doughty little British-made propjet, there had never been an incident remotely involving the electrical arcing of a stud.

There are, of course, other sources of aircraft electrical fires. But in delving deeply into every such possibility, the CAB found that all the evidence pointed away from an electrical fire as the primary cause of the crash.

First, there was every indication that the pilots did not find it necessary to follow standard emergency procedures for combating a serious electrical fire. Those procedures call for turning on the emergency power switch and turning off the battery master switch and the generators. The investigators found that key electrical components were still operating normally at impact. The DME (distance-measuring equipment) unit was functioning up to five miles before impact and this navigation device is generator-operated. The crew obviously did not execute electrical emergency procedures and the only conclusion was that there was no such emergency. As further evidence, the emergency power inverter was found not to have been rotating at the time of impact. The fuel boost pumps were running—they would have been turned off if there had been an electrical fire.

True, there was extensive fire damage in the area of the belly containing the Viscount's electrical innards. But in the Viscount and most low-wing planes, this area is close to and between the fuel tanks. In an impact severe enough to cause structural breakup, the electrical bay would be exposed to spilled fuel and inevitable fire.

Furthermore, there is a definite pattern of damage associated with in-flight fires originating in an aircraft belly. The flames invariably burn through the relatively light belly skin, leaving behind the plane a path of partially burned debris. Not a single witness reported seeing such debris falling from Flight 823, nor was any belly debris found away from the main wreckage area.

Exhaustive research eliminated all other normal sources of aircraft fire—hydraulic, combustible cargo or engines. Sabotage also was ruled out; no explosive residues were found. But the Viscount *did* catch fire and from its observed meanderings in the flight's final minutes, the fire was serious enough to have caused apparent loss of control. Flight 823's last known altitude was eleven thousand feet, at which time it was cleared to descend to eight thousand. Yet it was seen as low as two hundred feet with no word from the crew as to the reason for the descent. But where and how did the fatal blaze originate?

The cabin itself was the only logical answer, but it was an answer obtained only partially by the available evidence, and in large part by pure conjecture. For example, the Armed Forces Institute of Pathology conducted toxicological examinations of several victims. No elevated carbon monoxide levels were found and tests on respiratory tract specimens disclosed only a small amount of carbon particles.

On the other hand, laboratory tests on various samples of the aircraft's structure and components revealed the presence of a severe cabin fire. There was definite evidence of fire on seats, windows, forward bulkhead trim and the carry-on luggage rack. The latter was found to have been exposed to temperatures of nearly 130° F. The plastic material on one soundproof window had been heated to more than six hundred degrees. Significantly, there was considerable fire damage on passenger cabin material found some distance from the main impact area and not subjected to ground fire.

The body of the free-fall victim provided some intriguing and yet puzzling clues. He apparently opened the emergency window and jumped—ostensibly to escape the cabin fire. An autopsy disclosed that he died from injuries received on impact. His hands, face and neck were burned but only a few carbon particles were found in his trachea and the carbon monoxide level in his blood was low. Yet the upper portions of his clothing were impregnated with heavy soot.

The FBI ran his clothing through its superb laboratory and reported that the soot was the product of incomplete combustion of saturated aliphatic hydrocarbons. Such soot could come from kerosene, gasoline, paraffin, hydraulic fluid, naphtha and lighter fluid. Another product capable of producing liquid aliphatic hydrocarbon soot is ordinary hair spray.

The jet-powered Viscount does not carry gasoline. Nor was there any paraffin or naphtha known to have been aboard 823. There was, of course, kerosene and hydraulic fluid in large quantity. And carbon deposits taken from under floor wreckage at the crash site also were identified as aliphatic hydrocarbons.

This again seemed to shift the probable originating source of the fire away from the cabin to the belly. But such deposits also could have come from post-impact fire and not from an in-flight fire. The CAB called in an expert from the Massachusetts Institute of Technology for special tests.

The MIT technician exposed both painted and unpainted aluminum surfaces to severe heat generated by ignited kerosene, hydraulic fluid and turbine engine oil. All three left soot deposits but only on those portions of metal directly in the line of flame impingement. Tests also were run on aluminum dipped in the three liquids and left in ovens for five minutes under temperatures of up to 1000° F. Some of the test aluminum was scratched and cut to simulate crash damage.

The results were compared to the condition of the metal in

the underfloor wreckage of the UAL Viscount. The MIT expert's verdict: there was no positive evidence of a belly fire prior to impact and the soot most probably was from post-impact fire.

In that case, the deposits had to stem from ignited kerosene and/or hydraulic fluid. So, presumably, could the soot found on various cabin materials. But what about the clothes of the passenger who jumped?

Where and how did his clothing get covered with a hydrocarbon soot? Not from post-impact fire, for his body landed eighty-four hundred feet away from the crash site and his fall or jump occurred an estimated three minutes before Flight 823 hit the ground. It was pretty well established by this time that the fire broke out in the cabin, although investigators are still stumped on the reason.

The FBI provided another tantalizing clue. Its laboratory tried to duplicate the deposits on the clothing of the free-fall passenger by burning samples of the material. The technicians were best able to duplicate the heat damage by igniting and then quenching a fire from lighter fluid.

Investigators recalled that a cigarette lighter with a clear plastic fuel reservoir had been found near this passenger's body. But the lighter was about seven eighths full. It seemed improbable if not impossible that one eighth of the fluid in a tiny lighter could have generated a fire of such proportions as to wreck an airliner.

From this point, the investigation had to tiptoe cautiously into the area of educated guessing, based largely on the supposed actions of the crew. There were a number of indications that the two pilots and both stewardesses tried desperately to quell some kind of cabin fire. The portable cabin $CO_2$ extinguisher and the portable water extinguisher had been used. The walk-around oxygen bottle was found with an open valve. All this, the CAB deduced, suggested strongly that the first officer—Charles L. Young —went back into the cabin to fight the fire a few minutes before the crash, evidently because the stewardesses were unsuccessful and possibly because of panic among the passengers. Young's body was found in the cabin, not the cockpit.

In the cockpit itself, the left side window had been opened. Only a portion of one of the three installed pilot smoke masks was recovered and it could not be determined whether the captain and copilot had donned them. The CAB thinks they did as part of the smoke evacuation procedure. There was no indication that

$CO_2$ bottles had been discharged into any of the engines, but $CO_2$ had been fired into the baggage compartment. However, the investigators did not consider this latter fact as even hazy evidence of a baggage compartment fire. Rather, they reasoned that as the cabin fire continued to rage unchecked, the captain must have discharged the baggage-cargo extinguishers as a desperation measure and not because he thought the fire had originated in this area.

The only flammable liquid carried as part of the Viscount above the fuselage floor is hydraulic fluid in a reservoir located in a compartment between the carry-on luggage rack and the lavatory. The CAB found the reservoir damaged by impact and fire. It was empty but the fire damage pattern did not support hydraulic fluid as a contributing factor to the fire.

The cargo manifest was examined avidly for any clues and one item stood out as if it were written in braille. This was a one-gallon can containing a flammable commercial paint modifier. But the can was found in the wreckage area, crushed but with no sign of fire damage. It was still wrapped in paper.

The CAB's final report, issued almost two years later, summed up the fate of Flight 823 in these frustrated words:

"The combustible material and source of ignition that started the fire are not known. Although attempts to determine if any passenger had carried any hazardous material aboard the aircraft did not reveal this had occurred, the possibility cannot be ruled out. Such a material, either innocently or with malicious intent, may have been in the possession of a passenger.

"Leakage or spillage of a flammable fluid with accidental or intentional ignition is a possible situation. Substantial aircraft cabin fires are such a rare occurrence that a most unusual and possibly not readily conceivable circumstance is visualized in this instance . . .

"There is no probative evidence available to the Board on which to base a determination as to the cause of the final maneuver."

In simplest terms, unsolved.

Yet the CAB may have come close to the unknown truth in its phrase "a most unusual and possibly not readily conceivable circumstance . . ."

There were positive indications of panic aboard Flight 823—a hypothetical yet believable scene of a cabin filled with milling, frightened passengers. Take the case of the passenger who left the plane before it crashed. He was an elderly lawyer who made the Washington–Huntsville trip frequently. He did not like to fly and was nervous in a plane. He had told friends that if anything happened on a flight, he would prefer to jump rather than be trapped in flaming wreckage. He invariably sat next to an emergency window exit, apparently for that very reason—and it seems logical to suppose that he did jump deliberately. This adds credence to the hypothetical picture of panic.

"Leakage or spillage of a flammable fluid"—this was cited as a possible cause of the fire origin, with ignition either accidental or intentional. There is one kind of lighter known to be dangerous because of its susceptibility to a flare-up, and that is the clear plastic type, which has been known to cause severe burns.

It is hard to visualize a small lighter triggering a deadly chain of events. But add one more hypothesis to this attempted reconstruction. A passenger lights a cigarette with a clear plastic lighter. A woman sitting next to him decides to spray her hair—a logical act of feminine grooming as Flight 823 prepares for its scheduled landing at Knoxville. The spraying and the lighting process are simultaneous. The lighter flares up and ignites the spray—and remember, hair spray is extremely flammable, to the point of spray cans carrying a warning message.

One can imagine the panic that would develop in such a situation. Upholstery could have been ignited. The nervous passenger instinctively opens an emergency exit and the influx of fresh oxygen into an unpressurized cabin spreads the flames. Smoke fills the cabin. The copilot comes back to help. The smoke by this time probably has penetrated to the cockpit and the captain, unable to see, opens the cockpit window on the left side. The frightened passengers rush to the rear of the plane, shifting the aircraft's center of gravity so drastically that the pilot, half blinded and probably unable to read his instruments, loses control. There is no time to send word of any trouble; both pilots probably are too busy trying to quell both panic and fire as well as instituting various emergency measures, including smoke evacuation and a final, desperate firing of carbon dioxide into the baggage compartment. In the final seconds before the crash, the captain is alone in the cockpit and certainly unable to transmit a last message.

Farfetched? Possibly, but the entire story of Flight 823 is close to impossible. A number of United pilots felt strongly at first that the airline may have been shipping some dangerously flammable materials to the government arsenal at Huntsville without listing such cargo on the manifest. One captain even refused to take off a few weeks after the crash because an agent told him some kind of unlisted cargo for Huntsville was aboard. The captain insisted on an inspection and the cargo turned out to be some engine parts. Yet not for some time was United able to convince its crews that it was not shipping unlisted and potentially hazardous cargo over this route.

The captain of Flight 823 was Oliver E. Sabatke, forty-one, an ex-Navy pilot known to all his friends as Ollie. Soft-spoken, easy-going and rather deliberate, he began flying for Capital Airlines after World War II and went over to United when the two carriers merged. Capital was known throughout the industry as a "pilots' airline," but Ollie Sabatke was one of the few Capital crew members who privately liked the idea of going with the bigger, more efficient United.

He was a six-footer, slim and pixie-faced—always with the suggestion of a slight grin on his lean face. He had nearly sixteen thousand hours of flying time, including seventeen hundred hours on the Viscount, which he worshiped as only an airman can love a sturdy, easy-handling and dependable airplane. He loved to fish and once held up an entire Army transport ship in Hawaii because he was running around frantically trying to find a prized fishing pole.

On the day of the crash, his pretty wife Lois was in Detroit visiting her parents, accompanied by the two youngest of their five sons. She had talked to Ollie the night before, making arrangements to fly back to Washington the following night so they could meet at National Airport when Captain Sabatke flew the return flight from Huntsville to Washington.

Lois Sabatke was in her parents' living room when someone turned on the 7 P.M. news telecast. She heard the announcer say that "A United Viscount apparently has crashed near Knoxville." Calmly, she turned to her father and mother and said, "It's Ollie's plane."

United officials, meanwhile, were trying to reach her. The wife of another UAL pilot finally remembered that an ex-neighbor of the Sabatkes had the phone number of Lois's parents. The former neighbor lived in Cincinnati and United obtained the number from her. But meanwhile, Lois had called UAL Operations in Detroit and was put through to Washington Operations. A crew scheduler, his voice shaky, told her "the chief pilot wants to talk to you, Mrs. Sabatke." She knew then that it had happened.

Today, more than four years after her husband's death, she still remembers with vivid clarity a lot of poignant little things. The United stewardess who sat on the edge of Lois Sabatke's seat, all the way from Detroit to Washington, squeezing her hand in unspoken sympathy and understanding. The more than one hundred fellow pilots' wives who took turns cooking, cleaning and caring for her children while she arranged to bury her husband. The cooperation and thoughtfulness of United officials, who furnished the immediate members of her family with positive space passes so they could attend the funeral—eight came from Milwaukee, four from San Francisco and five from Detroit.

She still gets pass privileges from United for herself and her family. Originally, the airline gave her twice-a-year family passes for anywhere on UAL's system at a 75 per cent discount. This was changed later so that now she can take her family on one annual vacation trip for free but on a space available basis, plus six space available passes yearly. And she can fly any United flight for half fare on a positive space basis.

In May of 1966, the CAB sent her an advance copy of the accident report on Flight 823. She dreaded reading it, but knew she had to for her own peace of mind. So did Craig, her oldest son. They were disappointed that the crash was unsolved, but Lois was glad that there was not the faintest mention of possible pilot error.

"That I couldn't have lived with," she remarks. "Ollie was a fine pilot. If they had blamed him in any way, it would have been an unerasable stigma on his memory. I never worried about his flying. Maybe subconsciously I did, but it was his life and he loved it."

Only one of the five boys—a twelve-year-old—has any present desire to be an airline pilot, and for him it is not only a desire but a burning ambition. As for Mrs. Sabatke, she was conversing one day with a neighbor who mentioned that he was afraid to fly.

"Just remember the two or three guys up front," Lois Sabatke told him. "They want to get home to their families as much as anybody riding in the cabin."

In the pleasant Sabatke home, a two-story brick house in suburban Maryland just outside Washington, a display case hangs on the wall of the basement recreation room. Inside is the American flag that was on Ollie Sabatke's coffin. Above the flag are his Navy medals, his Navy wings and the gold oak leaf of a lieutenant commander. Next to the case is his picture, in Navy uniform.

It is a cheerful, happy room that somehow also manages to be an unpretentious shrine to a pilot's memory. In the world of airmen, those they leave behind grieve quietly and bravely.

# 8

## " . . . SKIPPER'S SHOT!"

To repeat the definition composed by Stuart G. Tipton, President of the Air Transport Association, safety is "the art of reducing risk to the least possible chance of occurrence."

Air safety *is* the product of reducing risk, and Tipton's definition also can be categorized as an industry-government policy as well as a kind of slogan.

"*. . . the art of reducing risk to the least possible chance of occurrence.*"

Item: The airlines are gradually adopting an electronic device that keeps track of engine wear while jets are in flight, thus giving them more than adequate advance warning when any part needs replacement or repair.

Item: The cockpit simulators used in pilot training are so realistic, even to reproducing motion, that they can induce airsickness.

Item: The test programs on such new airliners as the Boeing 737 and 747, the Lockheed 1011 and the Douglas DC-10 involve exposure to stresses up to 50 per cent stronger than what the FAA's certification standards demand—and those standards are considered capable of providing safe margins of structural strength. Boeing alone has tested or will test to total destruction one twin-engine 737 and two giant 747s—$47 million worth of airplanes—even though such testing is not even required under the government's certification process. The 737 was put through a cabin pressurization differential two hundred and twenty-five times greater than the plane will need in normal service.

Item: A jet's vital structural parts are X-rayed during major overhauls to make sure there is no trace of metal fatigue.

Item: A $9000-a-year airline dispatcher can overrule a $30,000-a-year captain or a $100,000-a-year airline president if he decides it is not safe for a flight to take off.

Item: Jets equipped with new automatic, all-weather landing systems have been landed without a human hand touching throttles or controls.

Examples of "the art of reducing risk" could be cited for another fifty pages. But there is one loophole in air safety through which death has been able to pour; one hazard which has thus far proved unconquerable. This is the sick human mind, poisoned by greed or hate or sexual desire or the black abyss of utter madness.

In one word: sabotage.

A small, dark, intense man named Francisco Gonzales was among the passengers who boarded Pacific Air Lines Flight 773 at Reno, Nevada, on May 7, 1964.

For one week he had been talking constantly about his impending death. On the previous day, he had purchased a Smith and Wesson Magnum revolver plus ammunition. At the San Francisco Airport that same night, before leaving on a Pacific flight to Reno, he displayed the gun to numerous friends. He even told one person he intended to shoot himself.

Gonzales also purchased two insurance policies at the San Francisco Airport, totaling $105,000. He wrapped the gun and ammunition in a small package which he carried aboard the plane to Reno. He also carried, in his mind and heart, a plan for self-destruction without a semblance of pity for what might be termed the innocent bystanders.

Francisco (Frank) Gonzales was a disturbed, frightened and tortured man so deeply in debt that half his income was committed to loan payments. He also was having marital difficulties. The friends who saw him off at the airport in San Francisco said later that he cried continually. Not one of them, however, notified Pacific or the police about the gun he was taking with him and his suicide threats.

In Reno he made the rounds of various casinos and gambled freely. One casino employee, noting that Gonzales seemed distraught, asked him how he was doing.

"It won't make any difference after tomorrow," the employee quoted Gonzales as replying.

Sometime during the evening, at one of the gambling establishments, he opened the package he continued to carry even while gambling. He took the gun out and apparently put it in his pocket after loading it. A janitor later found a cardboard carton for a Smith and Wesson revolver in a waste-paper container.

Shortly before 6 A.M., Gonzales went out to the Reno airport and climbed aboard Flight 773 with thirty-three other passengers. There were three crew members on the F-27—Captain Ernest Clark, who also was Pacific's chief pilot, First Officer Ray Andress and stewardess Marjorie Schafer.

The flight took off at 5:45 A.M. for San Francisco, stopping first at Stockton, California. Two passengers deplaned and ten new passengers boarded. At 6:38 A.M., the Oakland Air Route Traffic Control Center (ARTCC) gave 773 clearance to San Francisco, climbing VFR (visual flight rules) to six thousand and maintaining six thousand until further notice. The flight acknowledged the clearance and took off.

At 6:43 A.M., Oakland ARTCC shifted 773 to five thousand feet and advised the flight it was in radar contact.

6:45 A.M.—Oakland ARTCC instructed the flight to change heading for a vector into the San Francisco final approach course.

6:46 A.M.—ARTCC handed off the flight to Oakland Approach Control.

6:47 A.M.—Approach Control provided 773 with routine instructions and the current altimeter setting. It also informed Andress, who was handling communications, that his radio transmission was garbled. Presumably, at this very moment, passenger Francisco Gonzales got out of his seat and headed for the cockpit.

6:48 A.M—Andress was fiddling with his radio dials, trying to improve transmission quality. "How do you read now?" he inquired. Oakland replied, ". . . still the same. Sounds like overmodulation."

Fifteen seconds later, the Oakland approach controller received a final, puzzling transmission from Flight 773. It was garbled and unintelligible—merely a high-pitched voice that was almost a shout or even a scream.

The tiny blip that represented the F-27, its three crew members and forty-one passengers began to fade from the radar screen. Finally, it disappeared. Oakland tried to raise the flight but failed.

At 6:50 A.M., Approach Control asked another flight in the vicinity, United 593, if it had the F-27 in sight.

"Negative," 593 replied.

One minute later, United transmitted the epitaph of Pacific Flight 773.

"Oakland Approach Control, United 593. There's a black cloud of smoke coming through the undercast at . . . three-thirty, or four o'clock position right now. Looks like oil or gasoline fire."

The fire was the funeral pyre of an F-27 and forty-four human beings, including Francisco Gonzales, who had resolved his problems in his own way: suicide and mass murder.

The plane's flight recorder disclosed later that the propjet dove from five thousand feet to twenty-one hundred feet in less than twenty-three seconds—a descent rate of nine thousand feet a minute and an airspeed of nearly four hundred miles an hour. Clark or Andress, probably the latter, must have tried desperately to pull out; the recorder showed a sharp climb back to thirty-two hundred feet, followed by a final dive. Impact was so violent that a seismograph station at Camp Parks, California—about three miles from the crash site—registered a "disturbance of unknown origin."

The only traces left of the cockpit were four small pieces of the instrument panel, metallic rubble with no single portion of more than eight square inches, and a tiny section of the frame tubing from Captain Clark's seat. The tubing was subjected to an FBI microscopic examination which disclosed silvery metallic smears in an indentation. The smears were found to contain lead and antimony. Concluded the FBI: the indentation came from a bullet.

Searchers probing through the wreckage found a Smith and Wesson Magnum with the serial number S210645—the number of the gun purchased by Gonzales on May 6. It contained empty cartridges, freshly fired. The gun also had human tissue and clothing fibers embedded in the frame.

Investigators were almost certain that Gonzales had either entered the cockpit and shot the pilots, or had fired blindly through the flimsy cockpit door.

Ironically, that same day the FAA had adopted a rule, to become effective the following August 6, that all cockpit doors must be locked in flight. It was unlikely that Clark or Andress had locked theirs. The final proof of murder came from the tape of Flight 773's final transmission to Oakland Approach Control. It was undecipherable—just that high-pitched voice—but the tape was sent to the Bell Telephone Laboratories along with earlier recordings of the captain's and first officer's voices.

A spectogram (a visual tracing of the human voice) comparison showed that Andress sent the last message. As best as could be determined, it was:

"Skipper's shot. We're ben (or we've been) shot. (I was) try 'in ta help . . ."

Martha Andress, the widow of First Officer Ray Andress, is a tall, exceptionally attractive woman in her late thirties.

Her husband's death turned this mother of four into a crusader, and the union to which he belonged into an angry lobby against easy-to-buy flight insurance. Pacific itself financed a trip to Washington for Martha Andress, where she testified before Congressional committees on legislation that would ban the sale of insurance at airport counters or from vending machines.

The lawmakers listened respectfully and sympathetically, but the legislation died and at this writing similar bills have yet to be enacted. To this day, Martha Andress is convinced that the easy availability of airport insurance in heavy amounts triggered the crime—a conviction shared devoutly by virtually every airline pilot in the United States.

"If he [Gonzales] had been able to buy only a few thousand dollars' worth or none at all, my husband would still be alive," she told me in an interview.

The memory of the morning of May 7 remains cruelly fresh. Andress was filling in for a pilot on his vacation. He had called Martha the night before—from Reno—to be sure and have breakfast ready for him after 773 got in. Her first word of the crash came from another pilot's wife, who thought the vacationing crew member was on the flight—his regular trip.

"No," Martha Andress told her calmly. "It was Ray's flight."

All morning, pilot wives kept coming over to take care of the children and fix meals. In the afternoon, several officials of Pacific arrived. Martha grabbed them, without hysteria but with unconcealed emotion.

"Ray was a good pilot," she kept insisting. "And Ernie was even a chief pilot. No matter what you find out, you can't call it pilot error." [Note her defensive attitude even in grief, identical to that of Mrs. Sabatke.]

"I guess I knew quite early that it was murder," she recalls. "Ray's father was with the FBI for eighteen years. The FBI came over that night and told me that a gun had been found and that they knew the owner and knew he was on the plane. I think it was right then that I decided I'd do everything I could to keep this from happening again."

(Her crusade has been only partially successful. One state—Colorado—has outlawed "slot-machine insurance"—policies sold through "any mechanical device or vending machine." It became law July 1, 1967; significantly, Colorado was the scene of a previous sabotage case in which a cold-blooded killer named Jack Graham planted a bomb in his mother's suitcase before she boarded a United DC-6 at Denver. The plane blew up over Longmont, Colorado, killing all forty-four aboard. Graham, who had purchased flight insurance from an airport vending machine for his mother with himself named as the beneficiary, confessed later that he committed the crime for the insurance money. He was executed in a gas chamber.)

Six months before Flight 773 ended in senseless tragedy, Ray Andress had started taking aikido lessons—the art of disarming a man in a confined space. He got interested in the course at the urging of Oscar Cleal, a Pacific captain who in 1961 was shot and permanently blinded by a crazed, gun-wielding hoodlum at the Chico, California, airport in an apparent hijacking attempt. (The gunman, Bruce Britt, has been appealing at regular intervals for parole from a California prison where he is serving a forty-two-year sentence. His last appeal was rejected March 16, 1967, and he was scheduled for another hearing in November of 1968.)

Martha Andress believes that her husband would have used his aikido training if there had been the slightest chance. But she figures Captain Clark was shot and killed instantly, and that the wounded copilot tried only to save the plane. It was rather typical that Andress was one of the few Pacific pilots Captain Cleal could get interested in the art of aikido. Only seven or eight enrolled in the course; pilots traditionally are rather lethargic about any project that cuts into their off-duty time. After the Pacific crash and a rash of hijacking incidents, a couple of Bonanza pilots arranged for a course in the handling of small firearms (Bonanza, along with a few other carriers, gave their crews permission to put pistols or revolvers in their flight bags at their own discretion). Just six pilots signed up, although many of the non-participants shied away not from lack of interest but from fears that arming crews could lead to airborne gun battles and possible harm to passengers.

For more than a year, Mrs. Andress wrote letters to newspapers and pilots, trying to sustain interest in the sabotage problem.

"I know it's easier to go out and play golf on your day off," she wrote one pilot, "but it's also so easy to forget—after a few months—what happened last May 7."

Pacific gave her a lifetime pass. She likes to fly but she is terribly conscious of other passengers and their actions. Once she noticed a man who kept getting out of his seat and heading for a forward lavatory with a bag or sack in his hand. She was positive he was mustering up nerve to detonate a bomb.

"All I could think of was Ray and my heart wouldn't stop pounding the whole flight," she admits. "Believe me, pilots' wives aren't afraid of crashes; they're afraid of sabotage."

So, for that matter, are pilots, because they feel so helpless in preventing sabotage. ALPA officials concede that banning insurance machines or over-the-counter airport sales is no cure-all. But they argue that even an inadequate deterrent is better than none at all. They point out that insurance has been a factor in the majority of airliner bombing cases, with airport-vended insurance involved in most of them.

ALPA has just about given up hopes of getting Congress to ban all airport insurance sales. But it has succeeded in having several bills introduced that would at least limit such insurance to a maximum liability of $50,000. And the Association continues to plug for what it regards as the most acceptable and workable compromise—a $50,000 limit on over-the-counter insurance and an outright ban on insurance vending machines. ALPA officials are rather bitter about Congressional apathy. As one puts it: "It'll take another major sabotage case, involving cheap airport insurance as the motive, before they'll get off their butts and act to end what is so plainly just a lottery in lives."

The airlines themselves have quietly pondered ways to reduce or eliminate the so-called "lottery" aspect of flight insurance. Some carriers have discussed with major insurance companies the practicality of three measures:

—Sell trip insurance solely on an annual or semi-annual basis, or for a specific number of flights, instead of the quick "one shot" policies so readily available at airports. (This has little support mainly because restricting insurance to long-range policies would be unfair to millions who make only one or two trips a year.)

—Turn over all insurance sales to the airlines themselves, adding the cost of a trip policy to the price of the ticket just as car rental firms now offer extra collision-liability insurance for a small added fee.

—Reduce the maximum insurance a passenger can purchase from the present limit of $250,000, although there has been no agreement on what a new maximum should be; ALPA's suggested $50,000 limit is the amount most frequently mentioned.

Thus far, the discussions have been fruitless, although one more major tragedy traced to insurance as a motive would stir up renewed interest and possibly some drastic action that Congress and the industry presently are reluctant to take.

A few years ago, the FAA asked an insurance expert to determine the relationship of flight insurance to sabotage cases and to recommend whether airport sales should be forbidden. The expert chosen was Clarence Pell, Jr., who headed the aviation division of a large insurance firm. Pell reported back to FAA that banning or limiting airport flight insurance would not come anywhere close to solving the sabotage menace. He said the over-all benefits of such insurance outweighed the sabotage-prevention factor. Besides, he added, if a would-be mass murderer couldn't buy insurance at an airport he could obtain it elsewhere with comparative ease.

ALPA challenged Pell's findings as somewhat suspect. It questioned the wisdom of having an insurance executive judge the merits of a proposal that would destroy a lucrative business. The pilots' union claims that flight insurance sales total about $50 million annually. They also represent a considerable source of income to airport operators. ALPA says at least five cents and as much as seventeen cents out of every quarter paid for a trip policy goes to the airport for rent. However, while ALPA was naturally suspicious of Pell's objectivity, he was not alone in his conclusions. In 1963, a government-industry committee also recommended against eliminating airport insurance. Whether a new study would reach a different decision is another matter. Because the ALPA proposal at least is the only specific and possibly practical step anyone has suggested, airline passengers should be interested in these pros and cons on airport insurance:

Pro—Why penalize the public by removing an inexpensive form of protection for families and loved ones? Sabotage is a terrible but still rare crime.

Con—Passengers can get insurance elsewhere, through long-range travel insurance or regular life insurance. Anyway, the families of those killed in air crashes aren't being left destitute even without flight insurance. The by-product of every air tragedy is an avalanche of negligence lawsuits. Nor is there any great demand for flight insurance. According to one estimate, only 20 per cent of the passengers buy it and a good proportion of these are attracted by the large benefits available. They purchase trip insurance almost like they'd play slot machines or buy lottery tickets.

Pro—Not all travelers can afford to buy annual trip insurance or regular life insurance.

Con—Why single out airline passengers as having an apparently exclusive need for protection? At least eighty thousand Americans die every year in automobile accidents, falls, drownings, fires and other mishaps. Air transportation can no longer be considered in the "special risk" category and insurance companies admit this when they sell insurance to pilots and stewardesses at the same rate paid by those who do not fly for a living.

Pro—There is no evidence to show that elimination of airport insurance would end or even decrease sabotage. Motives other than insurance frequently are involved.

Con—Nobody claims that elimination is a panacea. But it would minimize the chances for sabotage by removing the temptation for an easy pay-off.

Pro—The record shows that not a single saboteur has ever collected from an insurance policy. This knowledge is the best deterrent against the crime of mass murder for profit.

Con—The widow of one suspected saboteur *did* collect on his insurance because it was impossible to establish definite proof of his guilt. Even if no saboteur himself ever collected, this wouldn't keep somebody else from trying it. Nor have non-pay-offs prevented the most recent sabotage cases. It must be remembered that an aircraft bombing usually results in total destruction. The potential saboteur invariably believes he has a chance of getting away with literal murder. Few laymen are aware of the clues that a bombing leaves behind. Sabotage is by no means a perfect crime, but there is considerable evidence that saboteurs regard it as such. Furthermore, what pilots dread more than anything else is an airliner bombing that occurs over water, where wreckage recovery not only would be difficult but perhaps impossible. This *would* be a theoretically perfect crime. The 1959 crash of a National Airlines DC-7 in the Gulf of Mexico is widely believed to have been caused by a bomb, but not enough wreckage was ever recovered to list this as a positive sabotage case.

Pro—If a person bent on sabotaging an airliner couldn't buy airport insurance, he could get a policy through other channels. Anyone insane or vicious enough to commit mass murder is not going to be deterred simply bacause he can't buy insurance at an airport.

Con—Regular insurance provides some screening of applicants, by no means perfect but at least more thorough than sales via vending machines or a girl at an insurance counter who is not trained to spot suspicious-acting customers. The availability of airport insurance probably tips the scales toward murder in the sick mind of a saboteur.

In discussing various means of preventing sabotage, it is essential to examine the history of mass murder—largely to determine whether there is a definite pattern to motivation for sabotage. Establishment of a pattern would have the effect of possibly narrowing the means of prevention. Unfortunately, there is no real sign of a pattern. The sabotage toll has been heavy. Since the first known incident occurred in the United States in 1933 (a United Boeing 247 was destroyed by a bomb), there have been at least twenty definite or suspected aircraft sabotage cases world-wide. In the past ten years, fatal airliner bombings have occurred at the rate of one and a half per year. Since 1955, a total of two hundred and ten persons (one hundred and eighty-three passengers and twenty-seven crew members) have died in U.S. sabotage cases alone. And there are numerous incidents of bungled sabotage attempts that only luck prevented from being catastrophic.

There *is* a pattern to mass murder and it is a chilling one—namely, the killer does not care how many die so long as he gets the target he is aiming at, whether it be himself or somebody else on the plane. But as for motivation, just examine the following cases and you will realize how difficult it is to establish a pattern of impulse that might be combated.

1949—A jeweler named Albert Guay planted a bomb on a Canadian Pacific Airways DC-3. He wanted to kill his wife so he could marry another woman. He succeeded and killed twenty-two persons in addition to his wife. Motive: sex.

1950—A laboratory technician named John Grant put his wife,

two children and a bomb on a United Air Lines plane in Los
Angeles, then lost his nerve and screamed a warning to baggage
handlers. Grant was infatuated with an airline stewardess. Motive:
sex.

1952—A bomb exploded in a luggage compartment on a Mexican
Airways plane. The pilot landed safely. Eventually, two men who
had insured seven of the twenty passengers aboard for $208,000
were convicted and sentenced to thirty years imprisonment. Motive: profit.

1953—A bomb exploded in a plane parked at a Mexican airport,
killing three airport employees. The bomber confessed planting the
explosive in his own luggage so his relatives could collect insurance.
The irony was that his luggage was put on the wrong plane. Motive:
suicide for insurance.

1955—A time bomb blew up an Air India Constellation, killing
fifteen. A Chinese aircraft cleaner at the Hong Kong airport had
been bribed to put the bomb in the aircraft's wheel well. Motive:
politics.

1955—The Jack Graham sabotage case. Motive: profit.

1957—Retired jeweler Saul Beinstock walked calmly into the
lavatory of a Western Air Lines Convair flying from Las Vegas to
Los Angeles. He carried a briefcase with a bomb inside and detonated the device after he was in the lavatory. Beinstock was blown
out of the plane but the Convair made a safe landing with no
injuries to passengers or crew. Apparent motive: suicide for insurance.

1959—National Airlines DC-7. Motive: unknown but evidence
pointed to a gangland-type murder, possibly for profit.

1960—A National Airlines DC-6B blew up over Bolivia, North
Carolina, killing all thirty-four aboard. Authorities suspected a passenger named Julian Frank, whose body was found some distance
from the main wreckage area. His injuries were not of the type
usually sustained in a plane crash. Foreign objects found imbedded
in his flesh turned out to be small pieces of steel wire, cloth fibers
and black deposits analyzed as manganese dioxide—a substance
contained in dry cell batteries. Frank was a Westport, Connecticut,
lawyer who in the previous year had taken out more than one
million dollars in life insurance and who was involved in various
legal and financial troubles. It was never proved that he was

responsible for the battery-triggered dynamite device that destroyed the plane. Probable motive: suicide for insurance.

1962—An unknown killer put a bomb in the rear lavatory of a Continental Air Lines 707 that blew up over Centerville, Iowa. The eight crew members and fifty-seven passengers all perished in what was the first fatal sabotage case involving a jet. (It almost was the second; the DC-6B on which Julian Frank flew was a last-minute substitute for a jetliner that was taken out of service because of a cracked cockpit windshield.) Authorities believe the Continental plane was sabotaged by a passenger who had taken out heavy insurance just before the flight. Probable motive: suicide for insurance.

1963—The Pacific F-27 cockpit shooting. Motive: suicide for insurance.

1965—A Canadian Pacific DC-6B was blown up by a bomb over the Canadian Rockies, with fifty-two fatalities. The case is unsolved and the motive is unknown, although some authorities suspect an insurance plot.

1967—A minor executive with a soft drink company planted a bomb in his wife's suitcase before she boarded an American Airlines 727 flying between San Diego and Chicago. The device was detonated by an alarm clock but fortunately damage was not great and the plane landed safely. The husband told police he intended to kill his wife, but at this writing he was trying to escape prosecution on the grounds that the FBI agents who questioned him did not advise him of his legal rights.

1967—A homemade bomb exploded in the cabin of a British European Airways Comet over the Mediterranean, blowing a huge hole in the fuselage. The crew tried to get down safely but the jet disintegrated during the emergency descent. Motive: murder for political reasons.

Is there any way to prevent sabotage?

Numerous recommendations have been made but none appear to be truly satisfactory as of yet, although a few appear to have some potential.

One suggestion is to coat all explosive substances, such as dynamite, with a radioactive tracer that could be spotted by Geiger counters strategically located at airport baggage areas. But if the counters were sensitive enough to pick out radioactive materials buried deep inside a piece of luggage, they also might trigger voluminous false alarms by sensing the radioactive substances used on many clocks and watches. Another weakness is the fact that explosives can be made at home, using common chemicals. And it is possible to import explosive materials from other countries; the radioactive seeding technique would have to be international in scope.

The most drastic and supposedly foolproof sabotage cure, of course, would be mandatory inspection of *all* luggage, either physically or through fluoroscoping. But this would involve hopeless delays and inconvenience to millions of passengers, and might not even offer a guarantee against any bombing attempts. Any customs inspector can testify to the ingenuity of people who want to smuggle something past inspection. There are numerous ways in which a small but deadly bomb can be hidden in a suitcase or on a person. One can imagine the irritation that would result from mandatory frisking of all passengers. As for fluoroscoping, which has been urged by no less than J. Edgar Hoover, this again would pick up scores of innocent objects that just look like possible bombs.

Several firms have developed devices which sense the presence of explosives and can trigger many bomb mechanisms. Presumably they would be installed in a bombproof room at airports, with all luggage going through the room on the way to planes. Any hidden bomb would be detonated *before* it reached an aircraft. There are drawbacks, however. None of these devices can set off *all* triggering mechanisms. And a room capable of withstanding a dynamite blast would be an expensive installation for an airport.

More practical and promising is the "Chemosensor," also known as the "Sniffer." This is an extremely sensitive device that "smells" the presence of vapors or odors emanating from explosive substances like dynamite. It has been under development since 1964 when the FAA awarded a $39,000 contract to the Illinois Technical Research Institute in Chicago for study of the feasibility of such a bomb-detection technique. Early test models were unsatisfactory; they sensed harmless chemicals as well as explosive materials. A so-called "second generation" engineering model has been delivered to FAA's research center in Atlantic City for field evaluation tests. FAA officials are cautiously optimistic but they have their fingers crossed and they warn against expecting any single solution.

Sniffing was the only surviving idea out of thirty-five plans considered by a government-industry committee on airline sabotage a few years ago. It also was tentatively supported by ALPA's Destructive Objects Detection Committee, whose members witnessed an ITT demonstration in which a rather primitive Sniffer model quickly picked up the vapors from dynamite placed several feet from the machine. The ALPA group was particularly interested in a recommendation that the sniffing device be put on planes themselves, rather than in airport baggage areas. This calls for a pressurization and release cycle that would allow the detector to sample air from throughout the cabin as well as from cargo compartments. The vapor-sniffing would be activated by the crew as soon as their aircraft moved away from the ramp. The pilot committee urged further study, even though it admitted that there are problems "to be encountered in sniffing 65 million people, 200 million items of baggage and 8 million items of air freight."

Even if the Sniffer turns out to be effective, it still will fall short of being the ultimate anti-sabotage weapon unless it proves capable of detecting *any* material with explosive qualities. For example, it may not be able to sense such items as a gasoline bomb, an acid-type explosive or a thermite bomb—any of which could destroy an airplane as thoroughly as dynamite.

The most provocative proposal for conquering sabotage was ably discussed by an Air Canada pilot, Captain F. E. W. Smith, in an article he wrote for the *Canadian Air Line Pilot,* which is published by the Canadian pilots' union. ALPA reprinted it in its own magazine in the belief that Smith's subject matter deserved the widest distribution. He went into the various anti-sabotage methods suggested for combating sabotage, pointing out the weaknesses of each, and then brought up an intriguing idea. To quote directly from his article:

There remains the possibility of being able to rob the bomb of its damage. Strangely, this has apparently not yet received much consideration. Aircraft, properly constructed, might be made able to survive bombs. Perhaps it is not necessary that they always be destroyed.

As we are inclined to think of an explosion as an uncontainable force acting destructively in all directions, this suggestion may seem preposterous. Anyone who has ever worked with explosives, however, knows that their force can often *be controlled.* As a matter of fact, it is sometimes surprising how *little* damage an explosion will do.

It is conceivable that aircraft could be constructed so that the force of an explosion could be vented with only moderate damage, and in any case would not destroy the essentials required for a safe, if emergency, landing.

Cargo compartments could be built with their inner walls much stronger than their outer, instead of the reverse, so that if an explosion occurred in one, its force would blow outwards.

The vitals of an aircraft—controls, electrical systems, hydraulics, fuel lines—could be located to be safe from possible explosions and shielded.

There could be longitudinal strengthening that would keep an aircraft from breaking in two or losing its tail.

If these various things were done, aircraft would have a degree of survivability from acts of sabotage which they do not have now. The suggestion may be received by designers and aircraft operators with some dismay, for design requirements are tough enough now without adding new criteria, and armoring aircraft may cut heavily into performance. However, the destruction of aircraft by bombs probably cannot be prevented. From time to time it happens. Therefore a need exists for *designed* protection, at least equal to the need of watertight bulkheads on ships.

If destructive pressure is offered an ample outlet in a safe direction, the retaining structure needs only to be strong enough to withstand critical stress for a very short time. The necessary material, while strong, may actually be quite light and if given a routine function as well, may even improve the airplane . . .

Surely the aviation industry cannot accept any situation of sure disaster without trying to do *something* about it. To date there has been talk and that is all . . . nothing has been done to make the murderer's job more difficult.

Captain Smith's plea that *something* be done should find sympathetic response from the entire aviation community. It must be admitted that some of the cures proposed are almost as bad as the disease. One recommendation made in complete seriousness was that all airline baggage should be carried on separate planes, thus theoretically removing passengers from any danger area. Aside from the obvious fact that this would require the approximate doubling of the commercial aircraft fleet and would raise air fares to impossible proportions, it would be an almost useless measure. Bombs have been carried aboard airliners in small briefcases and hand luggage, and these would have to be banned along with the larger baggage. There also is the untold inconvenience of having one's baggage arrive at a different time. An almost equally drastic preventive would be to ban *all* carry-on luggage, putting such items in protected cargo bins along the lines Smith suggested.

Explosions, of course, are not the only form of sabotage, as the fate of Flight 773 demonstrated. Violation of cockpit security is even more frequent than destruction of aircraft integrity. "Sky-jacking" (former FAA Administrator Halaby tagged aerial hijacking with this name) continues to be a major problem despite Congressional action in 1961 that made aircraft piracy a federal crime and provided stiff punishment—imprisonment for not less than twenty years or even death under certain circumstances.

The new law also made it a federal crime for any unauthorized person to carry a concealed weapon aboard an airliner—tacit recognition that sky-jacking is nothing but potential sabotage. Laws seldom are totally effective deterrents to crimes, however. In the first seven months of 1968, four U.S. airliners were forced to divert to Cuba, in each case the hijacker forcing his way into the locked cockpit by threatening the stewardesses and/or passengers. A fifth attempt was foiled when a flight engineer talked the gunman out of it. The 1968 sky-jacking wave seemed to prove the contention of pilots and the airline industry alike that the FAA's rule requiring cockpit doors to be locked is an uncertain precaution as far as hijacking is concerned.

An electronic device that could spot concealed weapons has been urged. Most prisons have it. Certainly a tough federal gun control law, while proponents have not had aircraft hijackings specifically in mind, would have at least some beneficial effects. The ALPA Destructive Objects Detection Committee has looked into the possibility of arming pilots with guns that fire plastic or wax bullets—or low-velocity shells—which could stop a hijacker without damaging the aircraft. Armor-plated doors and other means of bulletproofing cockpits have been considered but generally discarded because of the inescapable fact that a sky-jacker has only to threaten stewardesses or other passengers. One suggestion is to teach all stewardesses karate or judo.

The airlines have expressed great interest in a weapon-detecting device developed by the Lockheed Missiles and Space Company. It utilizes a magnetic sensor to detect the movement of magnetic fields associated with such ferrous metal objects as guns. Theoretically, it could spot guns concealed in clothing or carry-on luggage.

A little-publicized measure against sky-jacking is a specially trained corps of FAA "sky marshals," who wear civilian clothes and ride certain flights incognito. They are experts at karate and judo, and carry concealed weapons such as pistols, tear gas "pens" and blackjacks. Usually they are assigned to flights, mostly on the East Coast, suspected of being targets for a sky-jacking attempt. Other times they board unannounced in a kind of spot-check operation. The FAA has never disclosed the size of the corps. Its members are regular FAA inspectors who volunteered for marshal duty even though they get no extra pay. They are trained at the Border Patrol Academy in Port Isabel, Texas, and the training emphasizes disarming tactics over gunplay.

(Careless or deliberately malicious use of firearms may be more of a safety hazard than is realized. Over a one-year period, six airliners were hit by gunfire from the ground in the Vietnam war theater. In this same period, nine airliners were struck by ground gunfire within the continental United States!)

A dog trainer in Los Angeles has taught his animals to smell the presence of marijuana on a person, and the dogs are trained to grab any dope-user they sniff out. He and other canine experts believe it is possible to teach a dog to smell any gunpowder carried in a concealed weapon. Impractical? Maybe, but nothing should be left untried or untested in preventing sabotage or hijacking.

The partner of sabotage and sky-jackings is the bomb hoaxer, in his own way as vicious and demented as an actual killer. It is impossible to say how many hoaxes occur because some newspapers wisely have agreed not to run stories on them. The FBI, airlines and government aviation agencies are unanimous in feeling that hoax publicity leads to further incidents and that complete cooperation by all news media would be very helpful. It can be said, however, that in 1964—even *after* passage of a federal law providing for hoax prosecution—the airlines were averaging three a week, and there is little reason to believe that such incidents have diminished. A movie called *Doomsday Flight*, run on television in 1967, resulted in an avalanche of hoaxes the following day. The plot involved a pressure bomb placed on an airliner, set to go off when the plane descended to two thousand feet. The saboteur tells the FBI he will reveal where the bomb is hidden and how it can be disarmed only if the airline pays $100,000 in ransom. The pilot foils the scheme by landing at Denver, where the airport is a mile above sea level.

Some airline people, even though they deplored the hoaxes that resulted from the film, thought it might accomplish some long-range good because the movie portrayed the deep concern a bomb threat generates and the quick countermeasures taken by police and airline authorities. The hoaxer has it made in his cruel, perverted idea of humor—the word "bomb" to an airline is decidedly unfunny because planes *have* been sabotaged, and no hoax, even if obviously phony, is handled in any way but deadly seriousness.

As with saboteurs, it is hard to pinpoint what might be classed as the "average" or "typical" hoax perpetrator. He could be a prank-playing adolescent, a respected businessman or even a college professor. He also could be a drunk, a mentally ill person or someone with a grudge against a particular airline. In one unusual case, numerous bomb hoax calls were traced to a highly regarded priest. And there have been several instances where passengers, fearing they were going to miss flights, have phoned in false bomb reports in order to delay their planes!

Not even a joking remark is treated lightly, as many passengers have discovered to the detriment of their finances. Federal authorities are prosecuting a surprising percentage of "jokester" incidents—passengers who in what they thought was a kidding manner mentioned "bomb" to an airline employee.

An Air Force reserve captain was checking in his luggage just before a commercial flight. The agent asked him if he also wanted to check his briefcase.

"No," chuckled the captain, "this is the one with the bomb in it."

In less than two minutes, he was being questioned by airport police. In less than ten minutes, he was being questioned by the FBI. In less than two weeks, he was standing before a federal judge, who fined him $250 and placed him on probation for one year.

A stewardess told an insurance executive to remove his attaché case from the overhead rack and put it under his seat.

"Okay," he smiled, "but it's got a bomb inside."

He was arrested when the plane landed and eventually fined $100.

A space engineer boarded an airliner with a friend. He remarked jokingly to the stewardess as he nodded toward his companion: "Better watch this fellow. I think he's got a bomb in his bag."

The plane took off but not with the space engineer. He paid a $500 fine, drew a six-month suspended jail sentence and was placed on probation during that period.

One airline nabbed a hoaxer accidentally, thanks to an agent's habitual politeness. A man called the airline to advise that a bomb was on a certain flight. Without thinking, the agent instinctively asked, "May I have your name, please?"

Equally instinctively, the caller gave his name—and was arrested shortly thereafter.

The federal law on hoax prosecution does not differentiate between harmless and malicious intent. Title 18 of the United States Code, Section 35, states simply:

> Whoever imparts or conveys or causes to be imparted or conveyed false information, knowing the information to be false, concerning an attempt or alleged attempt being made or to be made, to do any act which would be a crime [aircraft sabotage] shall be fined not more than $1,000 or imprisoned not more than one year or both.

All airline employees have been briefed by the Air Transport Association and FBI on exactly what to do if a bomb call comes in. The procedures have not and never will be publicized, but if anyone reading this book ever gets the urge to pull a hoax, let him be reminded that the procedures are designed for one thing only: to nab the hoaxer and prosecute him.

Sabotage could be classed as aviation's greatest safety problem, even ahead of collisions and impact fire. The latter two may have caused far more deaths in the past than aircraft bombings, but at least there are specific and extremely encouraging steps being taken to solve these problems. There is no such optimism about sabotage or sky-jackings. Nothing is unsolvable in air safety, but sabotage comes uncomfortably close because it does not stem from technical weaknesses. And it may become a bigger problem as air travel expands into larger-capacity aircraft carrying a greater cross section of passengers.

In the course of researching this book, I was discussing with a top Boeing engineer various safety problems of the jet age. Curious, I asked him which of aviation's current safety perplexities bothered him the most when he himself was on a plane.

"I'm never concerned about the plane, the crew or the airport," he replied thoughtfully. "But damned if I don't wonder at times which of the other hundred or so passengers is a homicidal nut."

# 9

## COLLISION COURSE

"Aircraft accidents are seldom produced by a single, isolated event. Like most other accidents, they occur most frequently as the result of a chain of events with a final precipitating factor, usually induced by the person who makes the majority of decisions —the pilot . . . It becomes increasingly important for all people concerned with aviation—designers, operations and supervisory personnel—better to understand man's frailties and limitations to avoid exceeding his capacity to sense, integrate, make decisions and act."

The author of those words was Dr. Charles Barron, chairman of the Federal Air Surgeons Aeromedical Advisory Committee for the Federal Aviation Administration. They sum up why airline pilots bristle at the accusation "pilot error." But they also might be said to apply to the airman's growing dread, aviation's biggest accident-prevention problem and the one air safety hazard which threatens to get worse before it gets better—mid-air collisions.

You are going to read about two collisions, occurring under totally different circumstances but with three common denominators: each theoretically was preventable, each involved alleged pilot error and each took place because of existing conditions that made pilot error merely the culminating factor. And this is the real story of the collision menace, the so-called danger of our "crowded skies," which in a sense is the same oversimplification of the problem that has led to so many oversimplified proposals to solve it. Just as an air accident has many reasons for the occurrence, so is there seldom if ever a single means of preventing a similar accident.

That is the main thing to be kept in mind as you digest the following pair of events, which transpired six and a half years apart—the second coming to pass despite all the recriminations, resolves and reforms that followed the first.

The time was 10:33 A.M. and the date was December 16, 1960.

At that precise second in history, a United Air Lines DC-8 and a Trans World Airlines Super-Constellation collided in the murky skies over Staten Island, New York. It was another aviation irony—the same two airlines were the principals in the 1956 collision of two transports over the Grand Canyon, an accident that led to badly needed improvements in air traffic control. The tragedy that struck on December 16, 1960, was bitter proof that the lessons of the Grand Canyon collision had come unraveled.

The temperature in New York City that day was a blustery thirty-three degrees. A light snow was falling on the remains of a seventeen-inch blizzard that had clobbered the city five days before.

At 10:34 A.M., police sergeant Edwin Costello, running the communications bureau at Brooklyn police headquarters, couldn't repress a yawn and then suddenly reminded himself to keep plenty of men in the vicinity of nearby factories and check-cashing places. December 16 was a Friday, and Friday is both a payroll day and a holdup day. In a few minutes, sudden death and not holdups was to be his chief concern.

At 10:34, supervising dispatcher Anthony Lauritis at Fire Department headquarters on Staten Island received alarm 2047 from a box at Lincoln Avenue and Grand Place. He transmitted it immediately to the closest firehouses. Seconds later, eight more fireboxes in Staten Island sent in alarms. Lauritis's telephone switchboard lit up like an amuck computer, the callers excitedly reporting that a plane had crashed at a small military airport called Miller Field. It was used mostly for single-engine planes and Lauritis wasn't especially alarmed. He figured the aircraft probably was a private plane and he dispatched two pumpers and two ladder trucks.

Chief Roger Carmody of the 8th Division led the equipment to Miller Field, took one horrified look and radioed a second alarm that brought four more pumpers, and additional four-ladder trucks, police and fire rescue squads and every available ambulance. The reinforcements as well as the original trucks were useless. What was strewn all over Miller Field was the wreckage of the TWA Constellation, only a few minutes before a red and white airliner about to complete a routine flight from Columbus, Ohio, to LaGuardia Airport.

It had been at five thousand feet approaching LaGuardia, its blip moving steadily on a LaGuardia Approach Control radarscope. The controller spotted something else on the scope.

"Unidentified target approaching you . . . six miles . . . jet traffic," he told TWA.

"Roger, acknowledged," TWA replied.

The controller watched the two blips carefully. He paged TWA again.

"Unidentified object . . . three miles . . . two o'clock."

"Roger, acknowledged," TWA responded.

The two blips moved unerringly toward each other, like a pair of tiny bugs scurrying for the same piece of food.

They merged.

The second blip was the UAL jet coming into Idlewild International Airport from Chicago. An outboard engine of the DC-8 sliced into the Constellation's fuselage with the force of a giant meat cleaver. The smaller plane fell instantly to the ground. Aboard the faltering, mortally stricken jet, one engine ripped off by the impact, Captain R. H. Sawyer fought to keep it in the air long enough for a landing.

The jetliner staggered lower and lower over the rooftops of Brooklyn. One wing tilted as the plane surrendered to its wounds and cracked into the roof of a four-story apartment house. The plane roared into Sterling Place, hit the ground, cartwheeled and rammed the Methodist Pillar of Fire Church. Aircraft and house of worship burst into flames. Burning debris exploded in every direction. Ten more buildings on Sterling Place and nearby Seventh Avenue caught fire.

The tail of the DC-8 snapped off, hurtled through the air and came down squarely in the center of the intersection of Seventh and Sterling. Its tip rested on the engine hood of a truck that had just halted for a stop sign.

One hundred and thirty-four persons were dead, eight of them bystanders and the remainder in the two planes. It could have been worse. The TWA plane fell only one hundred feet from Public School 41, where the children pressed close to the classroom windows and stared at the destruction outside. The UAL jet crashed just one block away from two parochial schools with seventeen hundred students and teachers inside.

Riding in the rear section of the DC-8 was an eleven-year-old boy named Stephen Baltz of Wilmette, Illinois. His father had put him on the plane in Chicago that morning for a visit with his grandparents, who were waiting for him at Idlewild. When the jet's tail broke off, the boy was tossed into a snowbank. Two policemen and a woman rushed over. The youngster sat up, dazed.

"My name is Stephen," he grasped through blackened lips. "Mommy. Daddy."

There were burns over 80 per cent of his body. The only survivor, he fought hard for his life and so did a platoon of doctors. One leg was broken in addition to his burns. But he managed to talk to CAB investigators, who had tears in their eyes as they listened to his story. He said he remembered looking out of the plane's window at the snow-covered city below.

"It looked like a picture out of a fairy book," he told them. "It was a beautiful sight. Then all of a sudden there was an explosion. I held onto my seat and then the plane crashed."

A city and a nation rooted and prayed for Stevie Baltz. The hospital was flooded with calls offering blood donations or skin for grafting. Shortly after 1 P.M. the day after the collision, Stevie's father emerged from his son's hospital room. His fist was clenched so hard, the knuckles were icy white.

"Well, our Stevie passed away around 1 P.M," he said.

He blinked, fighting to keep his composure.

"Stevie tried awfully hard because my son was a wonderful boy," Mr. Baltz added. "Not because he was my son, but because he was . . . he was Stevie."

A nurse burst into tears. So did a reporter. Young Stevie Baltz was the one hundred and thirty-fifth victim.

In United Press International's New York bureau, an editor was looking up the background of the Pillar of Fire Church. The Revisionist Methodist sect had received its name from a biblical quotation about the children of Israel leaving Egypt, the editor read. Curiously, he thumbed through a Bible looking for the quotation. He found it—Exodus 13:21.

> *And the Lord went before them by day in a pillar of cloud to lead them along the way, and by night in a pillar of fire to give them light, that they might travel by day and by night.*

Only one month before the Staten Island collision, and after the
FAA had poured nearly a half billion dollars into air traffic
control projects since the Grand Canyon disaster, then FAA Administrator Elwood R. Quesada had proudly told the National
Press Club in Washington that jets were being monitored by radar
"from takeoff to touchdown."

The events of December 16 showed only too well that radar
coverage was not what the airlines and their flight crews had
been led to believe.

At 10:31, the Idlewild Air Route Traffic Control Center, which
was monitoring United Flight 826 on radar, informed the flight:
"If holding is necessary at Preston (a radio check point), south-
west one minute pattern right turns on the radical south of
Robbinsville . . ."

UAL confirmed these instructions for what was to be the usual
circular "racetrack" pattern for holding at an assigned altitude
until ATC cleared it for final approach.

At 10:32, Flight 826 advised Idlewild ARTC it was descending
from six thousand feet to five thousand. ARTC replied: "826,
roger and you received the holding instruction at Preston. *Radar
service is terminated* [author's italics]. Contact Idlewild Approach
Control. Good day."

At 10:33, United notified Approach Control: "Approaching Preston at five thousand."

Approach Control told the flight to maintain that altitude, advised that little or no delay was expected at Preston, and then gave
826 a weather report and landing instructions.

United never acknowledged receipt of either the weather or the
landing instructions although confirmation was mandatory. Obviously, the collision occurred while Approach Control was transmitting that information—a communication that took exactly *sixteen seconds.*

Sixteen seconds. It had been just sixteen seconds earlier that
826 had specifically advised it was "approaching Preston at five
thousand." Yet the collision took place over Staten Island. To fly
from Preston, where United said it was, to the point of collision
over Staten Island would have required a speed of more than one
thousand miles an hour!

In actuality, the timetable established two facts:

(1) Flight 826 was not where its instruments showed it was.

When it messaged "approaching Preston" it was eleven miles beyond and was racing through the buffer zone that separates Idlewild traffic from that of LaGuardia, where TWA was about to land.

(2) Radar could *not* have been monitoring 826 very efficiently. Only eighty-eight seconds before the collision, ARTC had informed the flight "radar service is terminated." The jet right then and there had to be far off course and this deadly discrepancy should have been spotted on radar.

If that much was clear, why did 826 sail through the Preston holding point like a motorist running a red light? A navigation error? Faulty navigation signals from the ground? The CAB's answer many months later sent United and ALPA into wrathful orbit.

The Board put the entire blame for the collision on the crew of the jet. The pilots had failed, the CAB ruled, to report one of their two key radio navigation instruments out of service. At the speed the DC-8 was making, the crew was unable to determine their exact position soon enough with only one of the navigation signal receivers working. If the malfunction had been reported, the CAB added, 826 would have been handled more carefully by ATC.

United protested the verdict with every legal weapon available and won a partial victory. No less than one hundred and fifteen damage suits were filed against the two airlines and the FAA. The CAB's own hearings were followed by five months of testimony before a federal judge, consuming about fourteen thousand pages of argument over claims totaling more than $77 million.

The FAA denied any guilt. But United, TWA and the Justice Department, in an effort to end the legal wrangling and speed up settlement of the claims, agreed to share damage payments in what amounted to varying degrees of admitted responsibility— United 60 per cent, the federal government 25 per cent, and TWA 15 per cent. Quesada's successor, Najeeb Halaby, went as high as Attorney General Robert Kennedy to fight the proposed compromise settlement. He argued that for the federal government to pay 25 per cent of the damages was an admission that FAA was 25 per cent responsible for the tragedy. The Justice Department rejected his protest, as well it should have. Halaby was trying to protect his controllers not only from a stigma but from fears of future legal recriminations, yet there was not the slightest doubt that ATC's existing deficiencies contributed to the collision. Based on actions the FAA took after Staten Island, it easily could be argued that those deficiencies were major causal factors, the CAB's blaming the United pilots notwithstanding.

A few days after the collision, the FAA drastically reduced speed limits for aircraft entering terminal areas. The agency began assigning extra controllers at high-density traffic centers, their specific duties consisting of watching radarscopes for any planes straying from terminal area clearances and holding patterns. The FAA also improved radar "hand off" protection—the process under which one ATC center hands off traffic to the next jurisdiction. There had been a decided lack of hand-off continuity in the handling of Flight 826 from ARTC to Approach Control.

Next came an FAA order for mandatory installation of two navigation aids in all jet-powered aircraft by the end of 1963 and in all airliners by the end of 1964.

One was the transponder, a device which ties directly into the ATC system. A signal from the ground sends out a radio beam which hits a transponder in the plane. The transponder returns to ground radar a coded signal which automatically identifies the target and pinpoints its position.

The second was distance-measuring equipment (DME). This transmits an air-to-ground beam to the next radio checkpoint on an airway. The ground station returns a signal telling the pilot precisely how far he is from the checkpoint, the information being displayed on a tiny meter that ticks off the mileage as an automobile trip speedometer does. DME is an almost foolproof navigation backstop now, in accordance with FAA regulations, on all commercial transports and many smaller planes.

During Halaby's regime and later under the administration of his less colorful but equally able successor, William F. (Bozo) McKee, FAA continued to make tremendous strides in air traffic control. By Janaury 1, 1964, FAA had expanded what is known as "area positive control" to virtually all airspace above twenty-four thousand feet within the continental United States. Positive control provides long-range radar monitoring protection to high-flying jets. Airspace under such control cannot be entered without permission. Aircraft using it must operate under instrument flight rules (IFR) and be equipped with transponders for quick and accurate radar identification.

The FAA, which assumed control of military traffic when it came into existence, has since taken over control of certain phases of the Air Defense Command's interceptor missions. This action put fighter planes practicing interceptor missions under jurisdiction of ATC, with their movements monitored by FAA radar and their whereabouts known to civilian controllers. The order was issued after several near-collisions in 1963, caused by interceptors operating without ATC knowledge in federal airways.

New "bright display" radars are gradually going into ATC centers throughout the nation, although not as rapidly as either the airliners or FAA itself would like. These solve an old problem—the inability of controllers to see radar targets on screens exposed to daylight, such as those in control towers. The ATC centers themselves have been reduced in number to improve efficiency and eliminate potentially hazardous and confusing hand-offs from one center jurisdiction to another.

In the fall of 1963, FAA announced a major break-through in collision prevention: the development of a system that adds the dimension of altitude to radarscopes. Radar's biggest weakness has been its inability to determine a target's altitude; a target blip at three thousand feet looks the same as one at thirty thousand. The new system, known as alpha-numerics, will be a vital part of the ATC of the future and already is in operation, on a test basis, at several major centers. It supplements the transponder identification system by adding a second ground radio signal, one that intercepts the target aircraft and receives a coded altitude report in addition to the flight identification and position. The alpha-numerics display puts altitude, flight number and even attitude next to the target blip, with tiny green arrows pointing up or down to indicate climbing or descending. The airborne altitude data are extremely accurate because they are supplied electrically instead of by barometric pressure.

The combined DME/transponder program cost the airlines $50 million for installation of the necessary airborne equipment, not to mention the slightly higher amount FAA spent for the ground hardware. The altitude transponder, scheduled to be installed on two out of every three airliners by 1970, is running $5000 per aircraft. The latter will not only vastly improve radar coverage but will also reduce the communications workload, which now hamstrings both pilots and controllers and is a potential collision hazard. Before the transponder system came into being, many ground-ordered course changes were for radar identification, and until alpha-numerics gets into full operation, there still must be air–ground communications to establish altitude. The communications load has lessened somewhat and will be reduced further in the near future, but there are seeds of trouble planted in possible verbal misunderstandings as well as in pilot-controller distractions stemming from workload. An example of a communication foulup that nearly caused a collision occurred when a controller in contact with two airline flights cleared Flight 126 to descend to ten thousand feet. A Flight 26, holding at twelve thousand, acknowledged and made an unauthorized descent.

Quite obviously and quite necessarily, the bulk of improvements in air traffic control has concentrated on the "crowded sky" aspects—reducing the chances of collision in heavily traveled airways used by the faster aircraft, and in the high-density terminal areas of major airports. But as in almost every phase of air safety, industry and government can plug major loopholes—as was done after December 16, 1960—and still find tragedy slipping unexpectedly through a relative pinhole.

And this is what happened on July 19, 1967, at an unlikely location for a terrifying mid-air collision—the peaceful community of Hendersonville, North Carolina, whose airport handled so little traffic that it did not have a radar surveillance set.

Piedmont Flight 22 was a Boeing 727, scheduled from Atlanta to Washington with intermediate stops at the Asheville/Hendersonville Airport (the field serves both cities) and Roanoke, Virginia.

The jet's seventy-four passengers included one dignitary, Secretary-designate of the Navy John McNaughton, who boarded with his wife and eleven-year-old son. They were returning from a trip to Weaverville, North Carolina, where the boy had been attending summer camp. News photographers took pictures of the newly appointed Navy secretary and his smiling family at the airport restaurant before they went out to their plane.

Shortly before Flight 22 took off from the Asheville/Hendersonville Airport, a twin-engine Cessna 310 was approaching the field. The pilot was David Addison, forty, experienced, competent and qualified to fly on instruments; he was on an IFR flight plan, as a matter of fact. The plane was owned by an aviation insurance company in Missouri.

At 11:58 A.M., he reported to the Asheville Control Tower that he was over the Asheville Omni—a navigation radio signal about seventeen miles from the airport.

"Cessna two-one Sierra," the tower said. "You are cleared to the Broad River radio beacon to maintain six thousand . . ."

At this point, the controller paused. Piedmont 22 was just taking off to the southeast. The controller's clearance to the Cessna would have taken Addison on a southeast course, toward the radio navigation beacon known as Broad River. The controller changed the clearance.

"Correction," he said quickly to Addison. "You are cleared to the Asheville radio beacon for an ADF [automatic direction finder] approach to runway one-six at Asheville. Maintain six thousand."

This revised clearance was an order to approach from the northwest, toward a different radio beacon and away from any possible conflict with the jet.

"Cessna two-one Sierra, roger," Addison confirmed.

At 12:01 P.M., the Cessna and the 727 collided, the smaller plane coming up from behind and below, ripping into the jetliner's fuselage just in back of the left wing. Eyewitnesses said bodies fell out of the airliner "like confetti." The Cessna disintegrated in a ball of fire. One wing separated from the 727 and the jet nosed down, going into a slow spiral just before it crashed into the ground. All seventy-nine aboard were killed, including five crew members. Addison and the three passengers in his plane also perished.

At Washington National Airport, Flight 22's final destination, Pentagon aide Colonel Robert Hixon was waiting for the new Navy secretary. Nearby stood Mrs. Lillian Hahlbeck, whose daughter Glenna had been visiting in North Carolina and was due back that day.

The airport loudspeaker system asked those waiting for Flight 22 to go to Gate 25. Hixon felt uneasy as he walked toward Gate 25. The plane was due at 12:57; it was now 1:35 and there already had been whispered rumors around the airport that "Piedmont dropped one."

Don Shanks, the airline's area manager, ushered the silent people into a private lounge, closed the door and quietly told them that Flight 22 had crashed, with no survivors. Colonel Hixon shook his head and went back to the Pentagon to report to his superiors. Mrs. Hahlbeck started to cry. Shanks called an airport nurse who stayed with the sobbing woman all afternoon until she boarded another Piedmont plane bound for Asheville.

If grief was the reaction in that small lounge, indignation was the reaction on Capitol Hill. As usual, those waxing indignant didn't wait for investigators to start putting the pieces of tragedy together. In the next forty-eight hours, there were at least a half-dozen demands that the FAA segregate all private plane traffic from airports used by commercial transports. This was the year's second collision involving an airliner and a small private plane. The previous March, a twin-engine Beech Baron had collided with a TWA DC-9, near Urbana, Ohio, the impact severing the jet's cockpit from the rest of the plane and taking twenty-six persons to their death. Some of the Congressional statements bewailed the dangers of inexperienced private pilots invading airways used by airliners—a legitimate concern and one shared fervently by airline pilots, but not exactly relevant to the Urbana and Hendersonville collisions. Both Addison and the pilot of the Beech were veterans, perhaps not as skilled as the average airline pilot, but far above the caliber of the average private pilot in experience.

There was no explanation for Addison's failure to follow the changed clearance, a failure that took him eight miles southeast of the airport when he should have been flying northwest. A number of possibilities were still under investigation at this writing—instrument malfunction, incorrect tuning of his navigational radio or a misinterpretation of his position as he approached the airport. One possible clue was the fact that his approved flight plan, filed with the FAA in Atlanta, had called for an instrument approach from the southeast. Without knowing why the Asheville controller had changed this, he might have been shifting mental gears—subconsciously delaying compliance because his mind still was fixed on the original course. He didn't have much time; the revised clearance was transmitted only three minutes before the collision.

Another possibility was that Addison may have been using a Coast and Geodetic Survey aeronautical chart which did not have the Asheville radio beacon marked, as did the more detailed Jeppesen charts. Whether he referred to the government or the Jeppesen maps could not be determined, but if it was the former it would have been easy for him to tune in on the one beacon that chart did list—the wrong one. Under pressure of time and proximity to landing, he could have glanced down at the chart and mistaken the listed beacon for the Asheville nav aid.

One thing stood out, however: the controller himself was operating "blind," without radar. The Asheville/Hendersonville Airport was not eligible for radar because it handled, in 1966, just under fifty-four thousand itinerant aircraft "movements"—takeoffs and landings. To qualify for radar, the FAA requires an airport to log at least one hundred thousand annual movements by planes not based at the airport. The qualification standard is economic, not arbitrary; it would cost an estimated $500 million to install radar at all airports used by the scheduled airlines.

There are five hundred and twenty-six such airports in the United States. On July 19, 1967, *four hundred and thirty-four of these lacked surveillance radar of the type that might have prevented the Piedmont collision.* But that is only part of the story. Of those five hundred and twenty-six airports, two hundred and ninety-two did not even have FAA-manned control towers! As with radar, this deficiency can be traced to the FAA's economy-dictated qualification rules: to get a control tower, an airport has to have at least twenty-four thousand itinerant airport movements. There is not the slightest doubt in the world that the Hendersonville collision could be repeated at any of the more than four hundred airports without radar or at the nearly three hundred devoid of control towers.

Bad-weather operations at these "blind" airports are severely limited, of course. But most collisions take place in good weather when pilots are supposed to rely on the old "seen and be seen" rule of collision avoidance. The rule is pitifully, pathetically obsolete because modern aircraft, even many of the smaller private planes, fly at speeds defying the limits of human vision and reaction time. The Cessna of the type involved at Hendersonville cruises about sixty miles an hour faster than the DC-3. And the local service airlines serving these towerless and radarless airports are operating such transports as Convairs, Martins and even jet-powered F-27s—all of them fast enough to provide nearly the closure speed of a bullet when on collision course with a high-speed private plane or one of their own kind.

The National Transportation Safety Board emphasized the vulnerability of "see or be seen" in its report on the collision between the TWA DC-9 and a Beech over Ohio in March of 1967. The Board actually pinned the majority of blame on the TWA crew, because the airliner was the overtaking aircraft and its pilots presumably were in a better position to spot and avoid the smaller plane. The investigation also disclosed that the jetliner was flying excessively fast for a plane entering a terminal area, in this case Dayton, Ohio.

But the Board softened its castigation by acknowledging that the air traffic control system itself was not without some responsibility—literally a sin of omission rather than commission. As the report put it:

"ATC cannot assure an appropriate level of safety between 'known' and 'unknown' traffic operations, nor can the pilots of high-speed modern aircraft safely operate these aircraft in accordance with 'see or be seen' VFR right-of-way rules in the short space of time available to them for detection and corrective action."

In essence, the Board was pointing to the overly frequent conflicts between IFR and VFR traffic, the former operating under the guidance and protection of ATC while the latter can be wandering into the same airspace, its presence unknown to controllers or their IFR traffic. In the Urbana tragedy, TWA was approaching the Dayton airport unaware of the Beech's proximity until eighteen seconds before the collision, when the Dayton controller warned, ". . . traffic at twelve-thirty, one mile, southbound, slow-moving." The tardy warning was not due to any lack of alertness on the part of the controller; his radar simply did not pick up the small plane's target until the last minute. Nor was ATC cognizant that the Beech was in the area, inasmuch as its pilot was flying VFR without a flight plan and was not communicating with Dayton because he was about to land at nearby Springfield.

The cockpit voice recorder recovered from the DC-9 revealed that after receiving and acknowledging ATC's warning, the pilots became occupied almost immediately with voluminous pre-landing duties. The last recorded words came from the copilot, who informed the man in the left seat, "Ready on the checklist, Captain." At this point, the jet was only two or three seconds away from collision. Obviously, the DC-9 crew was concentrating on their forthcoming landing and not outside their busy cockpit.

A year after the Urbana disaster, an Ozark DC-9 and a private plane collided near Lambert Field, St. Louis. The smaller aircraft, a Cessna 150, did not appear on the radarscopes monitoring the air-liner's flight. History then repeated itself five months later when a North Central Convair and a private plane rammed each other, the crew of the transport being totally unaware that there was con-flicting traffic in the area.

The FAA has ordered lower speed limits for planes operating below ten thousand feet, but the agency knows only too well that the new rules are a rather flabby safety step. On modern jets, even at low speeds, cockpit workload precludes any extensive "lookout" operations. This is particularly true in jets flown by two-man crews, who usually are occupied to the extent of relying almost totally on ATC for collision avoidance. When this reliance is placed on towers which lack radar or which employ obsolete sets, it is painfully easy to see why collisions occur.

It is illuminating to examine the record of Congress in supplying the FAA with funds specifically earmarked for airport radar instal-lations. In 1964, the agency asked for $177 million and got $140 million. In 1965 it asked for $177 million and received $90 million. In 1966, FAA requested $91 million and was granted $87 million. Not only has funding been inadequate, but what money the FAA does obtain is doled out mostly to the airports where traffic density makes radar absolutely essential. This was one reason for establish-ing a priority system based on total aircraft takeoffs and landings.

Nor is Congressional parsimony the only villain; through the years, the Bureau of the Budget has repeatedly emasculated air safety funds. For fiscal '68, the FAA asked the Budget Bureau to approve $80 million for new control towers, radar and instrument landing systems.

The Bureau cut this to $35.4 million and also slashed nearly $7 million for the FAA's operations budget—out of which controllers are paid—despite warnings that traffic and workload increases have aggravated chronic controller shortages.

The House, many of whose members expressed loud alarm and hand-wringing concern over air safety after the Piedmont accident, cut the fiscal '68 FAA appropriations *even below* the Budget Bu-reau's incredibly shortsighted and niggardly allowance. It took the

Senate not only to restore the FAA's full requested amount but also to add $30 million more—the extra funds earmarked for safety work. FAA's proposed fiscal '69 budget was a whopping $1.6 billion and it will be interesting, as you read this book, to see if Congress literally has put its money where its mouth is. Tragedy is so quick to shock, yet so easy to forget. Since the Grand Canyon collision of 1956, more than forty Congressional committees have held hearings on air safety, with little tangible results—except for the usual disclosure that Congressional lethargy and Budget Bureau butchery were at least partially responsible for whatever major disaster prompted somebody to call a hearing.

Some lawmakers, in the wake of every crash, immediately castigate the FAA for spending millions without achieving air safety. The charge is not only untrue but also ducks the responsibility of Congress itself. Certainly there have been inefficiency, foot-dragging and mistakes within the FAA's bureaucracy. But for every single boner the FAA has pulled that warrants criticism, it has a half-dozen accomplishments warranting praise. In the past decade, the number of controllers has doubled. The ATC system, once equipped to handle only ten thousand IFR flights daily, now fields more than twenty thousand. Obviously, this is impressive but at the same time insufficient. To quote a Washington *Post* editorial published the day after Flight 22 plunged to destruction:

> Six and a half years ago, General Quesada left the FAA with the warning that the Government needed to spend $150 million a year for the next ten years if our ability to control planes in the air was to keep up with the advances in the quantity and speed of aircraft. Five years ago, Mr. Halaby produced a plan to automate air traffic control over the next five years. It would have cost about $500 million. What happened? We know that the money was not forthcoming from Congress to do the job. We do not know how many Americans died because the job was not done.

In truth a considerable amount *has* been done, considering the scope of the nation's mushrooming air traffic. Talk about "crowded skies" has obscured the fact that most collisions have occurred in relatively empty airspace, in clear weather. From past statistics and experiences, Hendersonville was more likely to happen than Staten Island. David Thomas, FAA's Deputy Administrator and a former controller himself, points out that the majority of near-collisions and inadvertent traffic conflicts, as well as actual collisions, take place when traffic is not abnormally heavy and when pilots and controllers alike tend to relax.

Thus, in discussing what has to be done to assure safer expanding traffic in contracting airspace, we must consider the small problems as well as the big. And this includes the needs of the small airplane as well as the large.

There are approximately 200,000 commercial, business and private flights a day in the United States. The FAA's air traffic control system handles only about 10 per cent of that number, and ATC's workload is further compressed by the fact that 50 per cent of the nation's air travelers originate at just ten airports. Our so-called "crowded skies" are limited not only to a relative handful of terminal areas, but to the periods of the day (1) when air traffic peaks in these areas and (2) when weather is bad.

It is seldom understood that the ATC system figuratively is a gigantic safety valve, designed to withstand the buildup of dangerous pressures. In other words, the system will neither accept nor absorb traffic which it cannot handle safely. Thus, the current inadequacies of ATC result in delays far more than in danger. They create inconvenience to a far greater extent than they create near-collisions and collisions. Many of the reforms planned for ATC involve increased efficiency as much as safety, although achievement of the former would have a fall-out beneficial to the latter.

What worries the planners, in industry as well as government, is that the present system—barely adequate some of the time—will be hopelessly inadequate in the near future. About two thousand airliners, more than one hundred thousand general aviation (private and business aircraft) and twenty thousand military planes now use the airspace.

By 1977, the airline fleet will have grown to thirty-five hundred planes. General aviation aircraft will number an estimated one hundred and eighty thousand. Only the military fleet may decline, but this will be offset by an amazing increase in the number of business jets that will require the same judicious control as bombers and fighters do today. According to FAA forecasts, so-called executive jets in 1977 will total at least eight thousand, outnumbering the airlines' own jet fleet by more than two to one.

In 1967, FAA control facilities handled more than 15 million aircraft making nearly 50 million takeoffs and landings. This represents a doubling of traffic over the past ten years, but by 1977 the traffic volume is expected to triple—to about 139 million landings and takeoffs made by more than 31 million planes.

The blueprints for coping with this aeronautical explosion already have been drawn and some "hardware" has progressed from blueprint stage to field testing or actual operation. Alpha-numerics, as mentioned previously, is on the verge of full-scale implementation at major centers. The system has developed bugs, inevitable in a complicated electronics network, although not to the extent of proving unworkable, as some critics have claimed. Alpha-numerics is a form of automation, and automation in its early stages usually causes a temporary increase in manual workload. Alpha-numerics is no cure-all, however. Its expensive airborne transponders are intended solely for airliners and most business aircraft which can afford the equipment. Alpha-numerics is merely Phase A of ATC's automation plan; Phase B, scheduled to be in existence by 1977, calls for computers which will digest all flight plans and will have the capability of predicting traffic conflicts in sufficient time to prevent any plane from invading airspace reserved for another.

This futuristic world of virtually all-electronic traffic control, however, admittedly is geared for fielding traffic in high-density areas, such as major airport hubs, and along the aerial highways used by jets. It still may fall short of collision prevention because of conflicts with smaller aircraft lacking sophisticated electronic aids or flown by pilots with little experience. Thus, some of today's problems will not necessarily be solved by the hardware of the future.

The airlines themselves, through the Air Transport Association, have proposed a broad series of steps to be taken within ATC. In addition to supporting such developments as alpha-numerics and radar protection at all airports served by the scheduled carriers, ATA wants:

—Enlargement of "airport traffic areas." Presently, every airport with a control tower has theoretical jurisdiction over traffic flying within a five-mile radius of the airport, up to two thousand feet. This means a plane operating VFR can fly as low as two thousand feet and as close as five miles to a major terminal area without advising the tower of its presence. A VFR pilot could even fly under two thousand feet if he is landing at another airport within the current five-mile radius. This rule has led to more than one near-miss, and may have contributed to the collision at St. Louis in March of 1968. Not only are towers often unaware of this type of VFR traffic, but radar does not always spot it. Small planes do not register well on most radarscopes. Airline pilots frequently will take evasive action to miss a private airplane, ask the tower if it was aware of the conflicting traffic and receive the reply: "He wasn't on our radar." ATA wants airport traffic areas expanded to include airspace up to five thousand feet and embracing all traffic within at least a fifteen-mile radius.

—To require all pilots flying in and out of high-traffic areas such as Kennedy, O'Hare, Washington National, Los Angeles, Atlanta and Miami to be at least instrument-qualified and to have enough radio and navigation equipment to permit utilization of ATC facilities.

Expansion of "positive control" to lower altitudes. "Positive control" refers to an FAA regulation requiring all planes flying above a certain altitude to file flight plans and operate under ATC jurisdiction. Presently, the positive control floor is twenty-four thousand feet except in the northeastern and north central states, where the floor has been lowered to eighteen thousand. ATA believes positive control down to ten thousand feet should be in effect by 1969 within the "Golden Triangle" embracing New York, Washington and Chicago, and by 1970 between Los Angeles and San Francisco. The airlines also want positive control extended all the way down from ten thousand feet to the ground in certain high-density airport areas such as New York, Chicago, Los Angeles, San Francisco and Washington.

These three proposals, and other similar recommendations for stiffer restrictions on private pilots, are anathema to general aviation groups, who feel strongly that the airspace belongs to all airmen. The opposition ranges from the vitriolic reactions of the Aircraft Owners and Pilots Association to somewhat calmer objections raised by light-plane manufacturers and other private and business pilot organizations.

Early in 1968, AOPA mailed ten thousand copies of a twenty-four page booklet to newspapers and city officials titled "The Truth About General Aviation." It was a gloves-off attack on the airlines, accusing them as the prime cause of airport congestion and charging that the carriers are attempting to force general aviation from the nation's airports.

"Congestion and delay on the runways has been caused by airline scheduling practices and compounded by the insistence of the airlines that their aircraft operate under Instrument Flight Rules, designed for bad weather, even when the weather is good," the AOPA publication declared.

These two points deserve analysis. AOPA's complaint that the airlines insist on IFR operations even in good weather would be unbelievably naïve coming from anyone but an aviation organization. The carriers *do* demand all-IFR, and strictly from a safety standpoint. They want their pilots and planes under ATC guidance at all times, which is what IFR involves. They want controllers to know the whereabouts of every commercial flight as a means of avoiding traffic conflicts and possible collisions. And this is precisely why they also are seeking mandatory IFR for all planes operating at altitudes used by airliners. AOPA's persistent claim that high-speed aircraft can fly safely under the old "see and be seen" policy is as obsolete as the Ford Trimotor.

On the question of airline scheduling practices AOPA has more of a logical argument. The carriers estimate that air traffic delays cost them at least $50 million annually at airports with FAA control towers, with losses of about $30 million just at the twenty-three largest airports. But part of the delays stem from the industry's habit of peak-hour scheduling—which to the average controller provides the same pleasant sound that "Marching Through Georgia" gives a Southerner.

Peak-hour scheduling is when the airlines furnish the greatest number of flights at the hours the greatest number of people prefer to fly. The times usually are between 7 A.M. and 9 A.M., and 5 P.M. to 7 P.M. FAA figures show there is a 75 per cent increase in major airport traffic in the two-hour period starting at 5 P.M., both arrivals and departures. This overloading of facilities has an unhappy consequence: the 75 per cent increase in traffic winds up with a 125 per cent increase in delays. Washington's National Airport is just one example (and O'Hare, Kennedy and Los Angeles can be worse):

In a three-minute period between 4:55 P.M. and 4:58 P.M., Na-

tional has eight airline flights scheduled to arrive and five departing flights seeking takeoff clearance.

At 5:55 P.M., there are seven scheduled arrivals and only five
minutes later, the airlines have seven flights wanting to leave
—which adds up to fourteen flights trying to take off or land in a
five-minute period. That kind of scheduling would cause delays
even if National were closed to all but airline operations. Add private
and business pilots' preferences for late afternoon departures and
you have airport congestion.

The airlines are well aware of peak-hour scheduling problems
but like politicians who are all for economy in the other guy's
district, every carrier would be happy to see reductions in peak-
hour scheduling—provided competitors did the reducing. No single
airline dares to take the initiative; passenger departure and arrival
demands follow a set and apparently immovable pattern, so pronounced that one carrier which actually tried to ease congestion
by shifting a popular 5 P.M. flight to 4:30 P.M. wound up losing
20 per cent of its usual load to another airline with a competitive
5 P.M. flight.

Peak-hour scheduling is not the only source of delays, to be
perfectly fair about it. Weather is an obvious one. And a seldom
considered cause is overly frequent FAA equipment failures. A
single radar malfunction at Kennedy once caused traffic delays of
more than two hours and diversion of twenty-five flights to other
airports. The New York Air Route Traffic Control Center recently
reported communications malfunctions totaling about three hundred and thirty-five hours in a little more than a one-month period.
This, too, is a financial problem. FAA simply lacks the funds for
adequate backup and standby equipment at its control centers and
towers. After the famous New York City blackout of a few years
ago, FAA obtained the money to provide standby electrical power
for its runway lighting. But similar protection for radar and communication facilities is sadly lacking and represents a potential
collision hazard.

All segments of aviation agree that something must be done
about airport congestion. In just three short years—from 1965 to
1968—the United States has increased by 22 per cent its number
of airplanes, which, in turn, are flying 25 per cent more hours,
carrying 54 per cent more passengers, making 48 per cent more
landings and takeoffs at airports where FAA has towers, and con-

ducting 45 per cent more instrument flights. In that same period, the number of pilots jumped 31 per cent and requests for federal airport aid increased by 90 per cent.

Some of the proposed solutions are on the drastic side, but perhaps drastic action is the only solution. There is, for example, the concept of the circular runway, which is just what the name implies. Think of a wheel with spokes. The outer rim is the runway. The spokes are taxiways. The hub is the control tower and terminal building. No such airport exists, but military pilots have landed experimentally on a circular track at the General Motors Automobile Proving Ground near Williams Air Force Base in Arizona.

The circular runway, as is the GM track, would have to be banked to overcome centrifugal force. Obviously, pilots would have to learn new techniques, particularly in landing, because they'd be lining up in final approach with one wing low. But the theoretical advantages are many. There could never be an undershoot or overshoot at a circular airport because a circle is endless. The concept offers unlimited flexibility in planning approach and landing corridors. Traffic control would be simplified, with control towers parked in the center of a circle. And finally, a circular airport would require about one third less acreage than a conventional terminal facility.

The Lockheed Aircraft Corporation actually has proposed a network of circular airports to be located at mid-points along heavily traveled air corridors. They would serve as regional transfer facilities, each airport consisting of five concentric circular runways accommodating everything from supersonic transports to light planes. For example, a flight from London to Washington would land at one of these transfer facilities closest to Washington, and the passengers would be shuttled to the capital.

Money, of course, is the chief bone of contention in eliminating airport congestion as a factor in collisions. The airlines want general aviation to pay a greater share of federal airway user charges, arguing that general aviation use of FAA instrument landing facilities has jumped from 5.7 per cent of total instrument approaches in 1951 to 27 per cent in 1967, and will reach an estimated 50 per cent by 1976. General aviation spokesmen, on the other hand, feel that private pilots are being accused unfairly of constituting a major menace to safety and that increased user charges is a thinly disguised means of getting them out of the skies.

There is no doubt there has been too much generalization in depicting the general aviation pilot as the chief culprit in airport traffic conflicts. There also has been too much generalization by some private pilots that the airlines are irrevocably anti-general aviation. The Air Transport Association's official policy calls for increased facilities to serve *both* segments of aviation—perhaps, in the case of smaller planes, either new general aviation "reliever" airports as conveniently located as major terminals or construction of new runways at the latter for the exclusive use of non-airline traffic.

It is natural for an organization like AOPA, representing as it does the interests of thousands of private pilots, to fear new regulations that would require installation of expensive equipment as a prerequisite for operating at the bigger airports, plus proficiency rechecks of private pilots at regular intervals. Nevertheless, increasing general aviation traffic may inevitably result in stiffer rules to protect not only the millions who fly the scheduled carriers, but also to protect experienced private pilots from their less proficient brethren. It is true that the air is free and that a private pilot has a right to use the airspace, just as a Volkswagen has as much right to the freeways and turnpikes as buses and trucks. But rights are usually accompanied by responsibility toward their exercise; the airlines also have a right to the nation's airspace, yet they are by all odds the most regulated industry in the world. By contrast, approximately 30 per cent of private planes lack two-way radios, which the FAA does not require for such aircraft.

It is the inexperienced, "Sunday driver" type of airman that airline pilots fear, and also the irresponsible fool who drinks before he flies.

"I'd rather shoot a landing with a fifty-foot ceiling than come into an airport on a clear, sunny Saturday or Sunday afternoon," a captain once remarked to me. "Sure, a private pilot is a taxpayer with a right to use a public airport. But I've got about a hundred taxpayers on my airplane with some rights, too—a right to expect safety."

Drinking and drug consumption among private pilots, while its extent is a subject of statistical controversy, could be a major safety matter in the future—and definitely a potential source of a catastrophic mid-air collision. An FAA survey disclosed that alcohol was a factor in one third of all fatal general aviation accidents during the year 1963. AOPA considered FAA's publicizing that figure an unfair slur on the majority of private pilots, and also questioned its validity. But the fact remains that drunken flying can kill a lot more people in a single accident than any case of drunken driving. Dr. Stanley Mohler, head of FAA's Aeromedical Applications Division, has warned that one ounce of whisky or a single beer can dilute airmanship by a significant amount.

Common medicinal drugs also have been known to impair pilot performance. And there is at least one case on record involving the use of LSD, an incident in which a drug-crazed man jumped out of a light plane after announcing that he could fly, sans aircraft. LSD as a serious safety problem may seem farfetched, but it is something to ponder with concern when we consider the increasing use of harmful drugs by young people who may also be learning how to fly.

Certainly, the inexperience of many private pilots seems to play a definite role in collisions. Of two hundred and twenty-five collisions reported between 1956 and 1966, two hundred and nineteen involved general aviation aircraft.

Wayne Parrish of American Aviation Publications, in a 1967 speech to an audience composed of controllers, commented on the argument that if airports are built with public funds, any taxpayer has a right to use them. He employed this analogy:

"How far would a horse and buggy get on a busy interstate highway? The owner of the horse and buggy is a taxpayer. The highway was built with public funds. He should be entitled to use it. But the realities of today's traffic rules him off—and fast . . . I, for one, don't believe that general aviation, per se, should be excluded from any airport in the country. But I do say the general aviation equipment that uses high-density airports must come up to the highest standards, it must keep pace, it must be properly equipped, and it must have something better than an amateur pilot. If you can't travel seventy miles an hour on the freeway, you're thrown off. There are other highways and other streets and roads, and there are other airports.

"And this is because air transportation has become very big. The rules and regulations are needed not for the airlines because they're airlines, but because the public is flying."

General aviation is responsible for 98 per cent of the country's aircraft, 96 per cent of its pilots, 79 per cent of the civil hours flown, and 50 per cent of passengers carried. Obviously its needs must be considered, but not in any "we've got as much right to any part of the sky as the airlines" sense. The meat-cleaver tactics of the Budget Bureau and the perpetual procrastinations of Congress have done enough harm to air safety without the added burden of the general aviation-airline feud.

The federal government has been spending and intends to spend around $75 million annually on airway and airport improvements. Senator Mike Monroney, chairman of the Senate Aviation Subcommittee, terms this "a starvation diet." To bring the nation's airway and airport system to a level capable of handling the anticipated traffic of 1975, Monroney warns, will require $4 billion for modernizing air traffic control and $8 billion for new or improved airports, particularly new fields that general aviation can use instead of contributing to the mounting logjams at major airline terminals. ATA estimates a minimum necessary annual expenditure of $150 million through 1975.

Monroney was incensed at a Budget Bureau rejection of a plan to establish a federal trust fund for airport and airway modernization. The proposal was backed by the airlines, FAA, airport operators and at least part of general aviation. The plan, offered in the spring of 1968, would have each segment of civil aviation paying a fair share of the costs. But the Budget Bureau shot the trust fund down, on the grounds that no federal funds should be earmarked for a single purpose because the money might be needed elsewhere. The Bureau was supported by Treasury Department economists, which drew this tart response from Monroney in a speech to the Society of Air Safety Investigators:

"There is no such thing as safety-vs-economic theory. The opposite of safety is lack of safety."

The bickering and quarreling over how to pay for airport/airway modernization, compounded by woefully inadequate funds in the past, had an inevitable result: a partial collapse of the air traffic control system in the hectic New York area and, to a lesser extent, Chicago. This occurred in the midsummer of 1968, touched off by an alleged controller slowdown. In truth, the number of controllers involved was too small to create the havoc that ensued, and havoc is an apt word.

On a single afternoon in July, one airline alone was forced to divert seventeen flights to alternate airports because of excessive delays in the New York area. Airline on-time performance dropped from 90 per cent to less than 50 per cent, due solely to air traffic delays. On a single afternoon, there were sixty planes lined up at Chicago's O'Hare waiting for takeoff clearances. Flights to New York from cities as far away as Los Angeles and Miami were being held up for more than an hour on the ground, unable to take off because of congestion occurring thousands of miles away. Eastern's well-run "shuttle" between New York and Washington experienced delays of up to four hours on flights that normally take forty-five minutes. At one point, midafternoon on a Friday, Eastern tossed in the towel and simply canceled the shuttle for several hours until traffic conditions got back to a state approaching normalcy.

If just New York and Chicago had been involved, the situation would have been only regionally chaotic. But the U.S. air transportation system is so constructed that a delay affecting a single flight at just one airport can cause a chain reaction spreading to airports all the way across the country. Most large airports can handle a maximum of about sixty aircraft per hour. Congestion delays are generated when traffic reaches forty-five planes per hour. Such delays are minor, perhaps about five minutes per flight. But as traffic builds up to the sixty-plane maximum, so do the delays. An airport is likely to experience delays of more than an hour even before the maximum is reached.

And it is ridiculously easy to hit a saturation point. Peak-hour scheduling automatically results in saturation. Add a deliberate controller slowdown to built-in delays and chaos is certain. Toss in the simple factor of increasing numbers of aircraft (the airlines are putting a new jetliner into service every day, and twenty new aircraft are being added daily to the nation's general aviation fleet), and one has to sympathize with the average controller.

It may never be known whether the supposed slowdown was the major reason for the 1968 summer crisis. Certainly, it was a trigger. But responsible FAA officials sincerely believe a partial system collapse was going to come anyway. Air traffic control experts within FAA insist that a single controller should not be forced to handle more than six flights at any given time. In July of 1968, on a typical busy weekend evening, controllers in New York and Chicago were assigned up to fifteen flights apiece. Under these conditions, some kind of slowdown is necessary and the slowdown comes in the form of "flow control"—the point at which a control center advises other centers it can no longer field traffic safely unless the pace of incoming traffic is slowed.

There is only one way to accomplish this. The normal separation of three to five miles between aircraft must be increased to at least twenty miles. This is why you may be sitting in a jetliner on the ground at Los Angeles, wondering why you can't take off for New York under perfect weather conditions. It is because New York has instituted flow control, knowing that when your jet comes into the area it is going to have to wait an hour or more before it can land. On occasions, congestion has been so bad that New York-bound jets have started to hold over Denver.

Admittedly, the FAA itself has consistently underestimated the fantastic air travel expansion and failed to hire sufficient controllers—who, in turn, need about three years' experience before they can be regarded as thoroughly trained. But it does little good to dwell on past sins, whether committed by Presidents, FAA, Congress or the Budget Bureau. It is painfully obvious that the rather limited crisis of 1968 will be repeated on a far greater scale in future years unless something is done *right now*. There should be an airport/airway trust fund, financed by a 2 per cent increase in the airline passenger ticket tax and other user charges imposed as necessary, including higher fuel taxes for general aviation. There is not a single doubt in the world that general aviation, which uses the air traffic control system nearly 30 per cent of the time, has not been paying a proportionate share of maintaining and improving that system. In 1967, general aviation fuel taxes contributed only $7 million, which was less than 5 per cent of what the FAA considered a fair share. Yet any proposal to increase this share has resulted in anguished cries of "You're trying to destroy private aviation." AOPA has gone so far as to accuse Defense Transportation Secretary Boyd of trying to get a fat-salaried airline job by insisting on higher general aviation fuel taxes—an accusation that is not only libelous and unfair, but typical of the senselessly provincial attacks AOPA is so fond of aiming at the government and airlines alike. It is totally inconsistent for general aviation to proclaim it is vitally important to the air transportation system, which it is, and then to mouth AOPA-type assaults on the motives and integrity of the rest of the aviation community.

The feuding plays into the hands of those who have persistently denied aviation the funds it needs to accomplish both greater efficiency and safety. This goes beyond airport and airway modernization. It extends to basic air safety research, such as installation of instrument landing systems at all airports served by jets. Present ILS, because of terrain problems, does not work at some airports. Yet FAA, because of reduced research funding, is ten years behind schedule in developing an ILS that can operate anywhere. Collision prevention is another area in which achievement has been hamstrung by inadequate financial support, to such an extent that the airlines have been doing more in this field than the FAA.

Collisions, of course, are only one aspect of weaknesses in air traffic control; near-misses are equally important because many reflect a catastrophe that *might* have happened.

FAA's critics are fond of reciting near-miss statistics as evidence of ATC inefficiency. The statistics definitely are not reassuring— there have been an average of about five hundred a year since 1960—and the figure may be too low because some pilots have refused to file near-miss reports in fear of FAA punitive action. Administrator McKee early in 1968 announced a new policy exempting any pilot or controller from disciplinary action stemming from a near-miss report. McKee said the agency was making a year-long study of ATC procedures and possible weaknesses and badly needed full and honest reporting of all incidents.

The very phrase "near-miss" has a frightening connotation that is somewhat out of proper perspective. Some near-misses are hairy and involve real danger. Many merely represent a situation in which less than standard separation occurs, prompting a controller or pilot to submit a complaint. A near-miss may be a case of inches or a couple of thousand feet. Some are due to ATC personnel errors, many more are attributed to system weaknesses or carelessness by inexperienced pilots, and there undoubtedly would be a considerably higher percentage if it were not for the devotion and dedication of the unsung heroes who man the nation's control towers and radarscopes. Controllers make between $6,000 and $11,000 a year, not a particularly lucrative return for skills and judgment on which so many lives depend. The FAA's aptitude test for controller applicants has a 90 per cent failure rate. Controllers have a higher than normal rate of ulcers and heart attacks; many would like to be able to retire either at fifty or after twenty years' service, a goal which FAA officials would be happy to see realized if capable replacements (and necessary funds) are available. They work under such pressure that nervous breakdowns are not unknown and there has been one case of suicide involving a controller who had watched a mid-air collision between an airliner and a National Guard jet on his radar set. The investigation cleared him of blame, but the disaster preyed on his mind for several years until he finally took his own life.

Airline pilots, while frequently prone to assign controllers to purgatory, in reality have Brobdingnagian respect for them. A few years ago, the FAA demoted a controller at Washington National Airport for a mistake that endangered two airliners. He inadvertently assigned them to the same altitude for nearly an hour while they both were in a holding pattern. One was an Eastern Electra and the other a United Viscount. The faster Electra passed the Viscount four times in a thick overcast without knowing the United plane was circling at the identical level. Only the Viscount's shorter turning radius kept the two aircraft from colliding. A brief section of the transcript will suffice to express the sentiments of the pilots:

Controller: "Eastern 404, descend to five thousand in the holding pattern."

EAL: "Eastern 404, to five thousand. We're leaving seven."

Controller: "Eastern 404, you're leaving seven?"

EAL: "Roger."

Controller: "United 322, what is your heading?"

UAL: "One-five-zero."

Controller: "Okay Eastern 404, continue on your heading and your descent to five thousand."

EAL: "Roger, heading three-two-zero."

UAL: "How long has he been at seven?"

EAL: "About . . . ah . . . forty-five minutes almost."

UAL: "Holy Christmas! So are we."

EAL: "Where . . . where are you now?"

UAL: "Springfield."

EAL: "Oh, for Heaven's sake! . . ."

Yet after the controller's demotion to a smaller airport was announced, a group of pilots—including those aboard the two planes involved—signed a petition asking FAA to be more lenient and expressing confidence in the controller's ability. The FAA was impressed but not enough to reduce his punishment.

(If the agency's punitive action appears harsh, consider this: the Japanese government once inflicted a long prison term on a controller found responsible for causing a fatal collision.)

There is no chance that near-misses will be eliminated entirely by any current or future program to improve the techniques of controlling air traffic, not even with 100 per cent automation and foolproof electronic gadgets. It is impossible now or ever to give perpetually adequate separation coverage to every square mile of airspace; machines and men alike have been known to fail.

This is why the airlines themselves are preparing to buy the only insurance that promises last-ditch protection against collisions between large aircraft—development of a workable, airborne collision avoidance system (CAS) that operates independently of ATC and, in fact, supplements ATC.

The search for a practical CAS dates back at least thirteen years, and as recently as 1964, successful development was considered beyond the state of the art.

Industry and government research concentrated first on proximity warning indicators (PWI)—a means by which a pilot could be warned when another plane was nearby. But the PWI, even if perfected, would offer little real protection. Most models were merely devices for detecting the heat given off by an airplane in flight, such as heat from propeller blades or turbine exhausts. Unfortunately, the PWIs tested also picked up heat from non-aircraft sources—the sun, clouds and even objects on the ground.

Assuming a PWI could be developed that could resist sounding countless false alarms, there still remains the impracticality of using one around an airport where normal traffic would activate the device enough times to drive a pilot crazy. The research on PWI dwindled in favor of CAS; the former tells a pilot where to look but leaves up to him the task of detecting the intruder and taking evasive action, whereas CAS detects conflicting traffic, warns the pilot and provides almost instant data on which to base evasive action.

The airlines and FAA studied two forms of collision avoidance systems. The first and most desirable was known as "non-cooperative"—where the CAS could spot an intruder without requiring said intruder also to carry a CAS. The second was a "cooperative" CAS—where both conflicting aircraft must have CAS.

A non-cooperative CAS would be preferred because it could protect CAS-equipped airliners, for example, from non-equipped planes. But this type, while still being researched, appears beyond present technical know-how, and the airlines are just about committed to a cooperative system.

The Air Transport Association late in 1967 provided $150,000 for full-scale evaluation of CAS equipment, using flight simulators manned by regular airline pilots. The program is continuing through 1969, including actual flight testing and probable initial steps toward installing CAS on all airliners by the end of 1970.

The most promising CAS concept is based on a technique known as "time frequency." Aircraft carrying this CAS equipment would transmit their altitudes on a common frequency at extremely precise times, already recorded into airborne CAS computers. The distance between the transmitting aircraft would be determined by electronic measurement of the difference between time of transmission and time of receipt—so accurately that the difference is measured in microseconds.

How does this predict a collision? Adequate collision warning is provided when the courses of two CAS-equipped planes start converging. The frequency being transmitted by the intruding plane changes slightly from the common frequency both are using. The change is measurable, varies with the speed of the two aircraft and thus feeds their rate of closure, and a "time to go until collision" warning appears on the CAS display in front of the pilot, along with a recommended course change to avoid collision.

The McDonnell-Douglas Corporation has successfully flight-tested a time frequency CAS unit called "EROS" which apparently stands an excellent chance of airline adoption after further experimenting and refinement. The uniform time concept, the heart of this CAS, is provided by clocks repeatedly synchronized in each aircraft by radio transmissions. They are accurate down to two tenths of a millionth of a second. McDonnell's research on EROS included computerized analyses of every mid-air collision that has occurred in the United States for the past twenty years. EROS is designed to give a pilot a one-minute warning of aircraft closing at speeds of up to three thousand miles an hour. Within seconds after the computer determines the approaching aircraft is on an intercepting path, it alerts the pilot with a loud aural signal and in the same second lights an appropriate UP or DOWN arrow on the

CAS display panel. Simultaneously, the computer "logic" changes the normal time frequency signals so that the CAS unit in the other plane instantly instructs its pilot to maneuver in the opposite direction!

CAS will be a fantastic achievement and also expensive; a single aircraft installation is expected to cost between $30,000 and $50,-000. Obviously, it is intended mostly to keep airliners apart, because few private pilots will be able to afford CAS. Yet according to Frank White, ATA's expert on collision avoidance systems, general aviation planes could be equipped with a $50 crystal video receiver capable of detecting the presence of a CAS-equipped aircraft by tuning in on CAS frequencies. White believes it also is possible to add calibration to the crystal receiver that would provide a rough but adequate indication of range—for as little as $100 to $200. One of aviation's chief goals is to bring down the price tag of navigation and communications equipment for small planes. It is possible, too; the early DME units cost $18,000, but an airline can buy one now for $9000 and a general aviation DME unit is available for $1500. An inexpensive, simplified CAS for general aviation is not impossible.

CAS is still another example of an exceptionally promising safety device that shouldn't be regarded as a perfect guarantee against collisions as long as it is limited to large aircraft. Yet assuming continued steady progress toward collision prevention, utilizing all means from CAS to sensible, fair restrictions on inexperienced private pilots, the future appears hopeful, to say the least. As for the present, it calls for vigilant concern but not unreasoning fear. Considering the task involved in the safe, efficient movement of two hundred thousand daily flights, aviation has done a remarkable job of turning potential danger into mere delays. Someone with a computer mind recently figured out that the nation's two thousand airliners spend six million hours a year in the air, consuming one hundred and fifty thousand of these hours just waiting to land. Theoretically, there is exposure to collision in every hour of flight, yet the actual collision rate is about one for every four million airline flights.

One might say even that rate is too high. But before denouncing the ATC system as so many critics do, ponder this one statistic: there are an average of eighteen hundred ship collisions a year!

# 10

## THE CRITICS

The right to criticize in a free society is inherent, sacred and assumed.

Having established this, let us add that the right to criticize carries with it a moral obligation which is no less inherent, sacred and assumed—namely, a sense of responsibility toward the truth. There are no exceptions. A critic does not deserve serious attention if his attacks are based on prejudices, phony statistics, emotionalism devoid of facts or gloomy predictions built on the quicksand of ignorance.

This certainly applies to anyone who makes a statement about air safety. If he expects to be listened to or read with interest, respect and mature consideration, he must be speaking from knowledge and objectivity. There are many critics of commercial aviation who fit this description. There are others whose unfounded accusations, half-truths and outright falsehoods don't deserve a one-inch display on the want ad page of a weekly newspaper.

I have resisted titling this chapter "The Enemies of Aviation," mainly because it would violate my own guidelines of objectivity; to call every unjust critic an enemy would be to libel his motives. He is more likely to be well-meaning as well as ignorant, sincerely concerned as well as totally misinformed. But in a sense, he *is* an enemy when his lack of responsibility, his flaunting of common-sense judgment, his refusal to investigate both sides of an issue before leaping with angry snarls in one direction all result in undue public fear about air travel; in a loss of confidence toward the men and machines entrusted with providing safe air travel.

The loudest, most vocal and most frequently off-base critics of aviation come out of the halls of Congress. As inevitably as daylight follows the rising sun, a major air accident is followed by one or more lawmakers denouncing, demanding or deriding. Fortunately, they are in the minority, but unfortunately—because they are supposedly responsible members of the nation's legislative branch —their pronouncements are carried by the press, which has little or no opportunity to judge those pronouncements as to accuracy, motive or veracity.

To me it is highly significant that the very members of Congress who do *not* rush forward into print after an airline crash are the very ones best informed about aviation, who have without exception worked hard to support sensible air safety measures, who have a close and mutually respectful relationship with airlines, manufacturers and federal air agencies, and whose own statements in regard to safety problems are never issued without careful investigation of the facts. To cite one leading example: Senator A. S. Mike Monroney: when Mike Monroney speaks about air safety, he speaks with an authority based on background, knowledge and sense of fairness that warrants undivided attention. So does Senator Warren Magnuson of Washington. Sam Friedel of Maryland, Monroney's counterpart in the House, is another example of a lawmaker who looks before he leaps.

The activities of Representative Henry Gonzalez in connection with the Boeing 727 already have been recounted. Shortly after the Pan American 707 crash at Elkton, Maryland, the Texan blasted Halaby and the FAA for exhibiting a "dangerous indifference" to the hazard of turbulence.

"Although the probable cause of the Elkton crash will not be determined until the Civil Aeronautics Board completes its investigation," he proclaimed, "it is reasonable to assume that turbulence played some part in this tragedy. Why did not the FAA controller instruct the Boeing 707 to fly in a 'holding pattern' outside or away from a turbulent area?"

In effect, he had accused an agency of the United States government with responsibility for the deaths of eighty-one persons. Yet he made this patently ridiculous charge *after:*

—the CAB already had announced publicly that lightning had struck the jet and that an explosion had occurred in the wing area hit by the bolt.

—the press had carried a transcript of communications between another plane flying only one thousand feet above Pan Am and Philadelphia Approach Control, the communications record establishing beyond any doubt that turbulence was not a factor in the accident.

His "reasonable assumption" about turbulence could have been made if he hadn't seen either the CAB's report of lightning evidence or the transcript which so effectively demolished his claim. But if the latter were the case, Gonzalez had no right to issue a statement blaming turbulence—and FAA "indifference"—until he had looked into the facts.

Another sample of this lawmaker's premature accident "solutions" came after the crash of an Eastern DC-7 near Kennedy International Airport. The DC-7 had just taken off when its crew took violent evasive action to avoid an incoming Pan Am jet, in the belief that the two aircrafts were on a collision course. The Eastern plane's maneuver was so sharp that the pilots lost control.

Gonzalez promptly accused the FAA of failing to provide proper separation, and then of lying when the agency denied his charge. There was no statement from Gonzalez nineteen months later when the CAB released a report on the accident exonerating Air Traffic Control and blaming the accident on an illusion—the Eastern crew, flying into a darkened sky with no visual horizon reference, misjudged the jet's altitude and tried to avoid a collision danger which did not exist. FAA *has* tried to duck responsibility in at least two major accidents, one a mid-air collision and the other a fog-shrouded landing that went sour when the pilot attempted to go around. In both crashes, FAA personnel—through mistakes or because of inadequate procedures—were partially to blame. But this does not excuse anyone who rushes headlong into publicly expressed conclusions while the wreckage is still burning.

Early in 1967, a TWA captain named Vernon Lowell wrote a book titled *Airline Safety Is a Myth* (one of the most misleading, oversensationalized titles in publishing history). Gonzalez regarded the book as verification of his own views, although it might be noted that most aviation writers sharply criticized Lowell for a work they considered one-sided and "punching at pillows," as Wayne Thomis of the Chicago *Tribune* put it. Gonzalez even invited the pilot-author to Washington where the Congressman set up a press conference.

Lowell, who looked a bit uncomfortable through the proceeding, responded to several pointed questions by saying he was not equipped to answer. Gonzalez displayed no such reluctance. He answered questions that the veteran pilot ducked and dominated the entire session.

Two months later, immediately after a couple of mid-air collisions between airliners and private aircraft shocked the nation, Gonzalez once more announced publicly that his attacks on the FAA had been vindicated.

"On more occasions than I care to count," he said in a floor speech, "I have called the attention of the House to the appalling lack of safety in the air. Two months ago, I introduced Captain Vernon Lowell, who wrote a book, *Airline Safety Is a Myth*, which publication backs up many of the statements I have made during the past four years about airline safety and the lack of adequate control over the airlines by the control system of the Federal Aviation Administration.

"I regret to say that some of my colleagues scoffed at me and questioned the motives of my actions. Others tried to discredit me, and Captain Lowell, for criticizing the FAA. The FAA itself had repeatedly issued bland assurances that everything is all right in the sky, that the traffic control system is fine. Yet we keep having mid-air collisions . . .

"It is sad to see, Mr. Speaker, that the FAA continues to deny any responsibility in mid-air collisions. There is never any fault found with the control system, or with the controllers; it is always a matter of 'pilot error' or 'the planes were off course.' Naturally the planes are off course when they collide; the question is why were they off course when the job of the FAA is to keep them on course?"

There was an untruth or at best half-truth in virtually every sentence Gonzalez uttered. To wit:

—The Lowell book in no way bore out Gonzalez' repeated accusations of FAA indifference to air traffic control problems. Lowell attached no blame for collision hazards to anyone, but merely urged compliance with air traffic rules by all pilots—military, airline, private and business—as well as early installation of electronic collision warning devices on every airplane, large and small. In truth, the book in many ways negates its own phony title because Lowell's chief point was that air travel could be safer—a point with which nobody quarrels.

—The FAA has *not* "repeatedly issued bland assurances" about the collision problem. On the contrary, in seeking Congressional appropriations for air traffic control modernization and improvement, top FAA officials have consistently conceded imperfections in the present system and warned of future problems when air traffic expands even further.

—The FAA does *not* invariably deny any responsibility for collisions. Regrettably, it has in one instance. But it has shouldered the blame in others and controllers have been punished when investigation established their errors.

—The FAA has *not* always assumed pilot error or off-course flying as causes for collisions, for there is not a single FAA official or controller who has not or will not admit deficiencies in the present system. The "off course" crack by Gonzalez is asinine; the majority of major collisions involving airlines have occurred when both planes were on assigned courses. They resulted from factors other than the supposed navigation errors which the Congressman claims the FAA constantly uses as an excuse. The agency also has granted immunity to pilots who turn in near-miss reports even if the circumstances indicate pilot error.

Gonzalez went on to quote from a letter Lowell sent him in which the pilot said the collision problem "is a lot worse than anyone will admit." Lowell said the ATC system is not preventing collisions and that one major difficulty is the mixing of high-speed and low-speed traffic—i.e., private planes in airspace used by jets. As I have pointed out in the previous chapter, the system *does* prevent collisions or nobody would dare to be flying. That it has weaknesses is only too obvious, but FAA cannot be blamed entirely for their existence.

The Texas lawmaker concluded his speech with this comment:

"I wonder, Mr. Speaker, when improvements can be expected in air traffic control; I have seen no improvement in four years, but only excuses."

Mr. Gonzalez must have been looking in the wrong direction if he failed to see any improvement. During the four years of which he spoke, air traffic continued a steady expansion, but the actual collision and near-miss rates remained about the same. This couldn't have been accomplished without *some* improvement, contrary to his acute vision.

We come next to Representative Richard Ottinger of New York, self-styled gadfly of air safety. His correspondence with FAA and the Department of Transportation approximates the length of *Gone With the Wind,* much of it along the same lines as Gonzalez' in that it heaps abuse on FAA and the airlines for alleged failures to make air travel safer.

It was Ottinger who called a press conference in December of 1967 and opened it by producing a bottle.

"The bottle I'm holding," he announced importantly, "contains cyanide, the same deadly chemical used in executions. Fabrics commonly used in airliners contain enough cyanide to turn a modern airliner into a lethal gas chamber."

He was referring to the fact that some aircraft fires have been known to produce toxic gases, including cyanide fumes. He also quoted a CAB study which attributed some deaths to toxic fumes, implying that cyanide was one of them. Finally, he accused the FAA and the airline industry of lethargy in tackling the problem.

Ottinger was guilty of shabby dramatics and also woefully sloppy research. These were the facts behind his so-called exposure of the cyanide "menace":

—While it is true that some fabrics could produce cyanide fumes in a cabin fire, there is not one documented case in which such fumes caused death. Long before these fumes can be produced, smoke from fuel fires or burning interior materials already will have resulted in fatalities.

—The CAB study cited by Ottinger didn't identify cyanide as one of the toxic gases under suspicion.

—Ottinger said the FAA and the industry had known about fire toxicity hazards for two years without doing anything about it. He completely ignored an FAA research project that had been going on for more than a year and was still in progress. He also admitted later to a reporter that he didn't know about a $2.5 million Aerospace Industries Association research project directed at developing safer cabin furnishings, with some materials already approved for installation.

—Ottinger claimed it was not necessary for temperatures to exceed survivable limits "before the lives of passengers may be jeopardized" by toxic gases, and he cited as his source ALPA fire tests. But he failed to tell the reporters that these tests measured gases in a cabin nearly four minutes after the fire started; the required post-crash evacuation time is ninety seconds. The FAA and AIA projects already had established that the materials to which Ottinger referred will burn only in a sustained fuel-fed fire, which is going to kill people with heat and/or carbon monoxide long before toxic fumes can be generated.

Ottinger also has been lambasting FAA for not requiring runway arresting gears, three-dimension radar, fuel tank protection and collision warning devices. As with Gonzalez and a few other gadflys, one has to ask again why he doesn't investigate before he accuses. The new alpha-numerics system of air traffic control described in Chapter 9 is nothing but 3-D radar, as Ottinger would have learned if he had bothered to ask FAA before issuing a press statement demanding its adoption. Fuel tank protection is another subject of major research efforts, and so are collision warning devices. Yet both also are examples of safety hardware requiring much testing and complete perfection; Ottinger is only too representative of those who seize on unproven, experimental devices as easy and quick panaceas. Development of a workable collision avoidance system, for example, is one of the toughest tasks ever to face electronic science.

It is regrettable that Congressmen like Ottinger and Gonzalez can take so much admirable interest in air safety and then pervert it into unfair accusations and badly researched proposals. Not enough lawmakers display such interest and concern, as the Congressional record for air safety appropriations (particularly in the House) would indicate.

It is when the concern is expressed in terms of everything from conclusion-jumping to exaggerations that the whistle should be blown. Unfortunately, because Congress furnishes the FAA with its financial lifeblood, FAA officials are understandably reluctant to call any lawmaker an out-and-out liar, which occasionally would be not only warranted but applauded. Senators and representatives think nothing of making attacks on federal agencies and their personnel, but heaven help the official who tries to fight back verbally or in print against a thin-skinned lawmaker who regards any criticism of Congress as the equivalent of insulting Motherhood and the Flag.

One airline executive who is not afraid to defend his company or the industry is Robert Peach, president of Mohawk. A Congressman, after the crash of a Mohawk BAC-111, demanded that the jet be grounded because according to him it obviously had a fatal defect (it did not; the accident eventually was traced to a freak

fire in the tail). Peach publicly called the lawmaker a liar, for
which he deserved a medal. Another representative asked Mohawk for a free airplane to be used on campaign trips. Peach refused. The Congressman then wrote a letter to the FAA accusing
Mohawk of unsafe maintenance practices. A subsequent special
FAA inspection completely cleared the airline of the Congressman's charges. [Peach is a tough customer even for members of
Congress; he once sent the FAA a bill for nearly $3000, which he
said represented additional operating costs caused by inefficient air
traffic control on a single day. The FAA has yet to pay the bill but
Peach figures the principle was more important than the principal.]

Some of these gossamer-skinned Congressmen are the same ones
who use air safety or air tragedies as a means of getting their
names into print; their alleged concern can only be judged and
then challenged on what they say to get their names into print.
Again, I'll refer to the Pan Am crash at Elkton as evidence:

—One House member demanded that all 707s be kept out of
turbulence and cited the "vulnerability" of the 707 to turbulence,
basing his conclusion on specific incidents involving an Eastern
jet at Houston and the fatal crash of a Trans-Canada jetliner
near Montreal. When it was pointed out to the Congressman that
the Eastern and TCA planes were DC-8s, not 707s, he hastily
amended his recommendation to include all jets.

—Another representative questioned the wisdom of the FAA
controller in ordering the Pan Am flight into a holding pattern
during the storm and urged an investigation of this aspect. He
apparently forgot that quite a few other planes were being held
in the same area, for the express purpose of waiting until a dangerous squall line cleared the Philadelphia airport. How many aircraft
would have been endangered if they had flown directly into the
storm is something he failed to contemplate.

—A third Congressman called for an investigation of the person
or persons responsible for allowing the jet to take off for Philadelphia from Baltimore. He issued this absurdity without bothering
to find out that the Pan Am flight was dispatched under strict
observance of all safety regulations, that many other planes left
Baltimore that same night and flew in the same weather without
difficulty, and that there was no logical reason for questioning

Pan Am's Baltimore departure unless somebody was clairvoyant enough to predict the fatal lightning strike.

If the reader thinks I have selected unusual or rare examples of Congressional stupidity in reacting to an air disaster, let me assure him that they were picked at random and that similar comments have been made after the majority of major crashes. The statements on the Pan Am crash were typical, not exceptions.

The news media—newspaper, radio and television—might appear to be a logical source of protection against Congressional misstatements, but not with any consistency. Unhappily, there are relatively few newsmen with aviation background and knowledge. Then too, a surprising number of large-city newspapers do not have writers who specialize in aviation news. In the aviation community, it is axiomatic that papers employing aviation specialists have the best, fairest and most responsible coverage of air news.

By and large, the airlines have no quarrel with the news media. Most airline public relations men are ex-reporters who understand the needs, handicaps and idiosyncrasies of the press. The majority of reporters, in turn, are sympathetic to the special problems of an airline PR. Both sides have matured considerably since the early days of aviation when the airlines felt newsmen were always trying to uncover something and the newsmen were positive the airlines always were trying to keep something covered up—accusations which had a certain amount of mutual validity. And their relationship still can get strained under the pressures of a major accident.

It is crash coverage which simultaneously portrays the various news media at their best and also their worst. A major air disaster is one of the toughest stories to cover in all journalism. It may take place, and frequently does, in a remote area where reporters must work under conditions that would challenge the durability of a mountain goat and the resourcefulness of a commando. At the same time, it can be a painfully frustrating assignment; a good newsman seeks the "why did it happen" as well as the "how did it happen," and in an air crash there usually are no fast, pat answers. Reporters who know aviation and its problems understand this; newsmen who don't, fall into the trap of portraying rumors as fact, guesses as solid conclusions and unsubstantiated eyewitness accounts as accurate descriptions. Newspapermen are not the only ones at fault; so are reporters representing radio and television stations.

Bill Huebner, aviation writer for the Hartford (Connecticut) *Times*, cites an incident which has occurred too many times in similar fashion, as far as the airlines are concerned. A captain about to land at Hartford couldn't get his "gear down" light to illuminate after he lowered his wheels. Following the protocol for such situations, he alerted airport officials, who had fire, rescue and ambulance vehicles standing by in case the gear was not locked and should collapse.

The control tower, also following established procedures, informed state police in a call monitored by newspapers and radio stations in the area. The emergency was about as hazardous as a flat tire on an automobile—the trouble, as the captain suspected, was nothing but a burned-out light on the instrument panel. But as Huebner tells the story:

"A radio disc jockey [not a newsman] switched on the echo chamber and in a panic-filled voice cried: 'Bulletin . . . bulletin! We interrupt to bring you this special hot line bulletin. A jetliner loaded with passengers is in serious trouble right now and preparing for a crash landing. All available ambulances are speeding to the airport and hospitals are alerted. Stay tuned to hot line for the crash!'"

According to Huebner, a newspaperman called the airline's local station manager and asked, "What happened to the plane that was supposed to crash?" The infuriated airline official hung up without answering, mentally assigning all reporters to a place whose temperatures are somewhat higher than the inside of a jet engine combustion chamber. Adds Huebner:

"His anger cooled, but it took a long time to dry the tears of parents, relatives, etc. who were waiting for people aboard that plane."

Bad reporting is resented by more than just the airlines. Most pilots take a dim view of the press due mainly to their conviction that the average reporter, although he knows pitifully little about aviation technology, seldom can refrain from issuing pontifical advice or reaching hasty conclusions. I won't say that the following, written by Captain William J. O'Connell of Piedmont, represents the feelings of all pilots, but I suspect he'd get a very loud amen from most of his brethren. Said O'Connell, in a letter to the ALPA magazine:

"A pilot wouldn't deliberately fly his airplane into the ground if it could be avoided, any more than a journalist would indulge in a rash of self-criticism in public print.

"That may be why so little is said of inaccuracies in press reporting of aircraft accidents and other happenings of interest in aviation. Yet ask any pilot of his opinion of a press report of an accident and watch the eyebrows furrow and the color rush to his face as he grinds out the disgusted question, 'Who wrote that?'"

Nor are pilots alone in their antagonism toward news media in general (conversely, they have a great deal of respect for aviation writing specialists or any other newsman demonstrating a modicum of aviation knowledge). The trouble is that newspapers and the radio-TV stations often are forced to staff crashes with personnel almost totally lacking in aviation background. What such reporters have written or said in the course of covering an accident has dismayed their own colleagues. The broadcasting media, according to many airline officials, are worse offenders than the newspaper corps. In the April 1966 issue of *American Aviation*, editor in chief Wayne Parrish wrote an editorial which spoke for many in aviation who are naturally hesitant to scold any news media, but broadcasting in particular because of its huge audiences. Parrish, a man never afraid to speak his mind, had this to say about coverage of the Boeing 727 controversy.

". . . TV and radio are going completely haywire in their blatant reporting. Not for the world do we suggest that a major airline accident isn't news, but the handling of the news is something else again . . . Uninformed TV and radio people usually are not able to appraise and digest fairly some of the stuff issued or made available by specialized government people. The result is a horrible distortion on the air.

"Such bald-faced statements as appeared on [a station] in Chicago that 'officials have ruled that the Boeing 727 jetliner is in fact a death trap,' or on [a station] in Los Angeles that 'the safety chief of the CAB warned that the 727 was a potential fire trap' are plain, irresponsible reporting of the facts. Government people are all too prone to pass out labels or conclusions even when they don't mean to. The general news media know very little about assessing such statements—and usually give them the worst twist possible."

Parrish put his finger on one of the major problems in aviation coverage. Government investigative officials usually are the only sources of news during a crash probe. They are under constant pressure to release information, yet on too many occasions—as Parrish pointed out—they have seen this information distorted beyond belief into sensationalism and even libel. The result is a distrust of the news media, a growing reluctance to say anything in fear that it will be misinterpreted and twisted many degrees out of proportion. The CAB's recommendations to the FAA on the Boeing 727 did *not* label the jet "a death trap" or "a potential fire trap," but when it publicized those recommendations it was only too easy for a reporter—either through ignorance or irresponsibility—to make recommendation synonymous with indictment. And perhaps these reporters are not entirely to blame; it is a very human tendency to paint any hot issue either black or white, whereas in air safety many issues can only be shaded gray. It takes a skilled newsman, indeed, to grasp the shadings and depict them accurately himself in written or verbal text.

Captain O'Connell's comment that journalists don't indulge in self-criticism may have been true at the time and still true of some newsmen, but it definitely no longer applies to the aviation press. In 1966, the Aviation/Space Writers Association published a pamphlet, "The Newsman and Air Accidents," and sent more than ten thousand copies to newspapers, radio stations, television stations and broadcasting networks not only here but abroad. It set something of a precedent in that it frankly admitted shortcomings in accident coverage. As then AWA President James Cahill phrased it in his foreword to the booklet:

"Admittedly, it contains information already familiar to many reporters. Nevertheless, there have been sufficient incidents of inadvertently inaccurate and misleading coverage to convince AWA that some general guidelines of knowledge would be useful to a large segment of the press."

Interestingly enough, there was almost no reaction of the "who the hell are you telling how to cover a story" variety; no complaints that AWA had insulted the ability and integrity of the press. Some AWA members feared this would happen. Instead, there was widespread praise for the publication and hundreds of letters thanking the Association for helping uninformed or inexperienced reporters understand the problems of handling major aviation news. The response of newspapers and radio-TV stations to a book which, in effect, chided them for past errors was in notable contrast to the usual anguished reaction of a Congressman who's criticized.

The booklet itself explains the federal accident investigative process (many reporters believe FAA investigates all crashes), urges caution in interviewing eyewitnesses, advises against jumping to conclusions and explains how to handle—with restraint and fairness—the non-fatal accidents such as emergency or precautionary landings. One quote will suffice to give the tone of the booklet:

"It might be stated bluntly that many veteran investigators mistrust the media because the little information they have tried to provide, with emphasis on its tentative nature, has on occasions been magnified or distorted prematurely into supposed solutions.

"Such distrust is of genuine concern to responsible newsmen. Simply stated, investigators feel the press and radio-TV are prone to jump to conclusions before any conclusions are reached. Seldom are there simple answers to a crash. Data and evidence must be tested, correlated, sifted, examined and—above all—confirmed. The process only on rare occasions produces a 'probable cause' in the preliminary stages of a crash probe."

(The temptation to make one more observation on the AWA booklet is irresistible: it is too bad a similar common-sense pamphlet on crash investigations is not available for distribution on Capitol Hill.)

Jumping to conclusions after a crash is not a sin committed solely by Congressmen and news media. It is an overindulged practice of too many attorneys trying to collect damages for the families of victims, with negligence lawsuits often filed long before accident investigators have the vaguest idea of what went wrong or who was responsible.

The airlines are a fat target for legal action, even when a carrier has been *proven* guiltless, because frequently they are the only parties involved in an accident investigation with the financial resources for a lucrative settlement or award. There are numerous examples. In 1949, a fighter plane flown by a Bolivian military pilot rammed an Eastern DC-4 over Washington National Airport.

The CAB found the Bolivian and the government-operated control tower at fault, with Eastern totally cleared, yet the airline wound up paying a fat share of the damage claims.

The Piedmont 727-Cessna collision at Hendersonville, North Carolina (Chapter 9), although no official "probable cause" verdict has been issued, produced no evidence that the airliner crew was to blame in any way. Yet Piedmont already has been sued for a total of $10.6 million on the grounds of negligence. The legal justification, let alone the moral, for such action is beyond my understanding. Most lawyers represent their clients honestly and sincerely, but it is no wonder that I once heard a veteran accident investigator remark with bitterness, "There are some airborne ambulance chasers who'd find a way to sue Jesus if a crash was nothing but an act of God."

In one crash probe, three technical experts from a British aircraft manufacturing company were asked to testify at a U.S. accident hearing. When the trio arrived, a lawyer representing the family of one of the victims served them with subpoenas charging negligence. An attorney for the airline involved told the lawyer to his face that he was ashamed of his profession.

At the risk of seeming callous, I must state my conviction that bloated lawsuits have hurt the accident investigation process and thus air safety itself. More than one air safety expert has complained that the lawyers attending a crash hearing frequently outnumber the technical witnesses. Fear of unreasonably huge litigation claims has led to an alarming amount of buck passing on the part of airlines, government, pilot unions and manufacturers.

The badly undermanned corps of federal accident investigators operate under a superb "team" concept. Because they have been starved for money and technical resources, they have evolved a system under which representatives of the "interested parties"— the airline or airlines involved, manufacturers, FAA and pilot organizations—assist in the investigation. A "team" assigned the job of determining whether structural failure occurred, for example, would be headed by a Safety Board expert but would include technical specialists from the airline, airframe manufacturer, FAA and ALPA or APA.

The system has worked well in the past; it has been copied by most foreign governments, who not only use the U.S. method of accident investigation but often call on American personnel to assist them. Yet with increasing frequency, the "interested parties" spend a disproportionate amount of time trying to clear themselves instead of maintaining the complete objectivity required of anyone engaged in a crash investigation. This activity is extended into the hearing process and can be blamed only on the knowledge that millions of dollars can be riding on the outcome.

One prominent attorney has even recorded a lecture on how to sue the airlines; he sells the tape for twelve dollars. A number of lawyers specialize in such lawsuits, for which no one blames them. They can be lucrative, thanks to the propensity of U.S. juries to side with the plaintiff in the majority of these cases even when the technical evidence (which not many jurors can understand) is in favor of the defendant. The wife of a pilot who was killed when he took off in the face of a threatening and very visible thunderstorm collected $300,000 by charging the Weather Bureau with negligence.

Charles F. McErlean, executive vice president and general manager of United Air Lines, is a former lawyer (he once headed UAL's legal department) who is concerned over the present system, in which litigation is based largely on "fault"; in other words, finding someone or something at fault from whom plaintiffs can recover, instead of determining the technical or operational factors that caused the accident and implementing the best corrective measures.

The "fault" system, McErlean pointed out, tends to restrict the free flow of information that helps solve crashes and prevents further occurrences. Instead of that flow, he argues, the parties in an accident investigation are under pressure to hide or gloss over vital facts because they fear a finding of liability. McErlean's solution would be to impose on the airlines, via legislation, "liability without fault." Under this plan, an airline literally would insure every passenger for safe passage with a fixed maximum liability. The cost of this insurance would be added to the price of the ticket. Passengers could purchase the usual travel insurance if they wanted additional protection.

Flow of information has made major contributions to the U.S. air safety record. It is not always appreciated until crash investigators run into deliberate attempts to block objective probes, such as has occurred sometimes in accidents involving American-built or -operated planes that crashed on foreign soil. When a Boeing

727 cargo plane crashed in East Germany in 1966, for example, Communist officials refused to let U.S. safety experts visit the crash site and then returned only half the wreckage to the airline that owned the plane. The accident went unsolved, an unhappy blow at the axiom that air safety has no nationalistic borders.

It is heartening to observe the mutual respect that exists between government crash probers and the unofficial assistants with whom they work. The Society of Air Safety Investigators' membership roster includes pilots, airline safety officials, controllers, dispatchers and industry scientists. It would be disastrous if this respect were endangered by the ever present shadow of legal recriminations.

Perhaps one answer is to put a reasonable ceiling on damages, as McErlean suggested; passengers on overseas flights, for example, can collect only up to a certain amount under the Warsaw Convention. Another proposal is to have accident hearings conducted by a kind of "Admiralty Court," the type employed in investigations of sea disasters. Here the lawyers, judges and even juries are composed of men familiar with technical matters, and their verdicts have been consistently fair to all parties.

Certainly the cause of efficient crash investigation would be enhanced by giving the Safety Board the funds it needs and has never obtained, despite the enormous importance of its work. The solution of crashes is becoming more difficult in direct proportion to the increasing complexity of planes. According to one veteran investigator, if it were not for the development of cockpit voice recorders, a half-dozen accidents over the past three years might never have been solved.

It may seem illogical to put noise abatement into a book on jet safety and a chapter on critics of aviation. It is not only unhappily logical but also absolutely necessary, for the jet noise problem could very well have a direct bearing on both safety and air progress.

Let it be said right at the outset that no one in aviation is unsympathetic toward those bothered, annoyed and upset by the noisy beasts screaming over their homes. That includes airline pilots, the airlines, the airports and the federal government. But let this also be said: to appease people on the ground, lives in the air may be endangered and moves to increase air travel efficiency may be destroyed; there is a border line over which appeasement cannot be allowed to step and that border line is a combination of safety and progress.

At least four government agencies are pondering solutions to the jet noise problem, one born with the jet age. In the words of one official, "We're searching through the medicine cabinet before the headache becomes migraine." He may have understated the situation; to carry on his analogy, the headache threatens to become a destructive brain tumor.

Jet noise used to be limited to a handful of major airports. Ten years ago, only sixteen cities received jet service. Now more than two hundred airports are handling jets, by 1970 there will be three hundred and fifty and by 1975 more than five hundred. Potentially, any airport served by jets has a noise problem.

The airports themselves have been described as "the man in the middle." No single airport can solve a noise problem. What action it can take might be compared to irrigating the Sahara Desert with a pail of water. Runways can be lengthened, "blast fences" and isolated run-up areas for jet engines may be provided, but basically the average airport is helpless.

Yet airports legally are bearing the brunt of lawsuits filed in connection with noise annoyance. This is due chiefly to a disputed and controversial 1962 Supreme Court decision known as the Griggs case. It involved a home owner living near Pittsburgh's Allegheny County Airport who filed suit claiming that low-flying jets had damaged the property value of his house. The Supreme Court, in a seven-to-two decision, ruled that legal liability for such damage rested with the airport—not the airlines or the federal government which operates the air traffic control system.

Out of the Griggs decision and a number of rulings by state courts have sprung more than two hundred lawsuits involving at least forty airports and millions of dollars. The exact amount cannot even be estimated on a day-to-day basis because scores of similar suits are merely awaiting the outcome of those already filed.

Originally, the attack on jet noise was aimed at the source—the turbine engine. Noise suppressors were installed on the early engines at considerable cost to the airlines. They also added $10,000 per aircraft in monthly operating expenses because they reduced power and simultaneously increased fuel consumption.

The later development of the fan-jet engine helped somewhat—in ever increasing use, it is measurably quieter than older power plants, although any jet engine is noisy. Nor is any technical breakthrough in sight, even though there is an enormous amount of research under way to produce new quieter engines or modify the present ones.

The major anti-noise weapon currently is in the field of operating techniques. This involves such steps as reducing power as soon as certain altitudes are reached, using preferential runways whenever possible to take flights away from populated areas, and, finally, turns away from those areas at specified altitudes. But pilots have accepted these techniques under protest and with firm, unanimous warnings that many noise abatement procedures fall just short of compromising safety. If a four-engine jetliner lost two engines during a low-altitude noise abatement turn, for example, loss of control would be very possible if not probable. The power reduction requirement almost immediately after takeoff is part of this potential danger that to pilots, anyway, is an invitation to a major disaster.

"Noise abatement," commented one captain, "is like a married man going out with other women. If he does it long enough, he'll get caught."

What has frustrated the entire aviation industry is the lethargy, indifference and lack of cooperation on the part of many local interests. There is only so much that can be done at the airport, federal or airline level, and many in aviation believe too much may already have been done. The use of preferential runways, to give one instance, has been known to delay takeoffs of heavily loaded flights for as long as four hours; higher gross weight means noisier takeoffs and these jets often are forced to use runways clogged with both outgoing and incoming traffic.

Yet there are almost countless cases where noise complaints have stemmed directly from the practice of building homes and apartments close to airports, *when builders knew in advance there would be a noise problem!* The FAA from the start of the jet age has been pleading with local governments to apply proper zoning and construction restrictions on land adjacent to airports that obviously would need expanding in the near future. Too often homes and schools and apartment houses were built there anyway—because lax zoning allowed real estate firms to push residential areas so close to airports that noise problems were inevitable.

Not too long ago, builders started construction of two thousand new homes directly under the path of one of the heaviest-traveled approach airways into Kennedy International Airport. The area involved was one which the FAA warned two years earlier would be noise sensitive. There was no zoning action taken, the real estate developers barged right ahead and the area now boasts at least one citizens' group which has hired a lawyer to press noise damage suits.

At the same JFK Airport, officials and the FAA moved the approach paths to Runway 13 along the Jamaica Bay coast to take advantage of a sparsely settled area. The navigation aids had no sooner been relocated when a builder announced he had completed financing arrangements for a twenty-six-story apartment house, with seven thousand dwelling units, almost directly under the new approach path that had been established for the express purpose of alleviating noise complaints from other areas! As recently as mid-1968, there were new homes being built so close to JFK that it is impossible to fly more than three hundred feet overhead. Noise restrictions literally have turned JFK into a two-runway airport.

Oscar Bakke, at the time Deputy Administrator of FAA's eastern region, bluntly told one civic meeting in Queens it was time for local governments to get tough. It also was time, he added, for local governments and the citizens they represented to begin recognizing the importance of aviation to a community's economy.

Nobody, said the usually soft-spoken FAA official, objects to organization of noise abatement groups. But he suggested that citizens also might organize committees to promote local airports and protect the enormous investment a community has in its air facilities—even if a city has to buy up land and move families away from airports.

"Immediately there would be screams that this is intolerable," he declared. "But for one bridge, the Verrazano Bridge, the city [of New York] found its way clear to move almost six thousand families, to expend some fifty-one million dollars in land acquisition to provide approaches to a bridge, a bridge that will contribute only a very small fraction of the contribution which is daily made at the major airports of New York."

Chicago's Midway Airport, once the busiest air terminal in the

United States, was a victim of noise protests to a partial extent. The airlines finally pulled out of Midway and the area around the airport quickly turned into an economic desert. Now they have resumed limited scheduled service—supported by a citizens' committee whose chairman once headed a committee to keep jets out of Midway! He explained his switch by frankly admitting he had no conception of aviation's importance to community in cold-blooded dollars and cents, nor the realization that jets actually are no louder than other planes and furthermore reduce exposure to noise because they climb faster.

Midway's close-to-disaster experience easily could be duplicated in cities where well-meaning but shortsighted citizens are trying to shut down or cripple airport operations. Yet there is mounting technical evidence that some noise complaints have been generated by a loud vocal minority, by lawyers seeking easy fees and by overemotional persons who aren't being bothered as much as they think they are.

One British survey revealed that the underlying reason for noise complaints among residents living near a major London airport was fear of falling aircraft, not the noise itself. One proven deterrent to noise protests in cities about to get jet service for the first time is an educational campaign which explains the inherent safety of jets and the fact that their noise merely is different, not necessarily louder.

If that seems like hogwash, examine the results of an extensive FAA survey conducted at Washington National Airport shortly after the agency allowed the airlines to operate jet service there—a decision accompanied by voluminous and angry citizens' groups who regarded this as the worst calamity since the British fleet burned the nation's capital. The FAA took scientific measurements of noise levels generated by *all* aircraft. The results showed most piston-engine planes noisier than the jets. The only possible conclusion is that jet noise draws complaints because it is a new kind of noise, not because it is louder.

At Van Nuys, California, home-owner associations got some forty thousand names on petitions to ban DC-9 jet service at the local airport. School officials ran a noise study in which sound levels were recorded in classrooms while a DC-9 took off and landed at the nearby airport. Its noise levels registered less than readings obtained from ordinary classroom activities. How many

noise complaints, indeed, fall into the category best described by
that classic Groucho Marx line—"Even if it was good, I wouldn't
like it"? British and U.S. studies concluded that about 30 per
cent of people living near airports constitute a hard-core group
which will continue complaining about noise no matter what is
done short of grounding all jets.

Early in 1966, the FAA announced it would allow short- and
medium-range jets to operate at Washington National Airport. It
received its first batch of noise complaints about "those damned
jets overhead" *before* jet flights began! The FAA was not surprised.
Some years ago, the Air Force disclosed in advance that it would
run sonic boom tests over a metropolitan area. The test flights were
scrubbed because of weather, but the Air Force was hit by boom
complaints anyway.

There also is evidence that, the Supreme Court's Griggs decision notwithstanding, some courts are beginning to take dim
views of noise damage lawsuits. In California, a Los Angeles
Superior Court judge ruled that the noise to which the plaintiffs
objected "was not of a substantial nature and did not cause any
depreciation in value of the properties." The case involved suits
brought by property owners claiming that noise had caused damages to their homes ranging from four thousand to eight thousand
dollars. They also sought 7 per cent interest on the damages ret-
roactive to January 29, 1959, when jet operations began at Los
Angeles International Airport.

In another legal fight, a judge tossed out of court an attempt by
a small community near Kennedy to fine pilots who violated certain noise levels—their levels being only slightly higher than what
a truck would generate going by a sound-measuring device.

There is not really any solid evidence that jets have destroyed
property values. Value of land adjacent to the Los Angeles International Airport, for example, soared from $250 an acre to
$250,000 after jet service began. The financial facts of life, however,
don't seem to bother some protest groups, the lawyers they hire
and local politicians. The Los Angeles Airport, badly in need of
expansion, worked out a plan for removing nearby homes from the
loudest noise zones and soundproofing other residences. Part of the
project was to have land rezoned from residential to light industrial, which would have made possible higher valuation of
condemned properties. A home-owners' association rejected the

rezoning proposal and as of early 1968 temporarily had stymied the airport's development plans.

Invariably, the noise groups demand the construction of new airports instead of improvements on existing ones. In virtually every case, they propose locations which are impractical or which would create noise problems in a different area. Meanwhile, they make no effort to block expansion of home building adjacent to airports, which is one of the prime reasons for the noise hassle. Commented one airline captain I talked to:

"I took off from a major airport the other day and flew over some new split-level homes being built just beyond the runway. I suppose the owners will be forming a noise protest committee as soon as they're settled."

Efforts to cooperate with such committees often meet with derision and fresh lawsuits. At Washington National Airport, operated by the FAA, officials banned jet operations after 11 P.M. forcing the airlines to land flights at Dulles twenty-seven miles away and then ferrying the planes to National the next day. Several committees at last report were still hollering and claiming untold damages to health and property. Many aviation people seriously wonder where the protesters come up with what appear to be fantastically inflated damage claim amounts.

Attorneys for one group of twenty-four hundred persons living near Los Angeles International Airport filed suits claiming $36 *million* in damages allegedly caused by aircraft noise. Another citizens' association in the same area sued for $15,000 per home, charging that jet noise had damaged their houses structurally, harmed their children's education and resulted in personal anxiety, eye irritation and difficulty in breathing and hearing. Ten other families filed suits totaling $400,000 and another small group asked for $108,000.

"Are they really seeking relief—or easy dough?" asked one airline captain.

Airport officials have had it on the noise problem. They firmly believe they have been made the scapegoats in the noise controversy, and their own organizations, the Airport Operators Council and the American Association of Airport Executives, have pulled out of the National Aircraft Noise Abatement Council. The latter was set up in 1960 to work out joint solutions to noise problems. The remaining members are the Air Transport Association, the Aerospace Industries Association and ALPA—with the latter announcing its intentions of withdrawing. *Aviation Daily* neatly summed up why NANAC came apart at the seams:

"Attempting to distill a unified industry position on aircraft noise control from these five groups was, at best, almost impossible. ATA and AIA, which established NANAC and always paid more than 90 per cent of its bills, emphasize land use as a noise control method; this makes the airport people nervous. The airport interests push aircraft modification, which makes the manufacturers and airlines nervous. And when either group mentions flight procedures, the pilots get nervous.

The FAA has proposed new noise reduction standards for future jet engines and corresponding reductions for current engines if technical modifications are possible. Power plant manufacturers and the airlines think the standards are unrealistically low and beyond the present state of the art. They may also be unrealistically high, for one can almost assume that the quietest jet engine is still going to be drawing complaints and lawsuits from the "even if it was good we wouldn't like it" contingent.

If there has been one lesson well taught and simultaneously ignored, it has been the importance of planning for the future. This is what aviation wants to get across to cities just now becoming part of the jet age. Barring a technological break-through in the jet engine itself, the only proven noise weapons are land acquisition, proper zoning restrictions and public education on the role aviation plays in the economic welfare of any community.

Meanwhile, I dread the day when a jet through some freak multiple malfunction suffers loss of engine power in the middle of a noise abatement turn or after the pilot already has reduced power at low altitude for the sake of noise abatement. Some of the protest committees on the ground may find out the hard way that noise is preferable to a one hundred and twenty ton jet landing in the living room. I also have plenty of company in resenting the lunatic fringe so apparent in at least some of the noise complaints.

One of my closest pilot friends, Captain Ed Bechtold of Eastern, made a speech a few years ago in which he said it was "time we stopped asking pilots to appease the public." He was, of course, referring to takeoff and landing procedures designed to reduce noise which he felt were potentially dangerous to the public that flies. The speech was widely printed. He told me later:

"The phone in my home started ringing even before I got home from the meeting where I made the speech. People abused and insulted my wife and even told my son I was no good. Sometimes the phone would ring and when we picked it up, nobody would answer. This went on all day and night. To get any rest, we finally had to take the phone off the hook about midnight.

"I've never heard such abusive and filthy language. The least they called me was a Communist. Quite a few said they were writing the White House, my own airline or the FAA to demand that I be fired. At first I tried to reason with them, but I couldn't get a word in edgewise. I'd start trying to explain that pilots are sympathetic about the noise problem and that we've co-operated as best we can in an abatement program. I just wanted to get across our plea that pilots have a responsibility to passengers, too, and that a takeoff or landing accident could hurt more than eardrums on the ground. Usually, I never got past my first few words—they wouldn't listen and just kept calling me foul names.

"One guy phoned my wife while I was out and said to her, 'I hope your husband crashes one of these nights.'"

The caller got his wish. My friend Ed Bechtold is dead, killed in a crash on a fog-cloaked runway. When I read about noise abatement protest groups and "committees to shut down Blank Airport," I remember Captain Bechtold's experience. And wonder.

# 11

## THE YONDER IN THE WILD BLUE

The mind reels at the statistics . . . the facts and figures.

If you placed the nose of the plane on one goal line of a football field, the tail would be towering over the opponents' 25-yard line.

The tail section itself is the equivalent of a six-story building in height. The entire aircraft requires an acre of ground in which to park.

In the configuration ordered by most airlines, there are twelve lavatories (with enough plumbing for seventeen) and seven galleys—the latter loaded onto the plane as entire units, just as food containers are put aboard today's jets.

Twelve to eighteen stewardesses will be required to serve the passengers it will carry—between three hundred and fifty and four hundred and fifty depending on whether an airline wants to have a first-class section in addition to coach. American, for example, will have sixty-four first-class seats (about the same as an entire DC-6 or DC-7) and two hundred and eighty-eight coach seats.

The communications system between the cabin and cockpit operates with touch-tone dial phones. There are separate dressing rooms for stewardesses, a stand-up cocktail bar in the first-class cabin and a full-size cocktail lounge on the upper deck just behind the cockpit.

The first-class aisles are almost the width of a DC-3's whole cabin. The seating in the coach section is nine or ten abreast, but the cabin is so wide that the "sardine" packing of today's six-abreast jet coach seating has been eliminated. There are two aisles, not one.

The fuel tanks hold more than fifty thousand gallons—twice the capacity of the 707 or DC-8. The wiring, if laid end to end, would stretch one hundred miles. To bring subcontracted structural parts into the factory building the plane, special railroad cars had to be designed. The factory itself cost $200 million and covers seven hundred and seventy acres. To excavate the construction site, workers hauled away more dirt than was moved to build the Grand Coulee dam.

The plane flies higher and faster and farther than any jet operating today—a range of more than six thousand miles, a service ceiling of forty thousand feet and a cruising speed of six hundred and twenty-five miles an hour. Loaded for takeoff on a transatlantic flight, the aircraft weighs three hundred and fifty tons—one hundred and seventy tons more than the Pilgrims' *Mayflower*. Its fuel could drive an automobile ten thousand miles a year for seventy years. The cabin is the equivalent of fourteen average-size living rooms in a medium-price house. It could hold thirty full-size automobiles parked bumper to bumper.

This is the Boeing 747, first of the "jumbo jets." It is not an airliner of the future. Boeing's design, test and production schedule —laid down in July of 1966—called for completion of the first plane by the end of 1968 and entry into passenger service before the end of 1969. It is one of a family of new giants that includes the McDonnell-Douglas DC-10, the Lockheed 1100 and Boeing's own supersonic transport.

The faint of heart have looked on the advent of jumbos and the supersonics with all the unbridled optimism of a kamikaze pilot making a post-mission social engagement. The statistical and financial impact of a single 747 crash already has been discussed; no one ever has questioned what such an accident would do in terms of airline reputation, the carriers' proud safety record and public acceptance of aircraft some cynics claim are just too big to fly.

The manufacturers and the airline industry are very well aware that a major crash involving a jumbo jet will bring cries of the "I told you so" variety. It seems apt, therefore, to disclose what is being done to make such transports as the 747 the safest airplanes ever built.

Every component going into this $20 million monster is being approved by something new in airframe manufacturing—a special committee of five hand-picked safety experts. Boeing assigned to this quintet the job of determining the relationship of every part to safety. The five men can overrule any or all of the twenty-five hundred designers working on the 747 project, if any single design raises the slightest safety question.

The smallest, most outwardly insignificant item goes under the careful analysis of the safety group. Could the coffee maker cause a crash, for example? Sound ridiculous? The committee investigated the coffee maker to make sure that its drain outlet was located far enough away from any wiring so no short circuit was possible.

One 747 designer came up with an idea for a system that would wash the plane's windows in flight. The safety group turned it down with three pages of technical objections, every one based on safety. As one committee member told me:

"As the state of the art gets more sophisticated and complex, the job of the designer gets more specialized. The result is that one designer will produce a system or individual component which looks great on paper, but which could cause trouble when it's used in connection with other systems and components. We have to worry about these interactions, to make sure one engineer isn't inadvertently fouling up the work of another; to guide all our engineers out of possible design traps which they couldn't possibly be aware of, working as they do in specialized fields."

Boeing points out that the 747 is not a radically new airplane; it is more a grown-up, enlarged 707 but with far more redundancy and with the most extensive attention to the "fail-safe" concept ever bestowed on a commercial transport. The safety committee has utilized a new method of spotting potential hazards known as the "fault-tree analysis." The name is derived from the charts the group draws up to determine the safety relationship of a system or component to the rest of the airplane. The chart resembles the drawing of a tree; at a glance, for example, an engineer can tell what effect an autopilot failure would have on the control system. Or whether the breaking of a single control cable would spread to other cables by transferring too much load.

Fault-tree analysis was initially used on Boeing missiles, and the 747 is the first transport plane to utilize its amazingly accurate forecasting. Into the tree is fed computer data such as the probability of failure of any one part . . . even the probability of a pilot pushing the wrong button inadvertently. Before approving the 747's landing gear system, the committee cranked into a computer the details of every hydraulic gear malfunction ever encountered by jets to make sure the jumbo's gear design bypassed all sources of trouble. Any airline specification change—such as ordering a different type of galley or a new kind of pilot seat—was checked by the committee for the tiniest adverse effect on safety. If one was found, Boeing informed the airline it could not provide the offending hardware.

The unique group describes its function as "taking just one more second look to make sure." It likes to cite, as an example of one engineer undoing the work of another, the case of a certain fighter plane. When the aircraft was in the preliminary design stage, engineers working on the fuel vents decided on the basis of dye tests that vents had to be extended a few inches to prevent ignition during fuel dumping. Several years later, when the fighter was in military service, two of them blew up in flight while dumping fuel.

Investigators ran the dye tests over again and discovered that another designer, wanting to reduce drag, had eliminated the longer vents without telling anyone. Further investigation disclosed that the second engineer didn't even know about the dye tests or the reason for the vent extension. Only three inches were involved, but this was enough to destroy a margin of safety.

Out of the safety group's work and the efforts of Boeing engineers has come a transport incorporating every safety lesson learned in the past. Structural strength is of dreadnought proportions. Key wing spars are *150 per cent* of design limits—in other words, 50 per cent stronger than what Boeing determined would be safe. One spar which failed at 135 per cent of design limits was rejected. All wing-skin members from wing root to tip are continuous strips; there are no joints where stress could accumulate.

The 747 could lose two thirds of its horizontal stabilizers and remain flyable. It could lose 30 per cent of its rudder and still be maneuvered safely. The giant handles as easily as a Boeing 727, a plane which can be landed with two fingers. Cockpit instrumentation is enlarged with improved lighting and fed electronically for greater accuracy.

Boeing naturally was interested in pilot reaction to the world's biggest jet designed exclusively for commercial use. Would there be, for instance, a psychological resistance to the size of the plane and the height of the cockpit, which is in the upper deck nearly twenty-nine feet from the ground?

Engineers mounted a cockpit mockup on a truck to reproduce the exact height of the real plane. Then it asked a pilot evaluation group to ride around in the make-believe cockpit. Not a single airman expressed any apprehension. There was unanimous agreement that the 747's cockpit visibility is superior to that of any airliner built; the downward visibility, for example, is almost nineteen feet, compared to fourteen in a 707 or DC-8.

The 747 has four main hydraulic systems, three of them solely for backup purposes. It can lose three of them and still fly. There are four separate systems for activating the split rudder, the wing flaps and elevators. The quadruple landing gear is suspended from both the wings and the fuselage so that if any two gears should fail, the plane can be landed safely on the other two.

The seats on the 747 are of a new design with energy-absorbing qualities. An inner tubular frame stretches under impact and absorbs the force, thus extending the deceleration time. All cabin materials are of newly developed fire-resistant fibers or plastic and have passed all toxic fume tests. There are twenty-one life rafts, and the ten huge doors, described in an earlier chapter, allow emergency evacuation of a fully loaded 747 well within the FAA's ninety-second limit.

Boeing, to determine the plane's evacuation performance, built a seventy-foot section of fuselage and ran evacuation tests on nearly eight thousand persons. It found it could get one hundred and sixty eight passengers out of a single door in eighty seconds, a figure including the time it took to open the door and inflate the slides. The "passengers" ranged from seven years old to 71, one of the elderly being a man with a wooden leg. On the full-scale cabin mockup, Boeing evacuated three hundred and sixty passengers in 78 seconds using only five of the ten exits.

There is even redundancy in the 747's navigation system—three individual systems for overseas flights and two for domestic operations. These are the so-called inertial guidance type in which a pre-takeoff computed course is fed into the system and coupled to the autopilot. The result is as close as any aircraft has come to automated flight with navigation accuracy of pin-point quality.

Boeing's attention to minute safety details was even extended to the design of the spiral staircase that winds from the main deck to the upper cockpit and lounge area. The company invited a team of airline medical experts to look over the gigantic mockup to see if they could spot any safety flaws. One, Dr. George Kidera of United, shook his head when he saw the staircase.

"It's too close to the cabin wall in that one spot," he complained.

Boeing engineers looked puzzled.

"I can't see anything wrong with it," one argued. "What's the problem?"

"Suppose a passenger was going up the stairs and had his arm draped on the railing in that particular spot just as the plane hit turbulence," Kidera explained. "He could catch his arm between the railing and the wall and break it."

Boeing moved the staircase over a few inches. (It got some pilot complaints on the stairs, incidentally; the boys were not happy about the width, pointing out that they'd have to make two trips up the staircase to the cockpit if they had more than one suitcase because it wasn't wide enough for a man carrying two bags.)

Another design change had no connection with safety but deserves mention because it bears out the airline contention that no stewardess who ever flew was satisfied with the galley of a new airliner. Boeing showed a group of stewardesses from several carriers through the mockup, noting with pride their awestruck stares and whispered comments of incredibility at the 747's size. When the girls finished the tour, a Boeing official asked if they had any comment—expecting a chorus of ecstatic, unqualified raves. There was silence before a single stewardess spoke up.

"The damned coffee drains are too small," she said firmly.

Boeing made them bigger.

There is one more 747 anecdote which also does not concern safety but warrants telling. Japan Air Lines sent a group of its top officials to inspect the cabin mockup. Boeing guides were showing them three different sample installations of in-flight movie systems and the JAL representatives asked to see one of them work. A Boeing engineer, cognizant that the three systems contained actual movies for demonstration purposes, turned on one projector.

What the gentlemen from Japan saw was a scene from a World War II potboiler in which a regiment of bucktoothed sons of Nippon were getting their brains beaten out by a handful of heroic

American marines. The Boeing man quickly shut off the projector and hastened the frowning guests off to another section of the mockup.

"Maybe," he sighed later, "we should have had the safety committee check those movies."

It is impossible to say whether Boeing (or Douglas or Lockheed with their own slightly smaller jumbos) has anticipated every emergency, every contingency. Probably not, but it can be said that it isn't from lack of effort. The 747 has a vastly improved cabin PA system, not only for normal clarity but as a means of combating any development of panic in a cabin loaded with four hundred persons.

Anticipating the abnormal and the unusual has been a goal of airplane designers for forty years, but it is an extremely difficult task. Even the beloved DC-3 suffered a design mistake, or rather an overlooking of a remote possibility. A DC-3 coming in for a landing at San Francisco many years ago flew right into San Francisco Bay. The wreckage was fished out of the water and investigators found the copilot's earphones wedged into the socket of his control yoke. They apparently had fallen off and got stuck, locking the controls in a dive. Douglas had to change the yoke socket to prevent this freak accident from reoccurring.

Anticipation of the abnormal also will be the cornerstone on which the supersonic transports will be built. Boeing has created a twelve-man safety analysis committee for its SST and its job will be even tougher than that of the 747 group. The supersonics are invading new areas of speed and altitude which will present new challenges to safety planning.

The cynics, doubters and scoffers express fears that supersonic flight presents too many problems defying solution. Maybe, but some of these people were expressing the same fears about the jets more than ten years ago—they were too big, too complex, too expensive, too noisy, too fast and flew too high, all of which exposed them to an environment packed with unknown and even mysterious dangers.

It is true that the SST will operate in some uncharted areas. But to say that its environment cannot be conquered is to libel the dedication, skill and knowledge of thousands of engineers and scientists who say supersonic flight can be as safe and in some ways safer than subsonic flight. The designers of the British-French

SST (the Concorde) and Boeing's SST planners are convinced of this.

The Boeing supersonic transport is three hundred and six feet from the needle nose to the massive tail, or longer than a football field. The nose is hinged, drooping to provide better cockpit visibility in takeoffs and landings than present jetliner crews enjoy, and raising to provide the rapier profile needed for supersonic speeds.

As of April 1, 1968, more than twenty airlines had placed firm orders for one hundred and twenty-two Boeing SSTs—a remarkable display of confidence in American aeronautical integrity and ability, for at that time the U.S. supersonic transport still was a "paper airplane" that existed mostly in drawings and blueprints.

Boeing won the bitter competition to build the SST airframe over Lockheed, the final decision being the careful conclusion of both airline and government experts. The verdict was not unanimous, there being considerable support for Lockheed's double-delta design. Many aviation authorities (including Boeing and Lockheed themselves, interestingly enough) believed that the two companies each should build a single prototype, fighting out their battle in actual test flights to prove which was the superior design.

This, however, would have added up to $500 million in development costs to a program already carrying a $4 billion price tag. The decision was made to award the airframe contract to a single airframe manufacturer who would build two prototypes for testing.

The American SST's titanium construction promises maximum structural strength, plus resistance to heat and metal fatigue. The inboard wing fuel tanks will be lined with a new plastic that makes the tanks virtually rupture-proof—thus drastically reducing the chances of a post-impact fire in the event of a crash landing. The fuel tanks also are located so that constant transfer will not be necessary to maintain trim.

Boeing plans to test each prototype at least fifteen hundred hours for a total of three thousand hours. The original prototype of the 707, known as the Dash-80, first flew in 1954 and still is being used as a test airplane almost daily. Yet the accumulated test flight time on the Dash-80 in over a fourteen-year period is only twenty-two hundred hours. This is impressive proof that Boeing, the federal government and the airlines are determined that the SST will have passed every conceivable safety test before it is allowed to carry a single passenger.

The same is true for the Concorde, giving little reason for pessimism without discounting the problems that must be overcome before passengers can fly on supersonics with the same confidence they now display toward today's aircraft.

For one thing, the average test period for a new subsonic jet has been about one thousand hours of flight time. The flight test hours for both the Concorde and Boeing SST will far surpass this—principally because all concerned with supersonic safety recognize the high stakes involved, from financial investment to the trust the public places in commercial aviation. It cannot be repeated too often that *no* SST will be allowed to carry a single paying passenger until designers, government and airlines are convinced it is a safe plane.

Will passengers be exposed to unknown hazards?

Supersonic flight is far from new. The United States alone has accumulated more than two hundred thousand hours of experience with flights surpassing the speed of sound and at least six thousand hours with flights doubling the speed of sound.

Some anti-SST persons have argued that very little is known about the ability of metal to withstand the heat and stresses generated in sustained supersonic operations. They rightfully point out that metal fatigue is a very real danger if knowledge of metal behavior is inadequate, just as it was in the case of the Comet, the world's first jetliner.

The Comet *was* a victim of aeronautical inexperience, but it taught priceless lessons in the need for the "fail-safe" creed of aircraft design. Later models of the Comet and every jetliner built since then have incorporated that philosophy into their design. The SST will not only be no exception, but will boast a fail-safe concept exceeding that of any transport of the past, perhaps even the 747. As for fatigue, the Concorde's aluminum alloy has the strength of titanium at speeds below fifteen hundred MPH. Titanium itself is an immensely strong metal, so strong that the severest tests have shown a titanium airframe has an almost unlimited life span.

One fear expressed about titanium is that it is very susceptible to lightning strikes—the implication being that the Boeing SST might turn out to be nothing but a flying bomb in a thunderstorm.

Any metal aircraft is capable of attracting lightning. The SST's fuel tanks, however, are expected to have the added protection of a gas that inerts fuel vapors, thus preventing any possible ignition by lightning. To further demonstrate that the titanium SST will be safe from lightning, Boeing ran tests which exposed the metal to four times the number of strikes an SST could be expected to receive in twenty years of service.

Turbulence is another source of SST doubts, the critics claiming that at seventy thousand feet an SST which encounters clear-air turbulence might as well be ramming a brick wall. Yet the high-altitude environment of supersonic travel is no mysterious wilderness. The British-French designers and Boeing have been gathering data from high-altitude flights conducted by the Air Force. These flights have shown there is one-third less turbulence between forty thousand and seventy thousand feet than at lower altitudes. They also have shown that whatever turbulence is encountered at supersonic levels offers no serious problems of stress. The aircraft used in these experimental flights included the B-70, SR-71, B-58 and U-2. Only the B-70 pilots reported a rougher than normal ride, and engineers have been studying the B-70's aerodynamic design to see if the shape of the fuselage, far different from that of the SST, may have contributed to turbulence discomfort.

Some have charged that in the thin upper atmosphere of seventy thousand feet, SST crews and passengers will be exposed to cosmic radiation that exceeds the levels deemed safe for workers in atomic plants. It has even been argued that the more frequent exposure of pilots and stewardesses could make them unable to bear children and even result in fatal illness.

There has been a tremendous amount of research accomplished in the field of high-altitude radiation. Air sampling has been going on for years, much of it done by the famed U-2 "spy plane." All available evidence shows that the radiation "menace" not only has been vastly overrated but also is almost non-existent. The U-2 flights revealed that in one year of supersonic flying, a Concorde or Boeing pilot would receive less than one fifth the permissible dose of industrial radiation workers.

The chief radiation danger would come from solar flares, but these occur in most predictable fashion only once or twice a year at most. They definitely can be predicted far enough in advance to allow rerouting of affected SST flights or even operating them at lower altitudes for the duration of the flares.

For that matter, radiation exposure was one of the dire warnings issued concerning subsonic jet travel. Early in the jet age, United Air Lines equipped two DC-8s with special radiation-monitoring devices and, as a control measure, installed the same measuring device at its Chicago headquarters building. It discovered there was almost as much radiation on the ground as in the air. NASA and the Air Force currently are conducting a new two-year study of upper-atmosphere radiation, the results of which will be applied to SST operations.

Will handling a plane as big and fast as the SST present new and potentially hazardous problems for pilots? Will they literally have to learn to fly all over again, which would be no minor safety issue?

In a special program conducted by Lockheed, selected airline pilots have been flying supersonic military planes for several years —to get the "feel" of Mach 2 and faster flights. The airmen's unanimous verdict was that supersonic flight will involve a few new techniques, but none that cannot be learned with proper training. All agreed that pilots should have no particular difficulty in transitioning from subsonic jets to the SST, and many said there would be less difficulty than what pilots experienced when shifting from prop planes to jets.

It also has been feared that the SST couldn't fit into an air traffic control system already overburdened at major airports. It gulps fuel like a hungry dinosaur and there could be problems if one was forced to hold over at an airport or brought down through levels occupied by other planes if it started running out of fuel. Yet the Federal Aviation Administration for some time has been running simulated SST flights through its air traffic control system without encountering special headaches. It may be necessary to give the SST a slightly higher approach or landing priority if fuel supply is critical, but not to the extent of disrupting normal traffic.

It is only too true that the SST will consume fuel with incredible greed, and fuel management will be a critical problem in safe and economic operation. A subsonic jet uses about thirteen thousand gallons of fuel on a typical New York–London flight. The Concorde will require eighteen thousand and the Boeing

SST thirty thousand. In today's jet, the fuel needed to achieve cruising speed and cruise altitude amounts to roughly 3 per cent of gross takeoff weight. In the SST, which in climb configuration burns fuel at a rate of two hundred thousand pounds an hour, the figure shoots up to 10 per cent. Temperature may replace winds as the prime factor in SST flight planning, for every two degrees of temperature higher than anticipated could mean as much as three thousand pounds of additional fuel consumption. The SST will be a "cold temperature" airplane, meaning that it will operate most efficiently at lower temperatures. Winds still will be an important element of flight planning, however. A fifty-knot head wind on a four-thousand-mile trip would require an extra thirty-five hundred pounds of fuel—or the equivalent of seventeen passengers. But high fuel consumption was an expected problem in the early days of the jet age, too—a problem solved completely by careful and judicious planning. The same should be true of the supersonic age.

If the cabin pressurization on an SST should fail at seventy thousand feet, would total structural collapse result? This is another argument advanced against the SST. Would even the breaking of one window cause such sudden depressurization that human blood would boil and death would come instantly to all occupants?

Complete, instantaneous depressurization *would* result in instant death, but this also would occur in a subsonic jet flying at forty thousand feet. The SST will have the same structural safety margins that apply to any high-flying aircraft. For example, the loss of a window at seventy thousand feet would depressurize the cabin to thirteen thousand feet. Passengers would be supplied with emergency oxygen masks, just as on today's jets. There would be no boiling of blood. It might be noted that in the first ten years of subsonic jet operations, there was not a single case of cabin window failure. The SST's cabin pressurization and air conditioning system will have at least triple redundancy, including standby ducting, if a primary duct somehow should be blocked. And finally, the structural integrity of the SST will be superior to that of any plane ever built. Boeing alone is putting an SST fuselage through the equivalent of twenty-five years of pressurization cycles to make sure there will be absolutely no possibility of fatigue failure.

To make money, the SST must be operated at greater frequency than any previous jet, which has raised the question of whether this could "age" the airplane to the point of developing unsuspected fatigue problems. The SST *will* make more flights, but its hours in the air—due to its greater speed—will be no more than current jets have. Boeing estimates that its SST will operate about thirty-three hundred hours a year or about 9.5 hours daily. Daily utilization of the U.S. subsonic jet ranges between 7.5 and seventeen hours daily. Takeoff and landing frequency for the SST will be less than that of the average subsonic transport because by its very nature, the SST will be used solely on non-stop flights.

Perhaps the most frightening allegation is that the slightest fuel leak on an SST at cruising altitude could result in an instantaneous and catastrophic explosion, because the fuel would come in immediate contact with outer skin already heated to as high as six hundred degrees from friction generated by supersonic speed.

This amounts to uninformed nonsense. First, Boeing's plan to line the fuel tanks with a special plastic makes them leak-proof and the fuel lines themselves will be heavily insulated. Second, fuel leaking at seventy thousand feet can't ignite, no matter how high the temperature on the fuselage or wing skin. Ignition requires oxygen and there is too little oxygen at supersonic altitudes to provide an ignition environment. Even if it were possible for fuel to catch fire at seventy thousand feet, the result would be "cold ignition," which has no temperature at all.

Because this book is mostly devoted to safety, it will not consider such controversial SST subjects as the sonic boom or economic justification for an airliner that will shrink the world by 50 to 60 per cent and bring any two points on earth within ten to twelve hours of each other. The latter seems justification enough; as for the former, it is by far the most formidable objection to supersonic travel and may limit the SST to ocean flights, but this does not mean it cannot be overcome or that the sonic boom, by itself, is a *proven* reason for abandoning the whole thing. Many of the allegedly scientific statements made about the boom menace have been totally false, exaggerated or based on inadequate or uncompleted research. The boom, as is the case with jet noise, concerns a lot of people in aviation, but worry does not call for hysteria, unfounded incriminations and deliberate falsehoods such as have been expressed by some citizens who probably would have tarred and feathered the Wright brothers if they had been around Kitty Hawk, North Carolina, on December 17, 1903.

That date in itself hammers home the inconceivable story of the jet age, which began only fifty-five years after two bicycle makers from Dayton, Ohio, flew one hundred feet over the sand dunes of Kitty Hawk for twelve seconds.

There have been mistakes, but there have been miracles. What was once spectacular is now conventional. What was once dangerously exciting is now prosaically routine. What we once cheered as we devoured black headlines is now taken for granted. That all this came to pass in the age of the jetliners is reason enough for aviation's pride in its past and confidence in its future.

# POSTSCRIPT

This book was written as a sequel to one published in 1960, *The Probable Cause*, and its genesis was the conviction that air safety events transpiring since then deserved a detailed telling.

I wrote in the introduction to that first full accounting of air crashes, their causes and cures, that "there is no such thing as a last word on air safety; aviation is too dynamic and ever-changing to decree any problem positively solved or completely hopeless."

In 1960, the jet age was less than two years old. Now ten years have elapsed since the first U.S. jetliner carried the first paying passengers on a scheduled flight. The truth of my original comment is borne out by the record of the decade just concluded, as the reader has, I hope, seen for himself.

I take full responsibility for what he has read. Many have helped in the preparation of the volume, but the conclusions, except where I have quoted directly, are my own. I offer no apologies for the contents, for I have tried to present the facts even though their telling may have hurt not only the personalities involved but myself—because I have close and valued friends in every phase of aviation. Nor can I offer any apology for unfavorable remarks made about the United States Congress in general or Congressmen as individuals. I respect the legislative branch as an institution and I have admiration for most lawmakers as dedicated public servants, but when their activities and words have harmed the cause of air safety I felt it necessary to point out their transgressions.

A great deal of the research that went into this book was accomplished while I covered aviation for United Press International. I am grateful for UPI's training in objectivity and for the opportunity it gave me to make aviation writing a profession.

To my colleagues in that profession I must express deep appreciation. My files are filled with their products, to which I have referred constantly and on which I have relied with embarrassing frequency. I would like to list virtually the entire membership roster of the Aviation/Space Writers Association, but in the interests of printing costs I shall have to limit individual mention to the following:

Wayne Thomis, Chicago *Tribune;* Dave Hoffman, Washington *Post;* Ev Clark, New York *Times;* Jerry Hannifin, *Time;* Bob Burkhardt of many publications; Joseph Murphy, *Air Transport World;* Brent Welling, *Business Week;* Clair Stebbins, Columbus *Dispatch;* Chick Yarbrough, Washington *Star;* William Henzey and Eric Bramley, American Aviation Publications; Vern Haugland, Associated Press; Bill Huebner, Hartford *Times;* Bob Buckhorn, UPI; Bill Burk, Memphis *Press-Scimitar;* Keith Saunders, *Air Travel Magazine;* and, I fear, too many whose names are victims of fatigue, poor memory and space.

Publications to which I owe much gratitude include *Airline Management and Marketing, Air Transport World, Space/Aeronautics, Air Travel* and—above all—my bible, *Aviation Daily.* Special mention must be made of a brilliant *Reader's Digest* article by Warren R. Young which furnished excellent background on the TWA-Eastern collision.

Books consulted include Robert Burkhardt's *The Federal Aviation Administration* (Praeger, 1967); Harold Mansfield's *Billion Dollar Battle* (McKay, 1965); *The Boeing 707* by Barry J. Schiff (Arco, 1967); *It Doesn't Matter Where You Sit,* by Fred McClement (McClelland & Stewart, 1966) and *Airline Safety Is A Myth,* by Vernon Lowell (Bartholomew House, 1967).

Much material was derived from official government accident reports and from the minutes of the Air Line Pilots Association's valuable and vital Safety Forums. I am most grateful to Ed Modes of ALPA and his entire staff for the privilege of being allowed to attend these forums, and for his courtesy in furnishing me access to *The Air Line Pilot,* ALPA's official publication. A low bow, also, to J. A. Wahle, director of air safety and engineering for the Flight Engineers International Association.

Government officials who have been of tremendous help include Bobbie Allen of the National Transportation Safety Board, Irv Ripps, Charles Warnick and Dennis Feldman of FAA.

A low bow in the direction of Dan Priest and his ATA public relations staff and to the following airline PR people: Russ Scearce,

United; Gordon Gilmore, John Corris, Herb Richardson, Frank Gillespie, Dave Moffitt and Ken Fletcher, TWA; Frank Brunton, Dave Frailey and Jim Devine, American; Jim Ashlock, Eastern; Willis Player and Harvey Gatts, Pan American; Fritz Schwaemmle, Delta; and Ray Silvius, Western.

To Gordon Williams, Rick Kiefer and many, many PR and technical people at Boeing, I owe more than mere thanks; their cooperation, honesty and patience made much of this book possible. My thanks also to Leo Schefer of the British Aircraft Corporation and to Hugh Gagos of Douglas.

The distaff side of the airlines has to be thanked—in particular, Clancie Henderson, manager of American's stewardess service in Washington, and her staff; Dudney O'Guin, American; Kay Crum, Bonanza; Karen Jones, TWA; Karen Downey, Northwest; and Del Russell, Priscilla Arone and Maureen McKeel, Western. To list the airline pilots who aided me would necessitate a separate chapter, but I would like to single out Paul Soderlind and Ken Norgaard, Northwest; Howard Kelly, Piedmont; Don Heine, North Central; Vic Hewes, Delta; John McDonald, United; John Boyle, Bonanza; Jim Furr, Eastern; Bill Bettwy, Bill Davenport, Rod Coston, Bill Culbertson, Tom Latte, Jerry Brenden, Rick Davis and Hugh Clark, all of American; and Walt Reed and Barney Fairbank, Mohawk.

The cooperation of these airline industry officials is gratefully acknowledged: Najeeb Halaby, Pan American; Stuart Tipton, ATA; Ed Converse, Bob Henry and Larry Decker, Air West; Jack Sharkey, Delta; Hayes Dever, United; Russ Stephenson, Mohawk—and a special salute to a man who made air safety a personal philosophy, W. A. Patterson of United.

Appreciation is due to Joseph J. Hradecky, controller at Washington National Airport, and his colleagues, who have always made me feel a bit more comfortable knowing that men like these are at the radarscopes.

Finally, my most inadequate thanks and gratitude to two friends whose help, advice and unstinting hard work brought this book to fruition and reality: my editor, Walter Bradbury, and my typist, Joanne Lamb Nash.

Robert J. Serling
Washington, D.C.